Chi-Gung

Chi-Gung

Harnessing the Power of the Universe

Daniel Reid

Illustrations by
Dexter Chou

SIMON & SCHUSTER
A VIACOM COMPANY

First published in Great Britain by
Simon & Schuster Ltd, 1998
A Viacom company

3 5 7 9 10 8 6 4 2

Simon & Schuster UK Ltd
Africa House
64–78 Kingsway
London WC2B 6AH

Simon & Schuster Australia
Sydney

A CIP catalogue record for this book is available from the British Library

ISBN 0-684-82125-7

Printed in Great Britain by
Butler & Tanner Ltd, Frome and London

This book is dedicated to my father Daniel Reid Sr.,
who might still be alive and well today
had he practised chi-gung,
and to my father-in-law Chou Yun-yu,
who is because he does,
and
to everyone everywhere who cultivates the energy of life
with wisdom and compassion.

Acknowledgements

I wish to acknowledge and thank the following individuals for their encouragement, contributions, and support in the completion of this book: Lo Teh-hsiu, chi-gung master from Taiwan, for his illuminating insights and information on the theory and practice of chi-gung; Howard Brewer, for introducing me to chi-gung and chi-gung teachers twenty years ago in Taiwan, and for coaching me along all these years; Dexter Chou, for once again creating the illustrations for my book exactly to specifications; Peter Turner, my editor at Shambhala, for his meticulous editing; Moriah St Clair, for demonstrating the true healing power of universal energy, and elucidating its functional link with wisdom and compassion; Chou Tung Reid, my partner in chi-gung and daily life, for her astute assistance interpreting esoteric Chinese materials, and her bright companionship on the path of practice. Ingrid Connell and all the other fine editors at Simon & Schuster in London for their long-standing faith in my work and their excellent editorial attention to every aspect of my manuscripts.

Table of Contents

A Note on Romanization

For the convenience of Western readers with no previous background in Chinese studies, I have followed the Yale University system of romanization for spelling most of the Chinese terms used in the book. Although the Yale system is seldom used today, it nevertheless remains the least confusing and the most accurate method of spelling Chinese words for Western readers, because it cleaves closest to standard English phonetics. For formal names, such as historical figures, dynasties, texts and so forth, I used the old Wade–Giles system of spelling, which remains the conventional practice among more traditionally minded Western sinologists.

Recently, the so-called 'pin-yin' system of romanization used in China since the Cultural Revolution has spread to the West, misleading most Western readers, as well as many newscasters, into mispronouncing the Chinese terms that appear in the media. For example, words pronounced 'jou' are inexplicably spelled 'zhou', the word 'shiao' is illogically spelled 'xiao', 'tsai' for no rhyme or reason is written 'cai', 'chin' is spelled 'qin', and 'chi-gung' is written 'qigong'. There's no way on earth the average Western reader can fathom the proper pronunciation of Chinese words from such a spelling system. Therefore, to avoid confusing my readers with spelling that defies the standard phonetic conventions that evolved with the Roman alphabet, not only in English but in all languages that use this alphabet, I never employ the pin-yin system to romanize Chinese words.

In my previous books, I spell the word 'chi' as 'chee', because that is precisely how it is pronounced in English. However, since this book is devoted entirely to the subject of chi-gung, I do not wish to further confuse matters by creating my own spelling for this key word, so I hereby conform to academic convention by using the relatively logical Yale system to spell 'chi' and 'chi-gung', with the explicit reminder that the proper pronunciation is 'chee', as in 'cheek' without the final 'k'.

Foreword

For more than 5000 years, chi-gung was one of the best-kept secrets in the world. Practised quietly behind the high walls and barred gates of ancient Buddhist monasteries and remote Taoist hermitages, in the private villas of the rich and influential, and the guarded palaces of emperors, chi-gung became China's most esoteric tradition. It was an art personally handed down through oral transmission, from reticent masters to select disciples in unbroken lineages spanning thousands of years. Those fortunate enough to receive the secret transmission became members of an exclusive fraternity of practitioners known simply as *nei-jia,* literally the 'internal family', an informal confederation of chi-gung adepts that included princes and poets, monks and martial artists, warriors and wise men, all of them dedicated to cultivating the 'Tao of Life' (*yung-sheng dao*) by working with universal energy. The few classical texts in which information about chi-gung was recorded for posterity were deliberately written in such vague, obscurely encoded terms that only well-practised initiates could possibly decipher their true meanings, and therefore these texts were circulated and understood only among the inner circles of the chi-gung world.

Today, all that has changed. Like so many other esoteric teachings from the ancient world, chi-gung is yielding its long-guarded secrets to the age of information, and practices that were once revealed only to the most select circles of initiates may be called forth by anyone. However, unlike so many other ancient traditions, chi-gung remains as vibrant, appealing and universally relevant today as it was 5000 years ago, if not more so, for it still rewards diligent practice with the only two things in life that humanity has always valued, and continues to value, more than fame and fortune. Those rewards are health and longevity, and chi-gung bestows them alike to prince and pauper, man and woman, spiritualist and hedonist, at the cost of only a little time and a lot of practice. This makes chi-gung a real bargain, particularly in light of contemporary health hazards.

Small wonder, then, that in recent years a spate of new books about chi-gung has suddenly appeared on the market, some of them written by self-styled 'masters' of uncharted lineage, with information presented in ways that can be misleading and sometimes downright dangerous for uninitiated readers who take it too literally. Therefore, the purpose of this book is to present an authoritative account of chi-gung for Western readers, including its historical development in China, a survey of its many styles and forms, its philosophical context and its most important practical precepts for personal practice. The intention of this author, who studied chi-gung for twelve years with accomplished Chinese masters in Taiwan and who has practised daily for over twenty years, is to clarify chi-gung for Western readers by discussing it in terms you can relate to, without compromising the spirit and intent of the original teachings; to correct common theoretical misconceptions that might lead to deviations in practice; to construct a meaningful framework for Western understanding of the esoteric Chinese terms and ideas which inform chi-gung; and to establish a firm foundation for basic practice that will serve as a personal springboard to health and longevity, while also inspiring you to pursue the higher spiritual vision which prolonged practice of chi-gung sooner or later engenders.

Virtually all spiritual traditions, Eastern and well as Western, agree on two basic points: that the power which created the universe and sustains all life within it is guided by a set of primordial principles that transcend all cultural definitions and may collectively be referred to as 'wisdom' or 'truth', and that this universal power of creation has always been motivated by, and should therefore never be invoked without, the compassionate empathy for life known throughout the world as 'love'. Wisdom, love and power – these are the three inseparable virtues, the transcendent triunal forces of the universe. Known in Chinese tradition simply as the 'Tao', or 'Way', and respectfully attributed to the power of 'Heaven', the universal laws of creative energy constitute the basic code of chi-gung practice. But to paraphrase Shakespeare, 'the Tao by any other name would be as great'. Thus, in monotheistic Western traditions, the same triunal trinity of wisdom, love and power is known as 'God', in Hinduism it is the 'Trimurti' of Brahma, Vishnu and Shiva, in Buddhism it's the emptiness, luminosity and energy of 'Bodhi' or 'Enlightened

Mind', and in Native American tradition it's called the 'Great Spirit'. It is due to the sacred nature of this creative power that access to it was so carefully protected from profane practitioners and kept secret from mere curiosity seekers.

In today's world, power has come to be regarded as a virtue in and of itself, divorced from wisdom and love by the rationalizations of science and technology. The abuse and destruction wreaked upon our world by people who use technology to harness universal power such as nuclear energy for purposes that contradict the laws of universal wisdom and deviate from the compassionate motivation of universal love, are obvious enough for all to see. But few are willing to admit that the problem of wholesale mismanagement of the world's resources really starts with our own individual mismanagement of our most precious private resource – our personal energy. Suffice to say that without wisdom, power is blind, and usually arrogant and aggressive as well. Without love, power is cold, calculating, often cruel, always self-serving. Conversely, wisdom without the power to enact itself is useless, and love without the power to express itself is impotent. Thus all three factors – wisdom, love and power – carry equal weight in the grand equation of 'Triplex Unity' and everything in it.

This book is about chi-gung, and chi-gung is about working with energy to harness the power of the universe for the benefit of humanity. Since the theoretical and technical points of practice are of primary interest to readers who wish to learn about chi-gung, these practical aspects constitute the main themes of the chapters which follow. However, for those of you who wish to cultivate personal energy by harnessing the power of the universe through chi-gung, the author wishes to emphasize the over-riding importance of learning and practising this art in close conjunction with the 'Great Spirit' of wisdom and love that governs universal energy throughout the manifold realms of nature and the cosmos. This is how chi-gung is meant to be practised – as a wise and compassionate expression of energy – and this is the reason that – in the past – it was taught only to those who had already demonstrated a commitment to those spiritual virtues. It's also the only way that humanity can harness the power of the universe to enhance life on earth without ultimately running the risk of, as Taoist masters once warned, 'playing with fire and provoking demons' (*dzou-huo ru-mo*).

Enough fiery and demonic forces have already been unleashed in this world by those who try to wield the power of universal energies without regard for truth and compassion. Perhaps that's why chi-gung has suddenly shed its veil of secrecy and become universally available at this crucial time in history – to help draw sacred wisdom and the cool clear water of compassion into an overheated and unwise world. Perhaps chi-gung, by forging a direct personal relationship between each individual practitioner and the creative power of the universe, will foster a renewed respect for the wisdom and love that together render this power worthy of the name that the *Tao Teh Ching* gives it, 'the Mother of all things under Heaven'. Perhaps that's what chi-gung is really all about – to empower individuals to rescue themselves from the disease, malaise and self-destructive behaviour that arise from humanity's unbridled misuse of power, by showing them the way to restore our own personal links with the primordial wisdom and unconditional love which make the awesome power of the universe 'user friendly' to chi-gung practitioners. It is with these thoughts in mind that this book was written.

Happy Hill
Chiang Mai, Thailand
September 1997

INTRODUCTION

Basic Terms and Concepts

Chi-gung is an ancient Chinese system of self-cultivation developed specifically as a means by which each individual may take full personal responsibility for protecting health, promoting vitality and prolonging life, while cultivating spiritual awareness and insight. Based on the primordial principles of classical Taoist philosophy, chi-gung is simple and practical – the practitioner learns how to harness the fundamental forces of the cosmos (Heaven), balance them with the elemental energies of nature (Earth) and harmonize them both with the essence, energy and spirit (i.e., the 'Three Treasures') of human life (Humanity). Chi-gung thus enables the individual to amplify his or her personal power with the infinite power of the universe.

Known in traditional Chinese thought as the 'Three Powers', Heaven (*tien*), Earth (*di*), and Humanity (*ren*) represent the sum total of all the forces and factors at all levels of human existence within the universe as we know it. It is by virtue of the balance and harmony of these powers that we may enjoy health and vitality, attain power and longevity, enhance our mental awareness and spiritual insight, overcome our instinctive fear of death, and realize the primordial immortality of the human spirit.

Though usually associated in popular Western imagination with medicine, monks and martial artists, chi-gung was also practised in traditional China by ministers of state and judicial magistrates, princes and prelates, poets and painters, each of whom utilized its power to cultivate their own particular talents, improve their professional performance, protect their health, enhance energy and prolong life. In today's highly competitive, stressful world, chi-gung's versatile utility as a personal tool – for promoting productivity, preventing disease, balancing emotions and calming the mind – has greater practical potential for the individual, and for society, than it ever has before. For busy people without the time or inclination for elaborate exercise programmes, expensive sports and difficult to learn manoeuvres, chi-gung provides a quick and easy system of self-healthcare that is both safe and simple to learn, and can be practised any time of the day or night, at home or at work, indoors or outdoors, without requiring any special equipment, expensive facilities or athletic skills, and only the most basic training. Yet simple as it seems, so potent are the healing powers and other benefits of chi-gung that some of the cures and other effects it achieves are discounted as 'miracles' even by eye-witness observers – despite the evidence – or scoffed at by incredulous sceptics as 'anecdotal evidence'. That's simply because there is a lot more to chi-gung than meets the eye. In fact, what meets the eye in chi-gung is merely a small tip of a massive iceberg floating serenely in the vast sea of universal energy.

Chi means 'breath' and 'air', and by extension it also denotes 'energy' and 'vitality'. *Gung* is a general term meaning 'work' and is used in reference to any technique or skill which requires time and effort, patience and practice, to perfect. Hence the term 'chi-gung' may be translated as 'breathing exercise' as well as 'energy work', and indeed the subtle skill of breath control is the key to cultivating control over the flow and balance of energy in the body and harmonizing human energy with the elementary energies of nature and the cosmos.

Chi manifests itself in myriad ways throughout the realms of nature (Earth), the cosmos (Heaven), and the human system (Humanity). For the purposes of chi-gung, the three most important manifestations of *chi* are the following:

• *Chi* is the fundamental 'stuff' of the entire manifest universe, the basic building block of all matter, the immaterial energy that constitutes all material form. Modern quantum physics has recently verified a fact that has long been apparent to ancient Taoist science: that the essential nature of even the most elemental atoms and molecules is nothing more or less than an array of various energies organized in particular patterns. *Chi* is therefore the basic energy that comprises all matter and animates all living things, and the fundamental functional force that drives all activities and transformations in nature and the universe, from the galactic to the microscopic, from the birth, growth, decay and death of stars to the formation and dissolution of atoms, molecules and cells in the human body.

• *Chi* is the basic life force of all three levels of human existence – body, energy and mind. In constitutes the definitive factor in all facets and phases of human life, from the molecular level of metabolism and cellular division to the larger organic functions of digestion and excretion, respiration and circulation, all the way up to the highest faculties of feeling and thought, awareness and perception. *Chi* is the invisible master template behind all visible forms and vital functions of the human system, and therefore it is the primary factor responsible for human health and disease, the main gauge of vitality and longevity, the bridge that links body and mind, and the common denominator in all the complex equations of physical, emotional and spiritual life. Chi-gung provides an effective way to mediate and manipulate the vital energies of life, and to balance and harmonize them for optimum health and longevity, emotional equilibrium and spiritual awareness.

• *Chi* also constitutes the dynamic polar field in which all energy moves and from which all power springs. Every type of energy functions within its own specific force field, from the lowest vibrations of matter to the highest frequencies of spirit, from the heaviest to the lightest, from the most polluted to the purest forms. Therefore the purity and potency of one's own personal *chi* determines the type of universal energy with which one's system resonates, and this in turn governs the nature of one's relationship with the higher forces and spiritual realms of the universe. Chi-gung permits the practitioner to purify and potentiate his or her own personal energy field so that it resonates in harmony with the purest energies and most powerful spiritual forces in the universe, thereby empowering humanity with the infinite energy, wisdom and other primordial virtues of Heaven and Earth.

Most forms for chi-gung involve various degrees of gentle movement or stillness of the body, balanced with rhythmically regulated breathing, all quietly harmonized by a calm, unhurried and clearly focused mind. Soft, slow movement of the body prevents the stiffness and stagnation that lead to degeneration and death. As Lao Tse states in the classic verse of the *Tao Teh Ching*:

Truly, to be stiff and hard is the way of death;
To be soft and supple is the way of life.

The importance of soft flowing movement was also noted by Confucius. In the classical text called *Spring and Autumn Annals*, the sage says,

Flowing water never stagnates, and the hinges of an active door never rust. This is due to movement. The same principle applies

to essence and energy. If the body does not move, essence does not flow. When essence does not flow, energy stagnates.

Chi-gung exercises such as the graceful rhythmic dance of Tai Chi Chuan are often referred to as 'moving meditation' because they blend soft, gentle movements of the body with a calm, contemplative state of mind. However, to understand fully the role of movement in chi-gung, one must also comprehend the central significance of stillness, as well as the complementary connection between the two. In the sitting meditation forms of chi-gung, for example, there is also movement, but it is all internal – in the flow of energy through the channels and the circulation of blood in the vessels and the cyclic waves of breath – while externally the physical body rests in motionless serenity. In moving forms of chi-gung, the rhythmic external motions of the body can only be maintained and kept in harmony with the cyclic rise and fall of breath by a mind that rests serenely in an undistracted state of internal stillness. Thus, like the eternal ebb and flow of the waves on the sea and the cyclic turns of day and night in the firmament, movement and stillness constitute the essential Yin and Yang poles of chi-gung and comprise the complementary cornerstones in all forms of practice.

The term 'Tao' transcends precise definition in words and is better understood through the archetypal symbols traditionally used to represent it – the sexual act between male and female, the constant interplay of the elementary energies of nature, the rhythmic dance of macrocosmic forces in the external universe and their microcosmic reflections in the internal world of the human body. In the classic canons of Taoist literature, the mysteries of Tao are elucidated through the symbolic formulations of trigrams and hexagrams in the ancient book of divination known as the *I-Ching* (*Book of Change*) and the arresting allusions and crystal-clear metaphors of the *Tao Teh Ching*, the intriguing 5000-character treatise on Tao attributed to the sage Lao Tze. The terse verse of this ancient text is a source of such universal insight and incisive truth that it ranks among the most popular, appealing and widely translated books in the world today.

The original Chinese ideogram for 'Tao' consists of the symbols for 'head' and 'walk'. As a noun, it generally means 'way' or 'path', while as a verb it means 'to say' or 'to know'. This implies that the Tao is a path through life that one takes by following the mind rather than the body; it also indicates that the Tao is the original source of all real knowledge and true words. 'There was something formless yet complete that existed before Heaven and Earth,' states Lao Tze in the *Tao Teh Ching*. 'It's true name I do not know. "Tao" is the nickname I give it.'

Of all the myriad elements of nature from which Taoist terminology is drawn, water comes closest to expressing the fundamental essence and full potential of Tao, and thus it has become the quintessential symbol of the Tao in philosophy, art and science. The initially yielding yet ultimately omnipotent nature of water permeates every aspect of chi-gung and provides a convenient metaphor through which the theory of chi-gung may be understood and the practice readily learned. Blood and energy move through their respective channels in the body like water flowing through rivers – free, full, unimpeded – and any obstruction to their free flow and natural equilibrium causes deviations that give rise to energy imbalance and has serious repercussions throughout the entire system. The way the body moves and feels during chi-gung practice is like swimming through water – soft and smooth, slow and rhythmic. The long, deep, diaphragmic breathing employed in chi-gung rises and falls with the same rhythmic regularity as waves on the ocean, while the human mind resting in the unruffled stillness of meditation is often compared to the surface of a lake on a windless day, calmly reflecting the silent clarity of Heaven above.

Water also symbolizes the mutable relationship between matter and energy, stillness and motion, and the transformations activated in the human system by the 'internal alchemy' of chi-gung practice. The fluid Yin essence in the 'cauldron' of the sacrum is transformed and sublimated by the 'wind' of breath acting as a 'bellows' to 'steam' and purify it, and refine it into Yang energy. This energy rises up the spine under the guidance of mind and enters the head, where it is further refined to nurture spirit. The spirit condenses and cools it again, inducing it to flow down the front channel as Water energy and store itself in the 'lower elixir field' (*dan-tien*) below the navel.

Traditional Taoist terminology is rooted in the universal symbols of nature and the cosmos, which is why Taoist philosophy has endured through the ages and produced ideas with significance that transcends cultural boundaries. Rather than creating new words to represent new ideas, as is the custom in Western civilization, the Chinese have always expressed their ideas through the symbolic language of nature, and therefore it requires only a little imagination to grasp even the most esoteric Taoist concepts.

Taoist ideas, cloaked as they are in colourful images familiar to one and all, are refreshingly free of the fuzzy ambiguity and complex jargon that characterize philosophical discussion and scientific debate in other cultural traditions. Indeed, even the most technical scientific aspects of Taoist thought are often expressed in terms so poetically imaginative and universally symbolic that their meanings are rendered far more clearly to the layman than they are by the technical terminology of Western science, and this is what makes the Taoist view of nature and life so appealing to people throughout the world.

Contrary to common misconceptions, Taoism is not really a religion, but rather a whole way of life. While a popular religion known as 'Tao Chiao', complete with its own hereditary 'pope', did branch out from the main trunk of Taoist thought in response to the influx of Buddhism from India during the third to fifth centuries AD, the true line of Taoist theory and practice, traditionally known as 'Tao Chia', was a non-sectarian, non-theist philosophy devoted to the study of nature and the cosmos and their relationships with the human condition. The universal principles of nature and practical precepts of life discovered and developed by practising Taoist philosophers lie at the heart of all the traditional Chinese arts and sciences – from martial arts to medical science, poetry and painting to alchemy and geomancy, cooking to cosmology – and they gave rise to a way of life that brought the human body, energy and mind into balanced synchronicity and harmonic resonance with the primordial forces of Heaven and the temporal elements of Earth. In the Taoist system of thought and practice, chi-gung became an effective personal tool for unlocking the mysteries of life and harnessing the universal powers of Heaven to regulate the elemental energies of Earth so that both may serve the needs of Humanity.

Taoism is perhaps the only philosophic system in the world which revolves more around practice than preaching, and chi-gung constitutes one of its most important practices. You don't have to remind a true Taoist to practise what he or she preaches, for if a Taoist preaches anything at all, it's usually the central importance of practice. Thus the Taoist way of life precludes the common hypocrisy of preaching one thing while practising another, for by definition the only way to know the Tao is to experience its power in practice, not just to talk about it in theory. As the first line of the *Tao Teh Ching* makes perfectly clear: 'The tao which can be said is not the eternal Tao . . .'

Enough said.

*

The primacy of practice notwithstanding, in order to engage in a meaningful discussion of chi-gung, we must first define the basic terms and understand the key concepts which form the theoretical framework from which the practices developed. So let's start at the beginning.

Polarity

At some inconceivably prior point in the distant past, the undifferentiated primordial unity which preceded the formation of stars and planets and all the various elements and energies of the universe was rent asunder to produce two polar forces that set in motion the ceaseless flux of creation. Known in modern Western cosmology as the 'Big Bang', this primal event is sparely described in the *Tao Teh Ching*: 'One gave birth to two'. The two came to be known as Yin and Yang, and the polarity to which they gave rise, and which in turn gave birth to everything in the universe, is called 'The Great Principle of Yin and Yang'.

Polarity is the basic premise of all manifest existence, the ground of all creation, the basis of all movement and change, and the field in which energy and matter engage in their ceaseless play of formation and dissolution, interaction and transmutation. Yin, the ideogram for which originally meant 'the shady side of a hill', refers to the negative and the dark, the passive and the female, moon and water, the soft and yielding, the internal and the lower aspects in any field, formation or system of energy. Yang, which meant 'the sunny side of a hill', denotes the positive and the light, the active and male, the sun and fire, the hard and aggressive, the external and the upper aspects and parts. It's important to realize that Yin and Yang are not two distinctly different types of energy, but rather the two opposite but complementary poles in any given form, function or field of energy. Furthermore, as the original ideograms so clearly indicate, Yin and Yang are mutually transmutable, for as the planet turns and the angle of the sun changes, the sunny Yang side of the hill becomes shady and Yin, while the Yin side lights up and becomes Yang.

The polarity of Yin and Yang is manifested in every aspect of chi-gung, as well as in the human body and energy system. In breathing, inhalation is Yin and exhalation is Yang. In the body, the upper, outer and back parts are Yang, while the lower, inner and front are Yin. Blood belongs to Yin relative to energy which belongs to Yang. The head is Yang, and the sacrum is Yin. The 'hollow' *fu* organs are Yang, while the 'solid' *dzang* organs are Yin. Thoughts are Yang, and feelings are Yin, and so forth and so on throughout every aspect of body, energy and mind.

Polar terms crop up again and again in every facet of chi-gung, so let's take a brief look at some of the most common and important pairs, all of which represent various functional facets of Yin and Yang:

• *Prenatal* (*sian-tien*) *and Postnatal* (*hou-tien*). All levels of human life have their prenatal and postnatal aspects. The prenatal aspect is the primordial potential that we bring into our lives at birth, while the postnatal aspect is the temporal form it takes during the course of corporeal life. Thus prenatal essence is the creative potential we receive at the moment of conception from the fusion of sperm and ovum from our parents. This primordial essence is stored in the sexual glands of the male and female and is passed on from generation to generation by sexual reproduction. Postnatal essence is produced during life from food, water and air, and it takes form in the blood, hormones, lymph and other vital fluids of the body.

Similarly, prenatal energy, also known in Chinese as *yuan-chi* (primordial energy), is the energy converted from the prenatal essence of glands, as well as the energy assimilated from cosmic sources in the sky (Heaven). Postnatal energy comes from the earthly sources of food and water, herbs and air, extracted and refined by the digestive and respiratory systems.

Prenatal spirit is the 'primordial mind of the Tao', the immortal soul and original spark of consciousness which 'is not born and does not die'. Postnatal spirit is the human mind of temporal reality on earth, including sensory perception, thought and feeling, personality and ego. The purpose of the highest levels of chi-gung practice is to develop conscious awareness of primordial spirit, a difficult task that requires one to recognize and accept the artificial and fleeting nature of the ego. Attaining primordial awareness of the mind of Tao is known as 'enlightenment' or 'immortality'.

• *Fire* (*huo*) *and Water* (*shui*). Fire is the archetypal symbol of Yang, while Water represents Yin. In the human energy system, Fire is the temporal form of energy produced by metabolism and respiration, and Water is the primordial energy stored in the glands. In the ordinary course of life, Fire flares upward and dissipates itself in the discursive thoughts, conflicting emotions and physical activities of daily life, while Water energy from the glands flows down and out, dissipating itself through sexual activity and stress. The purpose of internal alchemy, known in Taoist practice as *nei-*

gung ('internal work'), is to reverse the course of Fire and Water and thereby retard the ageing process and prolong life. This is done by keeping Fire energy out of the head, heart and solar plexus, refining and recirculating it instead through the major channels and storing it in the lower elixir field below the navel. At the same time, the precious Water energy ordinarily dissipated through sex and stress is conserved and raised upward through the spinal channels into the head, where it is used to nourish the faculties of spirit.

• *Movement* (*dung*) *and Stillness* (*jing*). Movement is a manifestation of Yang activity, and stillness reflects the calm, cooling quietude of Yin. The hectic activity of daily life causes Fire to flare up and dissipates one's reserves of essence and energy, while the stillness of meditation calms the system, cools the Fire and conserves vital resources. Thus, the practice of stillness constitutes a primary method of preserving health and prolonging life in chi-gung practice. Stillness not only indicates physical stillness, but also means stillness of mind and emotional quietude. In chi-gung, movement and stillness are always balanced within one another, such as the internal stillness of mind balanced with the external movement of body in moving exercises, and the movement of internal energy which occurs in the stillness of sitting meditation. In conventional life, most people never experience true stillness, for their minds are always racing with thoughts, and even in sleep their minds and bodies thrash around in disturbing dreams prompted by the worries of the day.

• *Internal* (*nei*) *and External* (*wai*). External aspects of chi-gung practice are known as *wai-gung*, include all movements of the body, and belong to Yang, while internal work is called *nei-gung*, involves mainly the mind and the breath, and belongs to Yin. Achieving a harmonious balance between external and internal aspects of practice is a primary principle of chi-gung. Similarly, using foods, herbs and other material supplements to sustain physical health is regarded as an external method of practice, while working with the immaterial elements of spirit and energy belongs to internal practice.

In all of these various aspects of Yin and Yang polarity, the goal of chi-gung practice is to always achieve optimum balance between the two and to avoid extremes in either direction. According to the tenets of TCM (Traditional Chinese Medicine), imbalance in the Yin and Yang polarity of various energy systems within the body is the root cause of all disease, and therefore the best way to cure and prevent disease and halt degeneration is to restore and maintain a natural, healthy balance in all facets and phases of the human energy system. Chi-gung is the most direct and effective way of achieving this goal.

Trinity

A fundamental trinity of forces and factors runs throughout Taoist philosophy, as well as most other spiritual traditions. In Christianity, there are the Father, Son and Holy Ghost; in Buddhism we find the Three Jewels of Buddha, Dharma and Sangha; and, in Hinduism, there is the Trimurti of Brahma, Vishnu and Shiva. In Eastern traditions, the three primordial qualities of the universe are emptiness, luminosity and energy, which in turn are the sources of the primal virtues of wisdom, love and power.

In Taoist tradition, trinity manifests macrocosmically in the Three Powers of Heaven, Earth and Humanity and microcosmically within the human system as the Three Treasures of essence (*jing*), energy (*chi*) and spirit (*shen*), as well as their postnatal aspects of body, breath and mind. The locus of the primordial aspects of the Three Treasures in the human body are known as the Three Elixir Fields (*san dan-tien*): primordial essence resides in the lower elixir field below the navel and is associated with sexual glands; primordial energy resides in the middle elixir field in the solar plexus and is related to the adrenal glands; and primordial spirit resides in the upper elixir field in the centre of the head and is associated with the pituitary and pineal glands.

In Tibetan Buddhist tradition, these three facets of human existence are referred to as body, speech and mind, with speech representing energy. That's because speech is the most powerful expression of energy in the human system, which accounts for the central importance of mantra (chanting sacred syllables) in Tibetan practice. Taoist tradition also recognizes the potency of sound as a manifestation of energy, and chi-gung includes several special practices involving sound, such as the Six Syllable Secret used for healing, as well as particular tones used to activate and balance various energy centres (chakras).

The Three Treasures (*san bao*) and the Three Powers (*san tsai*) constitute the basis of Taoist internal alchemy, whereby essence is transformed into energy, energy is transformed into spirit, and spirit is harmonized with the essential emptiness, luminosity and power of the universe. Chi-gung is involved in all stages of practice to activate and balance the various transformations mediated by the internal alchemy of *nei-gung*. It serves as a functional link between the physical and spiritual aspects of the practices, and the conductor that channels, guides and balances the various energies involved.

The Five Elemental Energies

As modern physics has conclusively proven, all matter – from atoms and molecules to planets and stars – is composed of energy bound into various patterns of sympathetic vibration, held in place by electromagnetic and nuclear forces; i.e., by the power of polarity. In the traditional Chinese Taoist paradigm of creation and manifest form, all matter on earth is composed and regulated by what are known as the Five Elemental Energies (*wu shing*). The *Yellow Emperor's Classic of Internal Medicine* states, 'The Five Elemental Energies of Wood, Fire, Earth, Metal and Water encompass all the myriad phenomena of nature. It is a paradigm that applies equally to humans.' Another ancient Chinese medical text notes, 'The Five Elemental Energies combine and recombine in innumerable ways to produce manifest existence. All things contain the Five Elemental Energies in various proportions.'

There are two basic transformational cycles whereby these energies interact and counterbalance one another to sustain homeostasis. One is called the creative (*sheng*), or generative, cycle, in which one energy stimulates and amplifies the next. Thus Water generates Wood, which generates Fire, which generates Earth, which produces Metal, which completes the cycle by creating Water. The other is called the control (*ke*), or subjugative, cycle, whereby one energy impedes and reduces the activity of the next. In this cycle, Water impedes Fire, which reduces Metal, which impedes Wood, which reduces Earth, which completes the cycle by impeding Water.

Chi-gung provides a mechanism through which one can guide and balance the Five Elemental Energies that compose the human system by utilizing the control and creative cycles to restore normal balance and maintain natural equilibrium among the vital energies that govern the internal organs and regulate their related functions and tissues. All of the vital organs are paired in matched sets of Yin and Yang, and each pair is associated with one of the Five Elemental Energies. For example, the Yin heart and Yang small intestine, as well as the related functions of circulation and assimilation, plus the associated emotion of joy and the colour red, are all governed by Fire energy. Similarly, the Yin kidneys and Yang bladder are governed by Water, which also controls the associated tissues of bone, brain and marrow, regulates the fluids of urine and semen, houses the emotion of fear, and is reflected in the colour black. Since there are specific chi-gung exercises to influence the energies of each of the vital organ systems through their meridiens, a weak heart may be tonified by exercises which stimulate the Fire energy of the heart, and conversely, an overactive heart may be controlled by doing exercises that boost the Water energy of the kidneys, which then quells the excessive Fire of the heart through the control cycle of Water over Fire.

Similar results may be achieved by applying other associated elements to stimulate or pacify various energies. Thus, the Fire energy of the heart may be amplified by wearing the colour red and eating bitter Fire flavour foods and herbs, while the Wood energy of the liver may be boosted by wearing green clothing and consuming sour Wood foods. The Earth energy of the spleen and stomach is tonified by using sweet Earth energy foods and herbs, and the Metal energy of the lungs and large intestine may be strengthened by using the healing syllable *shee*. The permutations and combinations of this system are countless, and they reflect the vast potential of using chi-gung for curative healing as well as preventative healthcare.

The chart in Table 1 lists the various organs, functions, emotions, colours, flavours and other attributes associated with the Five Elemental Energies within the microcosmic system of the human body and mind, as well as the external macrocosmic world.

Meridians

While Western medicine recognizes and deals with only two circulatory networks in the human body – the nerves and the blood vessels – TCM includes a third system: the energy network of meridiens, which it regards as the primary functional network in the human system, the decisive factor in human health, and the system which must be dealt with first and foremost in the treatment of human disease. The *Yellow Emperor's Classic of Internal Medicine* states, 'Energy commands blood: where energy goes, blood follows', which means that the decisive factor in the circulation of blood to the organs and tissues is the free flow of energy to those areas via the network of energy channels. Similarly, disorders of the nervous system respond so well to acupuncture treatment precisely because acupuncture stimulates or sedates the flow of energy through the meridians, which in turn balances the whole nervous system and permits the nerves to function properly.

The human energy system consists of an invisible but highly

TABLE 1: The Five Elemental Energies and Their Macrocosmic and Microcosmic Associations

Category	*Wood*	*Fire*	*Earth*	*Metal*	*Water*
			UNIVERSAL MACROCOSM		
Colour	Green	Red	Yellow	White	Black
Flavour	Sour	Bitter	Sweet	Pungent	Salty
Climate	windy	Hot	Damp	Dry	Cold
Hours	3–7 a.m.	9 a.m.–1 p.m.	1–3, 7–9 a.m. 1–3, 7–9 p.m.	3–7 p.m.	9 p.m.–1 a.m.
Development phase	Sprouting, growing	Blooming, fruiting	Ripening, harvesting	Withering, decaying	Dormancy, storage
Direction	East	South	Centre	West	North
Season	Spring	Summer	Late summer	Autumn	Winter
Activity	Generates	Expands	Stabilizes	Contracts	Conserves
			HUMAN MICROCOSM		
Organ Yin	Liver	Heart, pericardium	Spleen	Lungs	Kidneys
Yang	Gallbladder	Small intestine, Triple Burner	Stomach	Large intestine	Bladder
Vital function	Nervous System	Blood, endocrine	Digestion, lymph, muscle	Respiration, skin	Urinary reproductive
Bodily secretions	Tears	Sweat	Saliva	Mucus	Urine, sexual fluids
Emotion	Anger	Joy	Obsession	Grief	Fear
External apertures	Eyes	Tongue, throat	Lips, mouth	Nose	Ears
Life cycle	Infancy	Youth	Maturity	Old age	Death
Healing sound	*Hsü*	*Her*	*Hoo*	*Shee*	*Chway*
Tissue	Ligaments, nerves, nails	Blood vessels	Fat, muscle	Skin, hair	Bones, marrow, brain
			PSYCHIC AND PERSONALITY TRAITS		
Energy type	Expanding	Fusing	Moderating	Condensing	Conserving
Ability	Initiative	Communication	Negotiation	Discrimination	Imagination
Mental preoccupation	Work	Stimulation	Detail	Ritual	Secret, mystery
Obsessions	Answers, choices, goals	Pleasure, desire, love, divinity	Manipulation, loyalties, security	Perfection, order, standards	Mysteries, death, visions, facts
Tendencies	Risk, busy work	Excitement, contact	Comfort, company	Follow orders, make judgements	Solitude, isolation
Emotional need	Arousal	Being in love	Being needed	Being right	Being protected
Psychic fear	Helplessness	Isolation	Confusion	Corruption	Extinction
Virtue	Benevolence	Propriety	Faith	Rectitude	Wisdom
Emotional weakness	Depression	Instability	Obsession	Anguish	Fear

functional network of channels that forms a complex grid throughout the human body. This grid serves as a sort of master template for both the circulatory and nervous systems, and for all the other vital organs and their functions. Any congestion or obstruction in the blood and nervous systems can usually be traced to a blockage or imbalance in the energy network, and may therefore be treated by clearing the related channel and rebalancing the flow of energy through it.

The most powerful energy vessels in the human system are called *mai*, or 'channels', and they constitute a sort of reservoir from which all the other pathways draw their energy. The main system of major channels is called *chi jing ba mai*, the 'Eight Extraordinary Channels', and this is the network that is activated, balanced and replenished with energy in most forms of chi-gung work, including still sitting and 'moving meditation' exercises. The three major channels in this network are the Governing Channel that runs up the back along the spine, the Conception Channel that runs down the front of the body, and the Central or Thrusting Channel, which runs from the crown down through the centre of the body to the perineum (Fig. 1).

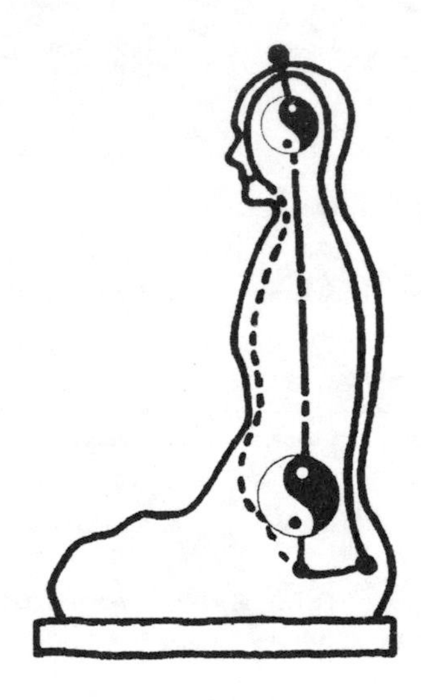

***Fig. 1* The Governing (back), Conception (front) and Thrusting (central) Channels; and the Upper (head) and Lower (abdomen) Elixir Fields**

Next in order of power and importance are the twelve organ-energy pathways, known as 'meridians' (*jing*). Each one is associated with one of the twelve vital organs recognized in TCM practice, including the Triple Burner* and Pericardium, which are

---

*Each 'burner' is associated with one of the body's three main cavities: thorax, abdomen and pelvis.

not considered organs in Western medicine. These twelve meridians flow like rivers throughout the entire body, carrying energy to their related organs and glands, regulating their associated functions and qualities, irrigating various tissues and limbs, and automatically balancing one another through the creative and control cycles of the Five Elemental Energies. Branching out like fine filaments from the eight major channels and twelve organ meridians is an intricate web of smaller vessels called *luo*, or 'capillaries', which transmit energy to every tissue and cell of the body.

Located at various spots on the body are sensitive energy terminals known as *shueh*, or 'vital points', which serve as relay stations through which the energies along related channels may be amplified or pacified by means of acupuncture, moxibustion, acupressure or massage. Acute sensitivity at these points serve as warning indicators of imbalances in those meridians and their related organs.

By replenishing the reservoirs of the eight major channels with energy drawn from external sources in nature and the cosmos, then guiding the energy to the organs and glands via the meridians and suffusing every tissue and cell with energy through the capillaries, chi-gung provides a simple, efficient way to recharge and rebalance the entire human energy system on a daily basis, thereby preventing and correcting the deficiencies and imbalances which give rise to disease and degenerative conditions in the body. Chi-gung pre-empts problems that may have already begun by restoring optimum balance and harmony to the entire system, thereby activating the body's own healing responses.

Types of Human Energy

In the parlance of chi-gung, a variety of different terms are used to describe the types of energy that exist and flow through the human system. These energies are the fundamental forces involved in chi-gung practice. The major types of human energy are briefly described below:

- *Yuan-chi* (*primordial energy*). This is the prenatal energy with which every human being is born into this world. Bestowed by the sexual plasma of father and mother at conception, it is stored after birth in the testes of men, the ovaries in women, and the adrenal cortex in both. It constitutes a reserve of vital energy which the body may draw upon when normal supplies of postnatal Fire energy extracted from food, water and air run low. However, since each individual is born with a limited potential of *yuan-chi*, the faster you use it up due to poor diet, frequent illness, chronic stress and 'fast living', the shorter your lifespan, and the weaker your immune response becomes. Sometimes also referred to as Water energy, *yuan-chi* is regarded as an important foundation for sustaining robust health and attaining longevity, and its conservation and tonification are fundamental principles of chi-gung practice.

• *Jen-chi* (*true energy*). This is the postnatal energy derived from digestion, respiration, metabolism and the other basic bodily functions, and constitutes the mainstay of daily life. Also known as Fire energy, it begins to supply the system with energy the moment a baby has its umbilical cord cut and draws in its first breath of air. True energy is produced in the blood when the nutrient energies refined from food digested in the stomach meet and fuse in the bloodstream with atmospheric energies extracted from air by the lungs. Chi-gung improves the body's capacity to produce True energy, especially when a healthy diet is followed, and the breathing methods used in chi-gung enhance the lungs' efficiency in extracting energy from air. Thus chi-gung helps conserve precious stores of *yuan-chi* by enhancing the body's supplies of *jen-chi*. True energy takes two basic functional forms in the human system: nourishing energy and guardian energy.

• *Ying-chi* (*nourishing energy*). *Ying-chi* is the fuel of metabolism and other vital functions of the organs and cells, and it travels within the blood vessels and the energy meridiens, which distribute it to every organ, gland, tissue and cell of the body, providing the basic nourishment and energy that activates the entire system. Its potency depends upon the quality of food and water consumed, the purity of the air one breathes, and the efficiency of the digestive, respiratory and circulatory systems. Correct breathing, clean blood, and strong heart and liver functions are preconditions for the unimpeded flow of blood and energy required for efficient delivery of nourishing energy to all parts of the body. Chi-gung gives a powerful boost to all of these functions, insuring adequate supplies of this energy to the whole system.

• *Wei-chi* (*guardian energy*). Guardian energy moves outside the bloodstream and energy channels and is distributed evenly throughout the surface of the body, in the subcutaneous tissue of the skin and around the exterior surface, where it forms a protective shell of energy that resists invasion by aberrant external energies from the environment, such as extremes of weather, radiation and negative energies from other people. The strength and density of one's Guardian energy determines the level of the body's overall resistance to the external factors of imbalanced energy that give rise to disease. *Wei-chi* responds automatically to shifts in ambient environmental energies to maintain optimum balance between internal and external forces. Perspiration, pores, pH balance and other vital functions of the skin play essential roles in the way Guardian energy responds to environmental challenges. Since the skin is an external extension of the lungs, chi-gung breathing helps maintain a strong defensive aura of Guardian energy around the entire surface of the body.

• *Dzang and fu chi* (*solid and hollow organ energy*). These are the energies associated with the 'solid' Yin organs (*dzang*) and the 'hollow' Yang organs (*fu*), each pair of which is governed by one of the Five Elemental Energies. These energies are involved in all the body's vital functions and associated qualities as outlined in Table 1 (see page 17). The vital organ-energies of the solid and hollow organs respond to external sources of the Five Elemental energies drawn from nature through food, water, air, weather factors, colours and herbs, as well as related internal factors such as emotions, thoughts, hormones and metabolic processes, and their mutual balance, which may be mediated by chi-gung, is a primary indicator of health and a major factor in overall vitality and longevity.

• *Jing-chi* (*essential energy*). This is a potent type of energy derived from the conversion of the purest, most potent forms of essence in the body, particularly sexual fluids, hormones and neurochemicals. When these essential fluids are conserved rather than dissipated, they may be transformed into the potent energy of *jing-chi* through the internal alchemy (*nei-gung*) of the Three Treasures. This sort of energy suffuses the entire body with a potent vitality that enhances immunity, promotes mental clarity, increases stamina and prolongs life.

• *Ling-chi* (*spiritual energy*). *Ling-chi* is the subtlest and most highly refined of all the energies in the human system and the product of the most advanced stages of practice, whereby the ordinary energies of the body are transformed into pure spiritual vitality. This type of highly refined energy enhances spiritual awareness, improves all cerebral functions, and constitutes the basic fuel for the highest level of spiritual work, such as gestating the 'Spiritual Embryo' (*ling-tai*) of immortality, attaining the enlightened state of mind and achieving the body of pure light known as the 'Rainbow Body', which serves as a vehicle of entry into the astral realms of existence beyond the material world.

Basic Modes of Moving Energy

In all forms of chi-gung, there is a variety of different modes of moving energy through the human system, as well as in and out of the human energy field. All of them are guided by the faculty of mind known as *yi* (intent, or will power) and regulated by breath control. At least several of these modes are generally involved in any particular style of chi-gung practice, and the modes selected for working with energy depend upon the overall purpose of the exercise. The basic modes of moving energy most frequently employed in chi-gung are briefly discussed below:

• *Shi-chi* (*drawing energy in*). This term refers to methods by which energy is drawn into the system from external sources through vital energy gates on the body. The points most often used for this purpose are the *yung-chuan* (Bubbling Spring) points on the soles of the feet, the *lao-gung* (Labour Palace) points on the palms of the hands, the *ni-wang-gung* (Medicine Palace) and *bai-hui* (Hundred Confluence) points on the crown of the head, the *hui-yin* (Yin Confluence) point at the perineum, and the *tan-jung* (Central Terrace) point at the heart. This method requires one-pointed mental focus on the energy gates selected for practice, the visualization of energy as light flowing through the point, and the concerted application of intent to draw energy in through the gates. Energy usually enters the system on the inhalation phase of breath.

• *Shing-chi* (*circulating energy*). This mode is used to circulate energy through the major channels, vital meridiens and minor capillaries of the human energy network. Its purpose is to clear obstructions and eliminate stagnant energy from the channels, irrigate the organs and tissues with fresh energy, balance Yin and Yang polarity throughout the system and harmonize the vital functions governed by the Five Elemental Energies. It may also be employed to target specific organs or tissues for treatment with healing energy, or to circulate energy in particular channels for refinement and transformation, such as in the Microcosmic Orbit meditation practice.

• *Pai-chi* (*expelling energy*). This method is used to expel stagnant, toxic, excess or other unwanted energies from the system by moving it out through specific energy gates, such as on the palms and soles, and the point between the eyebrows. This sort of energy is usually visualized as dark fog or smoke as it is driven from the system, and it is expelled on the exhalation phase of breath. It may be used to clear the entire system of stagnant *chi* or to purge specific organs via their related meridiens and points.

• *Huan-chi* (*exchanging energy*). Exchanging energy means intermingling one's energy with an external source in order to refresh, recharge and rebalance one's entire energy system. For example, practising *huan-chi* on the beach or high up on the mountains quickly recharges the whole system with the pure, potent energies generated by oceans and mountains. Practising in a forest allows one to exchange energy with trees, which produce very potent *chi*. In the Dual Cultivation style of Taoist sexual yoga, male and female intermingle and exchange their energies in order to boost and balance one another's vitality through the internal alchemy of sexual essence and energy.

• *Yang-chi* (*cultivating energy*). This refers to the phase of practice in which internal energy is concentrated and stored in the lower elixir field centre below the navel, in other major storage centres or in a specific organ targeted for tonification. For example, you may wish to cultivate Wood energy for the liver or Water energy for the kidney system, or cultivate the essential energy of hormones to boost vitality.

• *Lien-chi* (*refining energy*). Refining energy means to increase the purity and potency of a particular type of energy, and this is usually done in still sitting practice, using a fusion of mind and breath to refine energy in the 'cauldron' of the lower elixir field, then slowly drawing it upward along the spine into the upper elixir field in the head. This mode of internal practice is often compared with the external alchemy of trying to refine pure gold from baser metals, using the 'Fire' of internal heat, the 'Water' of vital essence, and the 'wind' of breath in the cauldron of the energy centre in the abdomen.

• *Hua-chi* (*transforming energy*). Transformation of essence into energy and energy into spirit is one of the fundamental formulas in the internal alchemy of the Three Treasures of life. The first stage involves the conservation, concentration and purification of vital essence, particularly hormones, sexual fluids and neurotransmitters. These fluids are then 'steamed' in the energy centres in order to transform them into higher forms of energy, the highest form being the *ling-chi* utilized for advanced spiritual work.

• *Fa-chi* (*emitting energy*). This is the mode of energy work used by master chi-gung healers to transmit healing energy from their own energy fields into the systems of their clients. Such energy is almost always emitted from the *lao-gung* point in the palm of the hand, although sometimes the fingertips, feet, brow point or even the entire body may be used for transmitting healing energy. In China, martial artists sometimes used this technique to deliver an 'energy blow' to vulnerable points on their opponent's bodies, or to envelope themselves in a protective shield of energy to deflect similar blows aimed at them.

Managing Energy with the 'Water Mind' of Intent

The postnatal aspect of spirit that governs our daily lives is known in Taoist practice as the 'human mind', and it has two distinctly different facets. One is the 'mind of emotion' or 'Fire mind', which resides in the heart. The other is the 'mind of intent', or 'Water mind', which resides in the head.

Like fire, the mind of emotion is volatile, hot and unpredictable, tending to run quickly out of control, and easily inflamed by the winds of external stimuli. By contrast, the mind of intent is like water – clear, cool, calm and stable, capable of reflecting 'everything under Heaven' without disturbing its own nature. While the Fire mind is linked directly to the five senses and responds emotionally to the constant play of sensory perceptions, the Water mind, when still and silent, enjoys direct access to the infinite wisdom and awareness of primordial spirit. Intent is the faculty by which the Water mind may take command of the human system, quell the flames of the emotional Fire mind, and manage human energy in accordance with the universal laws of wisdom and compassion rather than the dictates of personal ego and selfish desire. As the Taoist sage and chi-gung master Chang San-feng wrote six centuries ago, 'When wisdom controls desire, you live long; when desire overcomes wisdom, you die early.'

One of the primary goals of chi-gung practice is to learn how to harness passion with wisdom, control Fire with Water, and use intent to manage energy rather than letting energy be wasted by emotion. The purpose of transforming essence into energy, refining energy and raising it up the spinal channels into the head, then transforming it into spirit, is to nurture the awareness and volitional command of the Water mind, and to enhance the power of intent to control emotions and manage energy. Once this has been achieved, the second phase of internal alchemy may be practised, whereby spirit commands energy, and energy commands essence, which means that the mind gains firm control over the body through the medium of energy, realizing the primordial power of 'mind over matter'.

The ultimate stage of Taoist self-cultivation and internal alchemy is to fathom the mysteries of awareness itself and gain volitional control of our highest spiritual faculties. 'If you can open this one gate,' states an ancient Taoist axiom, 'all other gates will open naturally.' At the core of all chi-gung practice – whether moving or still, martial or medical – lies the deep still pool of the Water mind, in which is clearly reflected all the wisdom of the universe. The key point is to bring this primordial wisdom into the light of conscious awareness during one's lifetime, rather than leaving it to lie fallow in the dark recesses of the subconscious levels of the mind from one lifetime to the next. In order to do this, you must enlist the full power of intent to control the volatile responses of the emotional Fire mind and manage your life in accordance with the primordial principles of the 'Mind of Tao'. As the 2000-year-old *Wen Tzu Classic* states, 'When the spirit takes command, the body naturally follows it, and this arrangement benefits all Three Treasures. When the body leads the way, the spirit trails along, and this damages all Three Treasures.'

Chi-Gung as a Pillar of Life

Chi-gung is an integral and essential component in the ancient Taoist system of healthcare, life extension and spiritual self-cultivation known as *yang-sheng dao*, or the 'Tao of Cultivating Life'. This system is patterned on the eternal ways of nature and the transcendent laws of the universe and includes everything from diet and herbal supplements to breathing and exercise, sexual yoga and chi-gung, meditation and internal alchemy, awareness and attitude. In order to gain full benefit from chi-gung, it must always be properly practised within the overall context of the whole *yang-sheng* system of cultivating life.

Of all the various *yang-sheng* methods of cultivating health and longevity, chi-gung is the swiftest and most effective way to nurture, balance and manage the basic energies of life. As well as working on a physical level in the body, chi-gung enhances cerebral functions and awakens latent talents and abilities that might otherwise lie dormant for ever. It also pacifies emotions and balances moods, and stimulates the cultivation of the highest spiritual virtues by opening the mind to the universal wisdom of enlightened awareness.

Cultivating spiritual virtues such as wisdom, compassion, patience and tolerance is every bit as important in chi-gung practice as cultivating physical strength, health and power, for without the virtues of spirit, the power of chi-gung is easily bent towards deviant purposes by the fickle Fire mind of the human ego and selfish emotions. Using the power and latent abilities awakened by chi-gung for fighting, fortune-telling, gambling and profiteering are typical examples of what can happen when chi-gung is practised without guidance from the wisdom and intent of spirit. The end result of all deviant applications of chi-gung is the total loss of power, erosion of health, foreshortening of life and ultimate exclusion from the higher realms of existence after death.

The reason for this is quite clear: besides nurturing the energies required for life on earth and promoting longevity of the physical body, chi-gung also opens a gate to the infinitely powerful forces of the universe and establishes a direct link between the personal energy field of the individual practitioner and the universal energy fields of the cosmos and all creation. Anyone who tries to harness this power without respecting the wisdom and compassion with which it is inseparably linked at the source of creation is truly 'playing with fire' and is very likely to get badly burned.

In human life, most people enslave their minds and spend their energies to serve their bodies and satisfy their desires, thereby 'mistaking the servant for the master'. In the higher orders of the universe, which human life was designed to reflect, spirit is the master, and energy is the tool through which the spirit expresses itself creatively in material form. In order to harness the power of the universe for the benefit of humanity, human beings must pattern their bodies as well as their minds on the universal order of creation reflected in nature and the cosmos and known as the Tao, for this is the context in which human life evolved. When practising the Tao, one must learn to balance physical health and vitality with spiritual awareness and virtue, for that is the one and only way the Tao works.

CHAPTER 1

Historical Development of Chi-Gung in China

Chi-gung first took root during prehistoric times in ancient China, when a ceremonial tribal dance known as the 'Great Dance' (*da-wu*) was discovered to have therapeutic benefits for those who frequently performed it. This discovery probably occurred about 10,000 years ago and marks the birth of chi-gung, the earliest branch of Traditional Chinese Medicine (TCM) to develop. At that time, chi-gung and all forms of medicine were the exclusive domain of tribal shamans, whose role it was to commune with the powers of Heaven (*tien*) and Earth (*di*) for the benefit of Humanity (*ren*). By the third century BC, chi-gung had already acquired its role as the core practice in the three major fields with which it is still identified today: medicine, martial arts and meditation.

In Taoist lore, the original progenitor of the health and longevity practices with which chi-gung has been linked so long was the Yellow Emperor (Huang Ti), who ruled over a confederation of tribal clans in northern China around 2700 BC. The Yellow Emperor is said to have practised meditation and breathing exercises and cultivated the internal alchemy of Taoist sexual yoga, engaging in frequent sexual intercourse without ejaculation with his harem of 1200 women, thereby reaching the age of 111 years and achieving spiritual immortality. Huang Ti's discourses on health and longevity with his chief medical advisor, Chi Po, are recorded in the great medical text entitled *The Yellow Emperor's Classic of Internal Medicine* (*Huang Ti Nei Ching*), which first appeared in written form sometime around the third century BC.

The first written references to chi-gung in China are found in texts dating back about 4000 years, when another dance specifically developed to ward off disease, regulate breathing and balance energy was practised as preventative health therapy in the flood-prone basin of the Yellow River in northern China, where Chinese civilization first took shape. The heavy dampness in this region caused rheumatism, sluggish circulation and energy stagnation in the inhabitants living there. The chi-gung dance, which combined breath control with rhythmic bodily movements, patterned on those of animals in nature, was performed to drive dampness from the joints, muscles and other tissues of the body, to stimulate circulation of blood and energy, and to replenish the entire system with fresh infusions of *chi*.

Since those ancient times, many different branches of practice have sprouted and grown from the main trunk of chi-gung, each with its own particular style and purpose, all bestowing the same basic benefits of health and longevity, physiological balance and emotional equilibrium, mental clarity and spiritual harmony. Today the art and science of chi-gung continue to develop faster than ever before as new theoretical insights and practical applications are discovered by contemporary practitioners. As the scholar Fu Yi wrote nearly 2000 years ago, 'Chi-gung is an art that pleases the spirit, slows the ageing process and prolongs life.'

In this age of spiritual discontent, chronic degenerative disease and life-threatening ways of living, chi-gung's potential for both curative healing and preventative healthcare, as well as for personal self-cultivation and spiritual inspiration, is greater than it ever was before. So let's take a look at how this remarkable art and science of life developed and progressed through the major dynastic eras of Chinese history, gradually evolving to become one of Chinese civilization's greatest gifts to the world.

Yin and Chou Periods (18th–4th centuries BC)

One of the main figures referred to in texts of this early era is the legendary 'Methusela' of ancient China, Peng Tzu, who is said to have lived for 800 years due to the benefits of chi-gung practice. Credited as the progenitor of the *dao-yin* method of moving chi through the body with long slow extensions of the limbs combined with deep abdominal breathing, Peng Tzu is said to have risen every morning at 3 a.m. to sit in silent meditation until dawn. His favourite practices included massaging the eyes and other parts of the body with the palms of the hands, churning the tongue around in the mouth to stimulate secretion of the beneficial saliva known as 'sweet dew' (*gan-lu*) from the ducts below the tongue and swallowing it, and very slow, deliberate *dao-yin* exercises. Peng Tzu is therefore regarded as the founding father of chi-gung as a path to longevity.

During this period, China was a completely agrarian society and therefore paid very close attention to the recurring rhythms of nature and to cyclic cosmic phenomena. Shamans, who were the earliest 'medicine men', were responsible for the health of tribal people, and one way they performed this duty was by trying to harmonize human affairs with the enduring patterns of nature (Earth) and the cosmos (Heaven).

An important prince of the early Chou dynasty named Wang Chih-chiao is said to have practised the breathing method known as *tu-na* ('expel and draw in') while sitting in still meditation, as a means of restoring primordial vitality. This early historical reference to chi-gung practice in the royal household shows that ever since ancient times, chi-gung was practised as an integral element in the daily life of royalty and aristocracy in China, and this remained the case until the 20th century.

The early Chou period also produced the ancient book of divination called the *I-Ching* (*Book of Change*), one of the most important and influential texts in classical Chinese civilization. The *I-Ching* is based on a system of divination known as the eight trigrams (*ba-gua*), from which 64 hexagrams are conjured to predict the probability of future events and to invoke the universal principles of Heaven and Earth as solutions for the problems of Humanity. This is done by 'reading' the prevailing patterns and cyclic transformations of nature and the cosmos, as reflected in the arrangement of lines in the particular hexagrams which appear in response to specific questions. The concept of applying the universal principles of nature and the cosmos to the temporal affairs of human life became a fundamental tenet of early Taoist philosophy and a basic precept of chi-gung practice. Four important principles were drawn from the *I-Ching* during this formative period and adapted as a theoretical basis for chi-gung:

1. Human health and disease, happiness and malaise, all follow the cyclic transformations of Heaven and Earth.
2. When human thoughts, emotions and activities all reach a stable state of integral balance and functional harmony, this produces the most auspicious conditions for human life.
3. Whenever a person falls ill or encounters misfortune, the best way to correct the situation is to still the mind, pacify the emotions, harmonize the bodily functions, and cultivate a state of balance and equanimity. This approach results in the complete recovery of health, the full restoration of vitality and

the timely resurgence of good fortune by bringing the human system into a state of synergistic balance with the forces of Heaven and Earth, without resort to medicine or any other external means.

4. Movement and stillness are relative poles in a single unified state of existence, not separate phenomena, just as Yin and Yang are complementary poles of the same basic universal energy.

These principles constituted the fundamental philosophical roots of chi-gung in all subsequent eras.

Warring States, Chin and Han Eras (403 BC–220 AD)

As the Chou dynasty began to disintegrate, a period of political and social turmoil known as the Warring States Period dawned in China. But it was also a time of great intellectual creativity, giving birth to Confucius, Lao Tze and many other sages and scholars. Some of China's most important medical texts were compiled during this era, based on oral traditions handed down for thousands of years. Since the 'Old Sage' Lao Tze, to whom the *Tao Teh Ching* is attributed, was regarded as the pre-eminent Taoist philosopher of this period, Taoist tradition became known during this time as *Huang Lao Tao*, or 'The Way of the Yellow Emperor and the Old Sage'.

In 221 BC, the aggressive Chin kingdom swept down from the northeast frontier and united the warring states of China into a single unified empire for the first time in history. It is from the militant Chin kingdom that the West derived the name 'China'. The founding emperor, Chin Shih-huang, was deeply interested in alchemy as a means towards longevity, and he kept many alchemists in his court. However, he followed the misguided external school of alchemy, which, like its counterparts in medieval Europe, attempted to concoct a 'Golden Pill' (*jin-dan*) of immortality from minerals, heavy metals and toxic herbs. This 'magic bullet' approach to health and longevity, which in many ways resembles modern Western medicine's chemical approach to curing disease, was also encouraged by the emperors of the early Han dynasty, such as Han Wu-ti. Numerous princes of the Chin and Han eras met an early death after ingesting these toxic mineral concoctions.

Nevertheless, among the alchemists who served the royal courts of China were also a few genuine Taoist adepts who kept the true traditions of Huang Lao Tao alive and continued to develop chi-gung and other natural health and longevity techniques. For example, the Chin prime minister, Lu Pu-wei, compiled a text entitled *Spring and Autumn Book of Lu*, in which he collected and commented upon many ancient practices involving the 'Harmony of Heaven and Humanity', particularly the integration of human activity with seasonal cycles and other natural forces. The comprehensive Taoist healthcare system known as *Yang Sheng Tao*, 'The Way of Cultivating Life', became codified during this time and included such tried-and-true methods as balanced diet, deep breathing, *dao-yin*-style exercises and sexual yoga.

During the later Han period, there appeared one of the greatest figures in the history of TCM as well as Taoist internal alchemy – the physician Hua To, who systematized the exercise form known as 'Play of the Five Beasts' (*wu-chin-shi*) into a type of physical therapy for curing disease. One of Hua To's most distinguished patrons and patients was the famous military hero Tsao Tsao, who practised chi-gung as part of his own personal health regime. The Taoist adept Wei Po-yang also lived during the late Han and wrote one of the most important texts on Taoist alchemy ever produced, *Tsan Tung Chi* (The Union of the Triplex Equation), in which he discusses the internal alchemy of deep breathing and energy transformation and the Dual Cultivation of sexual yoga. The *Tai Ping Ching* ('Classic of Great Peace') also appeared at this time, summarizing many of the traditional teachings of the Huang Lao lineage.

Recent archaeological excavations at the Ma Wang tombs in Chang Sha, Hunan Province, have yielded concrete historical evidence that many of the most important chi-gung methods still used today were widely practised in China during the late Han era, nearly 2000 years ago. Documents and scrolls with detailed diagrams of the human energy system, illustrated instructions for performing *dao-yin* and other chi-gung exercises, and anatomical charts showing how deep diaphragmic breathing works were found in these tombs. These finds provided conclusive evidence that by the second century AD, the internal school of energy cultivation had supplanted the external school of toxic mineral compounds as a basis for the alchemy of human longevity, and that the human energy system had been clearly recognized as the key to health and longevity.

Thus, by the end of the Han dynasty, the emphasis on health and longevity practices had made a decisive shift away from 'magic potions' to the internal methods of energy management that have prevailed ever since. This was a crucial development in the evolution of chi-gung, because it reflected the recognition that the only true 'elixir of life' was the immaterial elixir of internal energy, and that the only way to obtain this elixir was through disciplined personal practice. This made health and longevity available to anyone who was willing to learn and practise the techniques, rather than only to the rich and influential segments of society who could afford expensive medicines. Medicinal herbs and diet remained important supplementary supports of chi-gung, but from this point on, the primary focus in human health and longevity rested on energy. The central importance of energy as the most decisive factor in health and longevity still remains the most distinctive hallmark of chi-gung as well as TCM in general, distinguishing it clearly from most Western medicine, which still attempts to conquer disease and extend life by the long discredited means of expensive drugs, toxic chemical compounds and mechanical devices.

The Three Kingdoms, and Northern and Southern Dynasties (200–580 AD)

After the disintegration of the Han dynasty, there followed another period of political turmoil and rapid social change that stimulated significant new developments in the field of medicine and chi-gung. Around 300 AD, in the Chin kingdom, an important text called *Huang Ting Ching* ('Yellow Court Classic') appeared, in which the internal elixir (*nei-dan*) school of thought became the prevalent theoretical basis of chi-gung, citing internal energy rather than external medicinal compounds as the key to its practice. The Three Elixir Field theory of internal alchemy was also clearly elucidated in this text, with vital energy centres located in the brain, solar plexus and lower abdomen serving as the three seats of energy transformation, with spirit, particularly intent (*yi*), firmly in command of the entire process. This text also describes practices whereby the hormone essence secreted by sexual and other glands is utilized as a source of essential energy, which is then further refined and drawn up through the spinal channels into the brain to nourish the higher spiritual faculties, a technique referred to as *huan jing bu nao*, or 'recycling essence to tonify the brain'.

During the early part of the fourth century AD, a Taoist philosopher, physician, and chi-gung practitioner by the name of Ko Hung wrote a milestone compendium of Taoist theory and practice entitled *Pao Pu Tze* ('He Who Embraces the Uncarved Block'). Still regarded as one of the most influential texts in the development of chi-gung practice, the *Pao Pu Tze* was the first book to clearly distinguish the two goals of physical longevity and spiritual immortality, which for many centuries had confused and misled many a practitioner into believing that immortality of the physical body could actually be achieved. Ko Hung pointed out that with disciplined practice, corporeal longevity could certainly be accomplished, but that the ultimate goal of practice was spiritual immortality, which could only be achieved by ultimately abandoning the corporeal body. These two goals could be pursued together, he pointed out, because the common element in both is energy. Thus, by cultivating internal energy, one could live a long and healthy life in this world, while also gaining sufficient time and energy to lay the foundation for immortal existence in the spiritual world after the death of the body.

Ko Hung stressed the importance of correct breathing as the key to chi-gung practice, citing breath as the postnatal manifestation of prenatal energy and thus the key to cultivating internal energy. He combined breath control with the soft, slow *dao-yun* form of exercise, resulting in the 'moving meditation' style of practice which still prevails in chi-gung today. In addition, he advocated the daily practice of still sitting meditation, using internal focus of attention (*tsun seh*), one-pointed awareness (*shou-yi*), and visualization (*guan-siang*) as the primary techniques for regulating energy directly with the mind. As part of his eclectic style of practice, he also discoursed at great length on the benefits of Dual Cultivation sexual yoga (*shuang-shiou*) as a swift means of building up internal energy for use in higher spiritual practice. This method involves prolonged intercourse without male ejaculation and with multiple female orgasm in order to build up strong polarity between male and female, so that at the moment of female orgasm, a fusion of Yin and Yang energies would occur spontaneously in both partners, balancing their *chi* and raising vitality to ever higher levels.

During the Southern Liang dynasty (502–557 AD), there appeared in China an eccentric old Buddhist monk from India named Bodhidharma. The Chinese called him Ta Mo. Dressed in tattered robes and professing an unorthodox style of tantric Buddhism, Ta Mo entered the famous Shao Lin Temple, retired to a cold stone chamber, and sat there in seclusion for nine years, meditating in total silence. It is said that a Chinese monk, eager to receive teachings from Ta Mo, chopped off his own hand and presented it to the master on a tray to stir him from his long reverie, but Ta Mo was not moved by this act.

When he finally emerged from his meditation, Ta Mo began to

teach the monks at the Shao Lin Temple how to strengthen their bodies as a foundation for higher spiritual practices. At the same time, he taught Chinese martial artists how to apply spiritual cultivation to enhance their martial skills. Prior to Ta Mo's arrival, Taoist adepts focused themselves single-mindedly on either prolonged still sitting meditation for spiritual purposes, or on rigorous physical training for martial prowess. Consequently, Chinese monks suffered from all sorts of physical ailments due to lack of exercise, while martial artists became violently aggressive pugilists with virtually no foundation in spiritual awareness. Ta Mo brought meditation and martial arts together in a single unified system of practice, completely revolutionizing both spiritual and martial cultivation in China. Introducing the *pranayama* breathing exercises and yoga stretching techniques of India, he combined them with the indigenous Chinese *dao-yin* and 'Play of the Five Beasts' regimes. The result was Chinese chi-gung and martial arts as we know them today.

Ta Mo went on to become the founding patriarch of Chan Buddhism, which blended elements of Chinese Taoism with the tantric Buddhism he brought from India. It was this form of Buddhism that later spread to Korea and Japan, where it became known as Zen. The subsequent paradox of martial monks and spiritual martial artists which henceforth characterized the Buddhist and Taoist scene in China developed as a direct result of Ta Mo's teachings.

Ta Mo is credited as the author of two pithy books of teachings that for many centuries were held in well-guarded secrecy by senior monks and martial arts masters. These two classics form the pillars of all the later schools of internal (*nei-gung*) style chi-gung practice in China and are probably the most influential written texts in the entire history of chi-gung. The first is called *Yi Chin Ching*, or 'Tendon Changing Classic', and the second, more esoteric, volume is entitled *Hsi Sui Ching*, or 'Marrow Cleansing Classic'. Together, these two volumes cover everything from basic stretching and loosening exercises that limber the body for meditation as well as martial arts practice, to the most advanced practices of internal alchemy, including techniques for transforming sexual essence and energy into spiritual vitality. The importance of these two texts in the evolution of chi-gung, martial arts and spiritual self-cultivation in China cannot be overstated, yet today they remain relatively unknown in the Western world.

Ta Mo's great contribution to chi-gung was to bring body and mind together for spiritual as well as physical self-cultivation, linking the two poles of practice by focusing attention on the common denominator of energy. This fusion also bridged the gap between internal and external, movement and stillness, power and awareness, and other dualistic qualities that still divide Western philosophy, religion and science into two hostile camps. According to Ta Mo's teachings, the key to entering the highest state of awareness is to avoid making arbitrary distinctions between 'this' and 'that' and to transcend all distinctions by finding the common ground in both. As he wrote in the *Tendon Changing Classic*, 'Of paramount importance is to seek movement within quiescence and to seek quiescence within movement, moving softly and continuously until one enters the sublime state.'

The sublime state might refer to spiritual awareness, physical vitality, emotional equilibrium or perfect health, depending on the focus of the practice, while the fusion of movement and quiescence may be found in slow-moving exercise or still-sitting meditation, depending on the form of practice. Ultimately, it doesn't make any difference, because when body and mind are linked together with energy, the goals of spiritual as well as physical practice are simultaneously realized. As an old Taoist maxim puts it, 'If you can open this one door, all other doors open as well.'

Tang Dynasty (618–906 AD)

Widely regarded as the 'Golden Age' of Chinese civilization, the Tang dynasty was a particularly fertile period for Taoism in China, and chi-gung continued to develop under the auspices of imperial patronage. Since the imperial family carried the same surname (Li) as the great Taoist sage Lao Tze, Tang emperors regarded themselves as direct descendants of this venerable figure, and therefore Taoism enjoyed immense favour during this period.

The physician and Taoist adept Sun Ssu-miao, who lived to the age of 101 during the early Tang, outliving several of the emperors he served, wrote an important treatise on medicine entitled *Chian Chin Fang* ('Precious Recipes'), in which he described several methods of healing the body with chi-gung. The method of healing with sound, known as the 'Six Syllable Secret', was explained in detail in this book, which also emphasized the importance of correct breathing as a means of regulating human energy. Another physician named Chao Yuan-fang wrote *Chu Ping Yuan Hou Lun* ('Discussion of Causes and Symptoms of Disease'), in which he described over 250 ways of enhancing the flow of energy in the human system with various forms of chi-gung.

The Taoist adept Ssu-ma Cheng Chen (647–735), who advocated strict adherence to the original quiescent spirit expounded by Lao Tze in the *Tao Teh Ching*, wrote extensively on the internal elixir (*nei-dan*) method of Taoist meditation. He stressed that the key to awakening *ling-chi*, or 'spiritual energy', was first to still the postnatal human mind, i.e., to stop thinking. In order to awaken the true primordial spirit and activate the energy of higher awareness, one must first silence the brain, particularly the cerebral cortex. Here again we see the subtle interaction of movement and stillness in Taoist practice. In this case, as long as the human mind (brain) is moving with constant discursive thought, the primordial spirit of higher awareness lies dormant. But when we still the brain, we thereby allow the original spirit to awaken and transform our mental energy into pure primordial awareness. Ssu-ma also recommended a strict vegetarian diet, claiming that animal foods such as meat overstimulated and polluted the body, making it more difficult for the mind to enter the states of quietude.

Some alchemists, however, continued to promote the 'magic bullet' approach as a short cut to longevity. However, when the Emperor Hsien Tzung died in the prime of life in the year 820, after ingesting a pill prepared for him from toxic minerals and heavy metals by the alchemist Liu Pi, this chemical approach to health and longevity finally fell into disgrace once and for all, and the internal elixir (*nei-dan*) school, which advocated internal energy work as the only effective path to health and longevity, gained permanent acceptance.

Another great name in Taoism during the Tang era was the adept Lu Tung-ping, who later became enshrined as one of the beloved 'Eight Immortals' of Taoism. Lu wrote extensively on the internal elixir school of practice, and emphasized the importance of the internal alchemy of the Three Treasures as the sole path to the primordial awareness of enlightenment. As Lu Tung-ping puts it:

> The human body consists entirely of essence, energy, and spirit, and these are known as the Three Treasures. Enlightenment and spontaneity are both achieved from these, yet very few people recognize the Three Treasures, even in their postnatal manifestations . . . Essence can only be concentrated with energy, but both essence and energy can only be regulated by spirit, and cultivating energy is only a matter of conserving the spirit. To conserve the spirit, one must stop thinking.

Sung and Yuan Dynasties (960–1368 AD)

During the Sung period, chi-gung continued to progress rapidly, particularly the internal elixir school. Among the many masters who appeared in China at this time, the most outstanding was Chang Po-tuan, the major lineage holder of the Complete Reality School of Taoism. Chang advocated intensive practice of the internal alchemy of the Three Treasures as the main path to health and longevity as well as spiritual enlightenment, but he also stressed the importance of other supplemental regimens such as diet and herbs, physical exercise and sexual discipline, to support the internal elixir practices.

Chang Po-tuan wrote many important texts on internal alchemy, including detailed instructions on practice and lucid explanations of theoretical principles. Among his writings, the most outstanding are *The Secret of Opening the Passes, The Four-Hundred Character Treatise on the Golden Elixir*, and his greatest work of all, *Understanding Reality*. Selections from his work have been translated into English by Thomas Cleary in *Vitality, Energy, Spirit* (Shambhala Publications), including these passages on internal alchemy from his text on the Golden Elixir:

> When the eyes do not look, the ears do not listen, the tongue doesn't speak, the nose doesn't smell, and the limbs do not move, this is called the five energies returning to the source.
>
> When vitality is transformed into energy, energy is transformed into spirit, and spirit is transformed into space; this is called the three flowers gathered on the peak . . .
>
> Refining the vitality means refining the basic vitality. It does not refer to the vitality felt through sexuality. Refining the energy means refining the basic energy. It does not refer to the energy of breathing through the nose and mouth. Refining the spirit means refining the basic spirit. It does not refer to the spirit of mind and thought.

Another important master of the early Sung period was Wang Che, a martial artist as well as an erudite scholar from northern China who retired from a flourishing professional career at the age of forty-seven in order to devote himself fully to internal practice of the Tao. He is most renowned for his rigorous training of seven devoted disciples who carried the torch of Complete Reality Taoism far and wide throughout China.

Chi-gung's central role in Traditional Chinese Medicine also received a major boost during this time, when the physician Wang Wei-yi cured the Emperor Jen Tzung of a serious ailment using acupuncture. As a result, the emperor himself took up acupuncture practice, established an imperial institute for research and training in acupuncture, and built a temple in honour of the ancient physician Pien Chueh, enshrining him as the patron saint of acupuncture. In 1026 AD, Wang Wei-yi designed the famous 'Brass Man', which today is still used as a master template for the major meridiens and points used in acupuncture therapy. These developments further established chi as the central factor in the treatment of disease.

During the later Southern Sung period, the great military hero Yueh Fei created a system of chi-gung exercises that is still practised widely throughout the world today. This famous set is called the 'Eight Pieces of Brocade', and it was designed to stimulate and balance the flow of energy throughout the entire human system, while simultaneously toning muscles, stretching tendons and loosening joints throughout the body. It remains one of the most effective and practical sets in the entire chi-gung repertoire. Yueh Fei is also credited with developing the well-known Hsing-Yi style of internal-energy martial arts.

The most renowned master to appear in the ensuing Mongol Yuan dynasty was Chang San-feng, the progenitor of what has become the most widely practised of all chi-gung forms in the world today – Tai Chi Chuan. But Chang was more than just a martial artist. He was also a master meditator, a medical practitioner and a highly erudite Taoist philosopher. The underlying theme in all of his practices and writings is the central importance of chi as the foundation of the internal elixir that confers health, longevity and spiritual awareness. Here's a sample of his writing from Thomas Cleary's compendium *Vitality, Energy, Spirit*:

> It is said that when you breathe out you contact the Root of Heaven and experience a sense of openness, and when you breathe in you contact the Root of Earth and experience a sense of solidity. Breathing out is associated with the fluidity of a dragon, breathing in is associated with the strength of the tiger. As you go on breathing in this frame of mind, with these associations, alternating between movement and stillness, it is important that the focus of your mind does not shift.

Let the true breath come and go, a subtle continuum on the brink of existence. Tune the breathing until you get breath without breathing; become one with it, and then the spirit can be solidified and the elixir can be made.

Ming and Ching Dynasties (1368–1912 AD)

The Ming and Ching dynasties were periods of consolidation and integration in all branches of chi-gung practice. Chi-gung's role in medicine became increasingly important as a primary form of therapy in the treatment of disease, while at the same time chi-gung became the central focus in the Chinese martial arts, resulting in the ascendancy of the soft 'internal' forms over the hard 'external' forms. The third great internal style of martial arts was developed at this time by Tung Hai-chuan. Known as Pa Kua Chang ('Eight Trigrams Palm'), this intricate, beautiful style of practice involves continuous circular manoeuvres around one's opponent, with graceful turns and rhythmic movements of the limbs and torso based on the cyclic transformations of the eight trigrams in the *I-Ching*. Together, Tai Chi Chuan, Hsing Yi and Pa Kua Chang have become the triumvirate of the internal martial arts style in which chi-gung plays the central role.

Distinctions between Taoist, Buddhist and Confucian applications of chi-gung also began to dissolve during this era, and chi-gung became a system unto itself, transcending arbitrary sectarian boundaries. In the past, the distinctions between 'prenatal' and 'postnatal', 'internal' and 'external', 'nature' and 'cosmos', and so forth had divided chi-gung practice into two stages, two schools, two aspects and other dualistic distinctions. During the Ming and Ching period, chi-gung masters increasingly emphasized the fundamental unity of the primordial and temporal, breath and energy, body and mind, movement and stillness, encouraging practitioners to seek results in actual experience and to dispense with debates about doctrine. This culminated in the syncretic approach set in motion by Ta Mo during the sixth century, and set the stage for chi-gung's dissemination throughout the world during the latter part of the 20th century.

A good example of the syncretization that occurred during this period is the work of the Ching dynasty adept and writer Liu I-ming. Liu spent most of his life seeking teachings from various masters of his time, practising what he learned, sorting out the real from the false traditions, and writing lucid expositions based upon his own inner realizations. A fine selection of his insights are collected in translation by Thomas Cleary in *Awakening to the Tao*, including this observant remark:

> The Tao is unique, without duality – why do deluded people divide it into high and low? . . . When you recognize that the principles of the sages are the same, you will realize that Taoism and Buddhism are alike. If you do not understand this and seek elsewhere, you will get involved in sidetracks, wasting your life in vain imagining.

Towards the end of this period, the wall of secrecy that once surrounded chi-gung began to crumble, and it became available to whoever was willing to learn and practise it. This unfortunately led to occasional abuses, the most striking example being the so-called 'Boxer Rebellion' at the turn of the century. Thousands of poverty-stricken peasants were recruited to participate in a mass uprising against foreign occupation in Peking, with tacit support from the notorious Empress Dowager and her decadent Manchu court. Briefly trained in rudimentary martial arts and chi-gung exercises and empowered with ersatz initiation ceremonies, this ragtag corps of insurgents was assured that their bodies were now immune to the bullets and cannon fire of foreign weapons, due to protection from the 'iron armour' of *chi*. They soon discovered the contrary to be the case, and thousands of them, armed with nothing but swords and spears, died in mass attacks against the well-fortified bunkers and blazing cannons of Western troops.

Modern Era (1912–Present)

Today, chi-gung continues to develop at a faster pace than ever before, supported by scientific research programmes in China and elsewhere, and its growing popularity throughout the world as a system of preventative healthcare. While chi-gung's central role in Chinese martial arts and meditation remains important, it is in the field of medicine that chi-gung has aroused the strongest interest and greatest support for further development. It is also in medicine that chi-gung arouses the most controversy and vitriolic opposition from die-hard proponents of chemical and surgical medicine.

The first such instance in China occurred in Shanghai, in 1929, when young Chinese students trained in modern Western medicine in Japan returned to China and demanded that all forms of Traditional Chinese Medicine be legally banned as superstitious hangovers from the past. This provoked widespread resentment among the elderly quarters of society, who still preferred the holistic therapies of TCM to the invasive, caustic techniques of modern Western medicine. A delegation of renowned Chinese physicians was appointed to petition the Nationalist government for formal support for their profession, and demanded legal guarantees that they could continue to practise alongside modern Western-trained physicians. Since so many of the ageing Nationalist government leaders themselves depended on TCM, the petition was accepted, and on 17 March a bill was passed to protect traditional practitioners from interference by proponents of modern medicine. This day is still celebrated in China as 'Chinese Doctor's Day'.

More recently, after the communist takeover of China, and particularly during the Cultural Revolution, radical revolutionaries once again threatened a wholesale annihilation of everything associated with traditional Chinese culture, including medicine and chi-gung. However, like before, chi-gung was spared from oblivion due to the support of Chinese leaders themselves. Chairman Mao was quoted as saying that Chinese civilization's two greatest gifts to the world would prove to be Chinese food and Chinese medicine, a prediction that is certainly proving true. Western observers often comment on the remarkable longevity of Chinese leaders, particularly the late Deng Hsiao-ping, who despite a lifelong habit of chain-smoking cigarettes, lax attention to diet, and many past hardships in life, managed to live to the age of ninety-two. Others have survived even longer. The reason for their longevity is well known in China: each leader is treated daily with emitted *chi* by master chi-gung therapists during their entire tenure of power, and this therapy continues throughout their retirement. While they also use herbal supplements and follow special dietary guidelines towards the end of their lives, the central factor in their amazing vitality and tenacious longevity is daily infusions of healing *chi* from recognized masters of this method. Indeed, one of the quickest ways to guarantee oneself a lifetime of security and comfort in China today is to demonstrate a gift for *fa-chi*, 'emitting chi', for such practitioners are in great demand among the wealthy and powerful elite in China.

Meanwhile, in society at large, chi-gung is being practised with growing enthusiasm in China and elsewhere in the world, both as a form of preventive health and as orthodox therapy in curative medicine. There are entire hospitals now in China where the only treatment provided is chi-gung, both in the form of self-practice and as emitted *chi* from master healers, without the supplementary use of Chinese herbs or Western drugs. These hospitals have treated tens of thousands of patients, including advanced cases of cancer, with a successful cure rate that exceeds anything ever accomplished with traditional herbal medicine or modern Western therapies. Examples of these cures are presented in Chapter 5.

Suffice to say here that chi-gung promises to become the next big wave in alternative medicine as we head into the twenty-first century, and that it will make a far greater impact on the world's approach to healthcare, and present a far graver challenge to the chemical/mechanical approach of modern medicine, than any other form of traditional therapy ever has before.

CHAPTER 2

Major Categories of Chi-Gung Practice

There are countless styles, forms and classifications of chi-gung in China, based on various theoretical schools of thought, different practical purposes and diverse points of focus in practice. Chinese sources cite anywhere from 2000 to 4000 distinctive styles of chi-gung practice. Some are founded on major philosophical traditions such as Taoism, Buddhism and Confucianism, others were developed to achieve specific results such as healing, martial power or spiritual insight, while still others are highly stylized forms named after the teachers who created them.

Despite this diversity, all forms of chi-gung practice share certain fundamental points in common. All of them work with energy, striving to achieve balance between Yin and Yang polarity and functional harmony among the Five Elemental Energies that govern the internal organs. All forms involve a subtle fusion of internal and external, movement and stillness, and all of them engage the Three Treasures of essence, energy and spirit as the fundamental elements of practice. Indeed, one of the most distinctive attributes of chi-gung is the broad range of its practical applications and its versatility in practice. Since it works with everything from the most basic biological functions and physiological factors such as sex and hormones, blood and digestion, to the most subtle spiritual faculties and higher cosmic forces such as intuition and intent, astral energy and psychic powers, chi-gung covers the full spectrum of self-cultivation, offering 'different strokes for different folks' without compromising its fundamental foundations in the universal principles of the Tao.

Five basic goals may be delineated as the primary points of focus in chi-gung practice:

- preserving health
- curing disease
- prolonging life
- developing physical strength and martial prowess
- cultivating spiritual awareness, enlightenment and liberation from the cycle of corporeal existence

Different schools of thought and styles of practice emphasized these various points to different degrees. The major categories introduced below are the ones with the longest historical pedigrees in China and are generally accepted in chi-gung circles today as the most important styles.

Major Schools of Thought in Chi-Gung

The three great philosophical schools of thought that moulded traditional Chinese civilization are Taoism, Confucianism and Buddhism. Each of these schools adapted chi-gung as a system of self-cultivation and geared the practices to their own particular purpose. In addition, two non-sectarian schools of practice evolved concurrently with the major philosophical schools, based on chi-gung's primary professional applications: the school of medical science and the school of martial arts.

The Taoist School

Taoism is the most ancient school of thought in chi-gung, as it is in all aspects of traditional Chinese civilization. Indeed, the basic theory and practice of chi-gung are based entirely on the fundamental principles of the Tao on which all of the classical Chinese arts and sciences are founded. In the Taoist school of practice, the ultimate goal of chi-gung is to 'achieve immortality' (*cheng-shien*). This involves the gradual gestation of a 'spiritual embryo' (*ling-tai*) that serves as a vehicle for transporting consciousness to a higher realm of existence after death, an immaculate immaterial realm of pure spirit and primordial awareness beyond the temporal bounds of space and time. To achieve this goal, the adept must conserve and continuously refine vital essence, cultivate vital energy, and transform them into pure spiritual vitality (*ling-chi*), from which the spiritual embryo of immortality gradually develops. The final step in this process, and the last stage in the internal alchemy of the Three Treasures, is called 'returning spirit to emptiness', or 'returning to the source'.

However, in order to reach this goal, Taoist adepts believed that one must first cultivate physical health and longevity as a foundation for the higher practices, and therefore they developed a comprehensive system of healthcare and life extension known as *yang-sheng* ('to cultivate life'). This system included diet and nutrition, herbs and exercise, sexual yoga and massage, as well as careful attention to harmonizing human activities with the rhythms of nature and cycles of the cosmos. The idea of harnessing the powers of the universe to assist humans in their quest for health, longevity and ultimate spiritual immortality was a uniquely Taoist contribution to chi-gung, and it led to the development of many arts and sciences that were later adopted for their practical value in other fields of practice, such as medicine, martial arts, astrology and geomancy.

The most distinctive points in the traditional Taoist school of chi-gung practice are briefly described below:

1. The concept of refining the spirit to ever higher levels of awareness by raising energy from the sacral and abdominal centres up to the head is central in Taoist practice. This refining process is a precondition for enlightenment and immortality and takes many years of disciplined practice to achieve.

2. The main focus of practice is energy, hence the term 'chi-gung', or 'energy work'. Energy is drawn from many sources – from air through breathing, from food through digestion, from nature and the cosmos in meditation, from the sun and moon and stars, from partners in sexual yoga, and so forth. All forms of energy are drawn into the human system, refined, cultivated and transformed for higher spiritual applications.

3. A unique aspect of Taoist chi-gung is the use of 'energy gates' on the body to 'breathe energy' directly into the human system from external sources.

4. The mental faculty of visualization is used to amplify the power and facilitate the flow of energy in chi-gung, based on the axiom of internal alchemy that 'spirit commands energy'. Visualization can therefore be used to guide energy into the body from external sources and to circulate it anywhere within the human system.

5. The 'interior elixir' (*nei-dan*) is the foundation of physical health and longevity as well as spiritual enlightenment. This elixir is refined from human essence and energy, not from medicinal substances. The purpose of internal alchemy in Taoist chi-gung is to produce the internal elixir by transforming the essence of vital bodily fluids and combining it with various other energy resources. The internal elixir constitutes the basic nourishment for the 'spiritual embryo' of immortality.

6. In addition to still meditation, Taoist chi-gung includes a unique form of 'moving meditation' used to develop the body, prevent and cure disease, stimulate vital secretions and help prolong life. These involve slow rhythmic movements of the body harmonized with deep abdominal breathing. Known as *tao-yin* ('induce and guide') and *wu-chin-shi* ('Play of the Five Beasts'), these exercises were originally derived from the way animals move in nature. They were further refined by the Indian monk Ta Mo, who combined them with *pranayama* breathing and meditation, and this 'moving meditation' style of practice later became the basis for all of the 'internal school' forms of Chinese martial arts.

7. Adepts of Taoist chi-gung also practise a type of periodic fasting called *bi-gu* (literally, 'abstain from grain'). This involves abstention not only from grains, but also vegetables, fruits and all cooked foods. During these fasting periods, the adept consumes only medicinal herbs and *chi*. The purpose of *bi-gu* is not only to detoxify and purify the body through fasting, but also to train the body to draw in energy directly from external sources through the body's energy gates and to produce internal energy from various forms of essence stored within the body by virtue of internal alchemy. During periods of *bi-gu*, chi-gung is practised more intensively to stimulate secretions of vital essence and catalyse its transformation into energy, and to keep the major energy gates open to the inflow of energies from nature and the cosmos. Sceptics who scoff at the possibility of living for prolonged periods on nothing but 'wind [energy] and water' should take note of the fact that in 1995, a seventy-year-old yogi in India fasted for 200 days, under close daily observation, taking nothing each day but two cups of water and plenty of *chi*, without losing weight or any other ill-effect. When food is completely withdrawn from the body, the internal alchemy of essence to energy transformation activated by chi-gung becomes far more efficient, and the human energy system naturally learns to tap into the infinite reservoirs of universal free energy. After each period of *bi-gu* is over, the amount of food one needs to consume each day thereafter decreases due to the increased efficiency of digestion and assimilation that results from this practice. The amount of sleep one needs each night also decreases due to the enhanced assimilation of energy from external sources.

8. Sexual yoga was a distinctive adjunct to Taoist chi-gung. This involves prolonged intercourse without male ejaculation but with multiple female orgasm. The idea is to amplify and balance the

energies of both partners by stimulating abundant sexual secretions and sexual energy, conserving them, transforming them, and drawing them up the spine into the head. The basic principle here was known as 'recycling essence to nourish the brain' (*huan jing bu nao*). Since a major component of male semen is cerebrospinal fluid, there is a sound scientific basis for the practice of retaining semen to nourish the brain.

9. Taoist chi-gung developed a system of total healthcare known as *yang-sheng tao* ('the tao of cultivating life') as an overall support for the central chi-gung practice. This system covered virtually every aspect of life in order to establish a synergistic 'Harmony of Heaven, Earth and Humanity', thereby insuring rapid progress on the path of practice. The basic principles of *yang-sheng* are the following:

- To achieve spiritual immortality, one must first take proper care of the body as the basic vehicle of practice.
- The body is composed of various vital energies drawn from Heaven and Earth. Therefore to cultivate life means to cultivate energy.
- The human system is a microcosm of nature and the cosmos, and therefore health and longevity can only be cultivated by harmonizing the human system with the rhythms of Heaven and Earth.
- The most fundamental conditions for practice are spiritual quietude and mental calm, emotional equilibrium and physical relaxation.
- There is a fundamental and indivisible union between body and mind, physical and spiritual practice, internal and external factors, bodily health and spiritual purity, with energy as the bridge. Therefore, progress and success in chi-gung depend on practising the whole system.

Of all the schools of chi-gung practice, the Taoist system is the most comprehensive and eclectic, for it places equal emphasis on physical health and spiritual awareness, regards a healthy body and a long life as the most important foundations for the ultimate goal of spiritual enlightenment, engages and integrates every aspect of life in the path of practice, and links everything together with the common denominator of energy. Moreover, in the Taoist approach, each individual practitioner is free to practise in a way that best suits his or her own personal inclinations, for the Taoist path is based entirely on the universal principles of nature and the cosmos, not on binding social or religious dogma. The only things required to practise Taoist chi-gung are one's own body, energy and mind, and a quiet place to sit or stand.

The Confucian School

Westerners usually imagine Confucius as a stodgy old scholar who liked to lecture the world with clever philosophical aphorisms, not as someone who might practise chi-gung. In fact, however, Confucius (Kung Fu-tze) took a lively interest in Taoism and is said to have held the great Taoist sage Lao Tze in high esteem.

Confucius and his philosophical heir Mencius (Meng Tze) regarded chi-gung as an important system of self-cultivation, but they approached it from an entirely different angle than the Taoist school. While Taoists used chi-gung as a means towards individual spiritual enlightenment and regarded the body as a vehicle towards this goal, Confucians approached chi-gung as a way to balance and purify the mind and control emotions so that people would become better members of society. Confucius believed that many physical diseases of the body are caused by mental and emotional imbalance, and by extension, the 'disease' of social and political disorder also arises from a disordered mind. 'To cultivate the body,' he wrote, 'first rectify the mind.' Mencius elaborated this idea when he wrote, 'To cultivate the mind, first eliminate desire and cultivate the pure primordial energy of nature.' What all this boils down to is the idea that the individual must purify the mind and balance the emotions in order to attain physical health and become a useful member of society. This applies particularly to those who wish to govern society: social and political leaders can only perform their duties properly after a period of intensive self-cultivation to eliminate greed, aggression, pride and other 'diseases' of the spirit that lead to improper behaviour and dereliction of duty.

The Confucian school of thought regarded nature and the cosmos as a blueprint for human society, and in this respect they agreed with the Taoist school. The difference was that the Taoists focused on self-cultivation and harmony with universal forces as a means towards individual enlightenment and spiritual immortality, while the Confucians focused on achieving social and political order, not individual freedom. Chi-gung thus became a method whereby the individual learned to take his or her proper place in society by cultivating the virtues of balance and equanimity. Since society was viewed as a microcosm of the universal order, by learning to obey the universal laws of nature one also learned to obey the laws of society. Thus a peaceful, orderly state of mind became the basis of a peaceful, orderly society.

The Confucian school of chi-gung enjoyed a brief heyday during the Warring States and early Han periods. Individual self-cultivation through chi-gung was practised as a means of restoring social order after a prolonged period of chaos, and instilling a sense of duty and selfless service among the scholars who came to power when Confucian philosophy became officially accepted as the state creed. But before long, as decadence and corruption once again spread among the ruling classes of China, the 'social school' of Confucian chi-gung faded away. Indeed, one of the main reasons that Buddhism and Taoism became increasingly popular in China from the Han through the Tang was the cynical self-interest and unethical conduct displayed by the Confucian elite who governed the empire.

During the Sung dynasty, in response to the growing influence of Buddhism, which was still regarded as a foreign religion, and Taoism, whose emphasis on individual freedom was seen as a threat to social cohesion, reformist Confucian scholars launched a revival of classical Confucian philosophy. Borrowing heavily from their Buddhist and Taoist rivals, these born-again Confucian scholars once more advocated self-cultivation through the practice of meditation, breath control and internal alchemy in order to cultivate social harmony and political correctness. The idea was to draw people back into the Confucian fold by offering them a system of spiritual development that could compete with the major religions and thereby satisfy the human need for spiritual nourishment. Known as the Neo-Confucian movement, the greatest proponent of this reform was the scholar Chu Hsi, who took a deep interest in the Taoist meditative techniques and advocated mental quietude as the best way to cultivate the peace, harmony and other ideal virtues of Heaven in the human heart and thereby instil them in society on Earth.

For Taoist and Buddhist practitioners, the first step on the road to spiritual development was to leave the family and abandon society and retire to a monastery or mountain hermitage to cultivate enlightenment. For the Neo-Confucian school, spiritual development was adapted to serve society, not the individual, and spiritual virtues were cultivated as a basis for fostering social virtues. Furthermore, by promoting physical health and vitality, chi-gung made the individual a more useful and productive member of society. This was a unique and typically practical Chinese way of co-opting an independent spiritual tradition and applying it to social and political purposes.

The Buddhist School

Prior to the arrival of Ta Mo in China, Buddhist monks focused their attention entirely on the attainment of 'Buddhahood', or spiritual enlightenment, through intensive practice of still meditation. The world 'Buddha' means 'one who is awakened', and thus the goal of Buddhist practice is spiritual awakening, pure and simple. In Taoist terms, this means subjugating the postnatal human mind of emotion and personal ego in order to restore the prenatal mind of primordial awareness and thereby escape the endless wheel of karma and reincarnation. Unlike the Taoist school, however, the Buddhist school of thought regarded the body as an impediment to spiritual practice, and Buddhists attached little importance to physical health and longevity.

With the arrival of Ta Mo from India, who taught that a strong body is an important foundation for spiritual cultivation, the Buddhist school in China began to incorporate physical exercise in their spiritual practice. The Shao Lin Temple thus became famous both as a centre for the martial arts and for meditation, and chi-gung became the core practice in physical as well as spiritual self-cultivation.

However, the Buddhist school still emphasized the primary importance of cultivating spiritual virtues, particularly the cessation of desire and aggression, and Buddhists took a dim view of the Taoist practice of sexual yoga as a means for cultivating energy for spiritual work. The Buddhists believed that if a practitioner achieved a high degree of power through the practice of martial and sexual chi-gung, without having first conquered his or her ego, the power obtained through such practices would be used for deviant purposes. Martial prowess, for example, was seen as a dangerous attribute in one who had not fully eliminated anger, and sexual yoga was seen as a mere pretext for lechery. Thus the traditional Buddhist virtues of celibacy, non-violence, compassion, abstention from intoxicants and so forth remained of primary importance in the Buddhist school of chi-gung, and this precluded many of the supplementary energy practices utilized by Taoist adepts.

In Buddhist chi-gung, attention remained firmly focused on the spirit, with physical exercise used only to counteract the stagnating effects of sitting for prolonged periods in still meditation. Cultivation of personal power through internal energy work was discouraged due to the risks of deviation. Breathing exercises were used primarily as a point of focus in *samatha* (tranquillity) and *vipassana* (insight) meditations, not as a means of cultivating energy through internal alchemy. These restrictions, however, applied only to ordained monks in established monastic orders. For secular Buddhist practitioners, there was an increasing tendency to combine the health and longevity practices and the personal freedom of the Taoist school with the spiritual virtue and disciplined personal behaviour of the Buddhist school, and today, virtually all Chinese practitioners of chi-gung follow this syncretic path.

The Medical School

Evidence suggests that chi-gung originally evolved in ancient China as a form of preventative and curative healthcare, and that it was in fact the first formal branch of Traditional Chinese Medicine. Subsequently, interest shifted more to chi-gung's applications in martial arts and meditation, and as a method of cultivating personal energy, emotional stability and peace of mind for daily life. Although Chinese physicians continued to prescribe chi-gung as supplementary medical therapy throughout Chinese history, the martial and meditative schools remained the predominant style of practice until the mid-twentieth century, when interest in the medical applications of chi-gung suddenly revived. Today, it is chi-gung's enormous potential as medical therapy in human health and healing that is drawing the strongest attention to the field, particularly scientific attention, and paving the way for chi-gung's dissemination throughout the world.

In medical chi-gung, the fundamental Taoist principles of Yin and Yang, the Five Elemental Energies (see page 15), balance and harmony, and so forth are applied to the diagnosis and treatment of disease. External physical symptoms of disease are viewed as signals indicating internal imbalances in energy. In TCM, the root cause of all disease is always traced to some sort of critical imbalance among the vital energies of the body, and therefore the cure always involves the re-establishment of normal balance among the energies of the human system and harmony between the human energy field and the forces of nature and the cosmos.

For example, whenever a patient's symptoms include aching eyes and blurry vision, the first thing a Chinese doctor suspects is an imbalance in liver energy, not an eye problem *per se*, because internal liver *chi* manifests externally in the condition of the eyes and vision. Similarly, earache and hearing problems usually reflect functional imbalances in the kidney organ-energy system. When the internal imbalance of energy is corrected and normal functions of the organ are restored, the external physical symptoms simply disappear and the disease is cured. Diagnosing and treating disease in terms of energy balance is the most distinctive hallmark of TCM, and it's based entirely on the principles of chi-gung.

The medical school of chi-gung also stresses the importance of physical exercise as a means for keeping the body toned and balanced and stimulating the free flow of blood and energy through the whole system. However, the type of exercise recommended in TCM differs greatly from the 'no pain, no gain' school of thought that still prevails in modern Western notions of physical fitness. Chinese medical chi-gung emphasizes soft, slow, rhythmic movements of the body synchronized with deep diaphragmic breathing. The purpose of these exercises is to stretch the tendons, loosen the joints, and tone the muscles, to promote circulation of blood, and to regulate all the vital functions of the body. The medical school adapted many forms of 'moving meditation' exercise for therapeutic use, including the ancient *dao-yin* and 'Play of the Five Beasts' forms based on animal movements, martial forms such as 'Eight Pieces of Brocade' and Tai Chi Chuan, and special exercises developed specifically to treat various internal organs. Massage and acupressure, which originally evolved as branches of chi-gung to help practitioners regulate internal energy, were also incorporated in the medical school of practice.

Although medical chi-gung focuses more on the links between energy and the body as a basis for diagnosing and curing disease, the role of the mind is certainly not overlooked. For example, visualization, which is normally used in Taoist meditation to manage energy for spiritual purposes, is also applied in medical chi-gung to facilitate the transport of energy to specific organs for therapeutic purposes. The importance of mental tranquillity and emotional equilibrium as preconditions for restoring balance to the human energy system is also a cornerstone of medical chi-gung, and sometimes still meditation is prescribed as means of first establishing mental and emotional balance prior to performing moving exercises that balance energy by working with the body and the breath.

There are basically two types of medical chi-gung – preventative and curative – and two forms of therapy: self-care through personal practice and transmission of energy from healer to patient. Chi-gung as a form of preventative healthcare is an integral aspect of every style and school of chi-gung practice, not just medical chi-gung. Indeed, one of the primary motivations for practising chi-gung in all schools of thought has always been to protect health and prevent disease, promote vitality and prolong life. In this respect, medical considerations constitute a common denominator in all styles of practice.

The curative applications of chi-gung are more specific to the medical school, and it is this aspect that is currently drawing such enthusiastic popular attention and serious scientific interest to the field. There are two ways to cure disease with chi-gung. One is by practising specific exercises designed to correct the basic imbalances responsible for particular diseases. These are basically the same sort of exercises used in preventative chi-gung, except that when used for curative therapy the exercises are practised for three to five hours and sometimes up to ten hours per day, rather than just an hour or two.

The other way of applying chi-gung as a curative therapy for disease is by transmitting healing energy from a master healer to the patient. Known in Chinese as 'emitting energy' (*fa-chi*), this technique is currently under intensive scientific scrutiny in China as a means of treating diseases such as cancer, AIDS, Parkinson's and Alzheimer's disease, multiple sclerosis, muscular dystrophy, and other scourges that modern medicine has failed to deal with effectively.

Healing energy is transmitted from healer to patient through the *lao-gung* points on the palms of the healer's hands. Usually there is no physical contact involved: instead, the healer stands or sits near the patient, with hands held anywhere from six inches (15cm) to three feet (90cm) from the parts of the patient's body to be treated. After making sure that the patient is as physically relaxed, emotionally calm, and mentally tranquil as possible under the circumstances, the healer proceeds to emit energy from his or her palms and channels it into the patient's system. Depending on the nature of the patient's disease, the healer modulates the energy beamed to the patient so that it has specific therapeutic effects. To dissolve a tumour, the healer uses a laser-like energy that destroys cancerous cells without harming healthy cells. To cure infectious diseases such as hepatitis B or tuberculosis, the healer emits a sort of 'killer *chi*' specifically geared to destroy the specific pathogen involved. For Parkinson's, Alzheimer's and other cerebral deficiency diseases, a type of energy is emitted that balances electromagnetic polarity in brain cells, stimulates circulation of blood and energy throughout the brain, and activates the synthesis and secretion of vital neuro-transmitters whose depletion gives rise to these conditions. Thus the energy emitted from the healer's hands carries both therapeutic power and specific information imprinted on it by the healer's mind.

Fortunately, modern technology has now made it possible to record and measure the healing effects of emitted energy, so that it can no longer be discounted by sceptics as mere 'anecdotal evidence' or 'voodoo medicine'. Scientific studies demonstrating the curative power of chi-gung in almost every type of cancer have been presented at international medical conferences throughout the world, and these papers are readily available from several medical institutions in China. Predictably, major Western medical journals have not been excessively eager to publicize these studies, because their results indicate that drugs, surgery, chemotherapy, radiation and other forms of expensive high-tech therapy favoured by conventional modern medicine are not only less efficient in treating cancer, heart disease, AIDS and other degenerative conditions, but may actually further aggravate these conditions by damaging the vital organs, polluting the blood, inhibiting immune response and throwing the whole system off balance. Nevertheless, sufficient numbers of professional Western physicians have now personally witnessed the curative powers of emitted *chi* under scientifically controlled conditions to bring medical chi-gung into serious scientific consideration in Western medical circles.

The Martial School

The martial applications of chi-gung developed in two distinct stages in Chinese history. Prior to the arrival in China of the Buddhist monk Ta Mo from India, only the external physical aspects of chi-gung were applied in martial arts. Exercises based on the movements that animals use when fighting were practised to build muscular strength, develop speed, and learn tactics, but there was no concept of using the mind to guide energy or synchronizing physical movements with breathing.

After Ta Mo began training Chinese monks to integrate physical exercise with their meditation practice and taught Chinese martial artists how to enhance their physical prowess with spiritual cultivation, the martial and meditative schools of chi-gung both built their practices on the 'internal elixir' (*nei-dan*) of energy as the foundation for physical power as well as spiritual awareness. Ever since the time of Ta Mo, the Chinese martial arts have followed the path of internal energy practice, using spirit to cultivate command over energy, and energy to cultivate martial skills. The three main schools of internal 'soft-style' martial arts that evolved in China as a result of this shift are Tai Chi Chuan, Hsing Yi and Pa Kua, each of which developed countless variations.

The martial school also borrowed certain techniques from the medical school of chi-gung. For example, the meridiens and power points of the human energy system were carefully studied to learn how energy moves in the body, and specific fighting techniques were developed to incapacitate an opponent simply by striking a particular point in such a way that the body became immediately immobilized. Known as *dian-shueh* ('Pressing Points'), this technique requires careful timing and great precision in striking, but its effects in fighting are far more devastating than anything that can be done with sheer physical strength.

While fighting prowess was the primary goal of martial chi-gung in traditional China, today the martial arts are practised more as a form of preventative healthcare than for fighting. Since all of the internal martial arts forms are designed to 'martial energy' under the command of mind, they may be practised just as well for purposes of health and longevity as for fighting. Soft-style Chinese martial arts are practised as much to strengthen and coordinate the body, enhance health and vitality, and cultivate spirit as they are to develop fighting prowess. These are basically the same goals pursued in all forms of chi-gung practice. The only real difference between martial, medical and meditative schools of practice is how the universal energy cultivated through chi-gung is applied in human life.

Moving Forms and Still Forms

Still practice (*jing-gung*) and moving practice (*dung-gung*) are the Yin and Yang of chi-gung, the two complementary poles of practice in all styles. This mode of categorizing chi-gung forms is based on the relative balance of stillness and movement in body and mind and in any particular form of practice.

Moving forms are generally defined as those which involve external movements of the body mediated by internal stillness of mind. Thus all of the martial arts and 'moving meditation' styles of practice are regarded as moving forms. The basic principles governing all moving forms include softness (*rou*), slowness (*man*), and smoothness (*ho*) of movement, balance and equilibrium in physical postures, and rhythmic regularity in the synchronization of bodily movements and breath. The purpose of moving forms is to keep the moving parts of the body limber and flexible, to promote circulation of blood and energy throughout the system, and to harmonize external movement of the limbs with internal flow of energy. One of the major guidelines in the practice of moving forms is summed up in the phrase, 'Seek stillness within movement'.

Still forms are basically defined by the external stillness of the body, combined with the internal movement of energy, or 'seeking movement within stillness'. Still meditation forms of chi-gung may be practised in sitting, standing or reclining postures. Rather than focusing on the synchronization of body and breath, as in moving forms, the main focus in still practice is keeping the mind fully attuned with the breath. Prior to practising any still form, however, the body should first be balanced with a series of stretching and loosening exercises, just as the mind must be stilled and the emotions calmed in preparation for the practice of moving forms.

In a nutshell, moving and still forms are the two great divisions that run throughout all the styles and schools of chi-gung practice. The moving forms are associated more with the body and the external aspects of practice, while still forms are related more with the mind and the internal aspects of practice, with breath serving as the functional link between movement and stillness, internal and external, body and mind. Moreover, all schools and styles of chi-gung employ both moving and still forms of practice, regardless of where the primary focus lies.

Ever since Ta Mo brought the martial and meditative traditions of Chinese chi-gung together at the Shao Lin Temple, movement and stillness have shared equal importance in chi-gung. Those whose primary goal is spiritual enlightenment through still meditation practice also practise moving forms to protect the health and extend the life of their physical bodies, while those who cultivate martial power by practising moving forms also practise still meditation to develop the volitional command of mind over energy and cultivate spiritual virtue as a preventative against the abuse of their martial powers.

Cultivating Nature and Cultivating Life

Cultivating nature (*shiou-shing*), cultivating life (*shiou-ming*), and cultivating nature and life together (*shing-ming shuang-shiou*) are terms that have been bandied about in chi-gung circles in China ever since they first appeared during the Tang period, but no two teachers or texts seem to agree on precisely what these terms mean.

'Nature' here basically refers to 'human nature', as reflected in the propensities and proclivities of human beings in their daily lives on earth. These include sexuality, personality, psychology, ego and self, family and work, and other aspects of postnatal human life. In terms of the Three Powers of Heaven, Earth and Humanity, 'nature' reflects the earthly pole in human beings, the temporal concerns of life that define day-to-day existence.

'Life' refers to the primordial aspects of human existence, the immortal spirit and universal energy that animate the human body during life, but survive it after death. These are the prenatal attributes of Heaven with which every human being is born but which remain dormant in most people until the moment of death. They include primordial awareness, the basic life-force of primordial energy, such esoteric spiritual faculties as clairvoyance and telepathy and so forth.

Forms for cultivating nature would therefore include all practices that engage the postnatal essences and energies of the physical body and the ordinary human mind. Sexual yoga, for example, is a practice for cultivating the sexual aspect of human nature. Diet and herbs work with the energies of the internal organs, and the slow rhythmic movement of 'moving meditation' exercises cultivate the essences of the physical body.

Forms for cultivating life work primarily with the primordial aspects of the human system, using still meditation as the main method of practice. This was the sort of single-minded spiritual cultivation practised by Buddhist monks in China prior to the arrival of Ta Mo. Those who exclusively cultivate the primordial spiritual powers of mind, while paying no attention to the temporal requirements and sensual proclivities of the body, often end up suffering from physical ill health, psychic imbalance and emotional malaise, as conditions in many monasteries throughout the world today reflect. Similarly, those who cultivate only physical health, bodily power, sexual potency and other temporal assets of human nature, without any consideration for the higher aspects of spirit which ultimately transcend life on earth, end up entirely immersed in the material aspect of existence, lose sight of spirit, and often abuse the powers of their practices for deviant purposes. This is the fundamental conundrum of chi-gung that was ultimately resolved by 'cultivating nature and life together'.

What this means is that chi-gung should always be practised in a comprehensive, balanced way that cultivates both the earthly aspects of human nature as well as the universal facets of primordial spirit. Chi-gung masters recognize the fact that humans must live with their bodies and their emotions, that appetites for food and sex are as basic to human nature as flesh and bone are to the body, and that the demands of family and society must be met even by those who wish to devote their lives to spiritual cultivation. Similarly, even the most materialistic, sensualistic hedonist is endowed with the same fundamental energy and immortal spirit as the most high-minded saint. The only way to resolve the basic contradictions in human life between body and spirit, temporal and spiritual concerns, human nature and universal spirit is to cultivate both aspects together so that they balance and mutually support each other.

This has been the trend in Chinese chi-gung as a form of self-cultivation ever since the so-called Neo-Confucian revival during the Sung dynasty, when Confucian scholars began to apply the very same practices used by Buddhist and Taoists for spiritual enlightenment to the individual self-cultivation of social virtues and political order. By erasing the distinctions between secular and spiritual applications of practice, attention focused increasingly on the fundamental factor of life that links body and spirit, intersects the temporal and universal, and bridges the practical and spiritual aspects of self-cultivation in chi-gung, and that factor is energy. Therefore, cultivating nature and life together means cultivating the fundamental energy of life that connects individual human nature with the primordial source of all creation throughout the universe. When that energy is strong and well balanced, physical as well as spiritual health are gained, the needs of the body as well as the mind are met, and the individual's primordial link with the universe is restored. This sort of balanced development of body and spirit by cultivating the basic energy upon which both depend has become a common thread in all forms of Chinese chi-gung.

Forms Based on Physical Posture

This way of classifying chi-gung forms is based on the posture adopted for practice and includes four basic categories: walking, standing, sitting and reclining.

- *Walking*: These are forms which involve ambulatory movement of the body, not just rhythmic movements of the limbs. Most traditional martial arts based on chi-gung fall into this category, such as Tai Chi, Hsing Yi and Pa Kua, although there are also 'walking meditation' forms used for spiritual practice, and walking forms of medical chi-gung for curing disease, such as the Guo Lin

Chi-gung developed recently in China as a cure for cancer. In all cases, the walking is done slowly, deliberately, and in rhythmic synchronicity with breath.

• *Standing*: Standing forms include many of the chi-gung exercise sets that are performed in the traditional 'Horse stance'. This is a very stable stance with a low centre of gravity designed to cultivate physical balance and a strong 'root' connection with the earth. In moving meditation exercises such as 'Eight Pieces of Brocade', the feet remain firmly planted to the ground, while the arms, head and torso move in various prescribed patterns, tuned to the inhalation and exhalation phases of breath.

There are also still meditation forms of chi-gung that are practised in the standing position, which facilitates the free flow of internal energy from head to feet. The standing posture takes maximum advantage of an energy factor called 'potential gradient', which determines the strength of the polar field in the human energy system between the Yang pole at the crown of the head and the Yin pole at the soles of the feet. The greater the distance between two poles in any given energy field, the stronger the potential gradient and the more powerful the flow of energy between poles. The enhanced field polarity in the standing posture increases the magnitude and accelerates the flow of energy through the meridians, and helps establish harmonic resonance between the human energy field and the greater force fields of nature (Earth) and the cosmos (Heaven). In sitting postures, the field is narrowed, with the perineum at the base of the spine rather than the feet serving as the negative Yin pole, and thus the overall polarity of the human field is proportionately reduced, resulting in a gentler, less dynamic flow of energy that may be more conducive to subtle spiritual work.

• *Sitting*: Sitting forms are those performed either in the traditional cross-legged postures such as Full Lotus and Half Lotus, or else seated on the edge of a low stool or chair, with feet planted firmly on the floor and a 90-degree angle between thigh and calf. While these forms are usually associated with still meditation styles of chi-gung, there are also some moving exercises that may be practised in the sitting postures, including the Eight Pieces of Brocade set.

The most important aspect in all sitting postures is the spine, which must be held erect and kept in alignment with the neck and head. While the standing posture encourages the full circulation of energy throughout the entire system, including the arm and leg channels, sitting postures tend to channel energy primarily into the

Microcosmic Orbit circuit of the Governing and Conception channels that run up the spine, through the head and back down the front of the body to the lower abdomen. These are the main channels involved in the internal alchemy of the Three Treasures, and in the transformation and transportation of energy in the Three Elixir Field centres located below the navel, at the solar plexus and in the head. Sitting forms are therefore most frequently employed in chi-gung practices which cultivate spiritual energy and focus on internal alchemy, while the standing forms are used more to cultivate energy for physical strength, martial power and overall vitality.

• *Reclining*: The reclining postures are used only when standing, sitting, or walking forms cannot be practised, such as by the weak or elderly, or by those recovering from serious illness. Only the breathing and meditative aspects of chi-gung are practised in the reclining postures, not the moving physical exercises. In the reclining position, visualization is used as a substitute for physical movements of the limbs to guide energy to various parts of the body. The reclining forms are used primarily for healing work in medical chi-gung, although disabled people who cannot maintain an erect sitting posture may also use these positions for meditation practice. Due to the parallel alignment of the body with the surface of the earth in reclining positions, the field polarity of the human energy system is reduced to virtually zero, which means that energy must be mobilized entirely by breath and mind control, with very little boost from the potential gradient between sky and ground. This makes it particularly difficult to balance the internal energies of the human system with the force fields of Heaven and Earth in the reclining postures, but they are very useful for cultivating conscious mental command over breath and energy and applying visualization, intent and other mental faculties to guide energy through the body.

Forms for Balancing Body, Breath and Mind

This way of classifying chi-gung forms is based on the main aspect of the human system that is brought into balance by a particular exercise. All of the various forms and schools of chi-gung practice work with the same basic three attributes of postnatal human life: the body, the breath and the mind. Each of these factors must be brought into balance as a precondition for working with their primordial prenatal aspects – essence, energy and spirit – to harness the power of the universe to enhance life. Various chi-gung exercises may therefore be classified according to the aspect of the human system which they bring into balance.

• *Balancing Body* (*tiao-shen*): In chi-gung, balancing the body is achieved by performing a series of stretching and loosening exercises that eliminate all tension from the body and establish a state of complete physical relaxation. Total relaxation of the body is a prerequisite for maintaining proper posture during practice, freely circulating blood and energy, breathing correctly, and establishing a stable state of mental quietude. Any tension in the muscles and tendons, or tightness in the joints, tends to throw the body off balance, obstruct circulation, inhibit deep abdominal breathing and distract the mind.

This category of exercise includes manoeuvres designed to stretch and loosen specific parts of the body, such as legs, shoulders and neck, slow rhythmic calisthetics to stimulate circulation and warm up the whole body, and various types of massage, tapping, rubbing and acupressure to soothe and balance particular muscles, joints and other tissues. As the body becomes progressively more relaxed, the autonomous nervous system switches over to the calming, restorative, parasympathetic branch, which balances the endocrine (hormone) system and activates the body's internal healing mechanisms. Since prenatal essence is stored mainly in the glands, these body balancing exercises ultimately balance essence by regulating the healing responses of the endocrine system.

• *Balancing Breath* (*tiao-shi*): Balancing breath means establishing volitional control over breathing and cultivating a pattern of rhythmic breath driven by the expansion and contraction of the diaphragm. Our normal breathing patterns are anything but balanced: they are constantly interrupted by talking, accelerated or inhibited by emotional swings, impeded by tension, strained by physical exertion and left unattended by distracted minds. Since breath is a reflection of energy in the human system, erratic breathing patterns reflect and induce erratic energy flow and therefore, in order to balance energy, one must first balance the breath.

The various phases of breath may be brought into balance by practising different breathing exercises, such as bellows breathing, compression breathing, alternate nostril breathing and so forth. This category of exercises therefore includes all of the various modes of deep abdominal breathing used in chi-gung practice. Just as the physical exercises may be used alone to balance the body in preparation for chi-gung, so the breathing exercises may be done by themselves to balance the breath prior to performing the main practice.

Bringing the breath into balance also balances the energy system. Breath control establishes emotional equilibrium, harmonizes the Five Elemental Energies of the organs, balances Yin/Yang polarity, stimulates energy circulation in the meridiens, and synchronizes the human energy field with the electromagnetic fields of earth, planets and stars.

• *Balancing Mind* (*tiao-shin*): Balancing the mind means bringing the postnatal cerebral functions of the human mind under control so that the prenatal powers of primordial spirit may manifest. This involves clearing the mind of discursive thought and shifting attention from the external world perceived by the five senses to the internal world of essence, energy and spirit. A calm, tranquil state of mind, free of thought and sensory distractions, is an absolute prerequisite for any form of internal energy work with chi-gung. Neither body nor breath can enter into and remain in a state of balance unless the mind is also balanced.

There are various methods that can be used to balance the mind, such as establishing 'one-pointed awareness' by focusing attention on a particular object or image, allowing thoughts to dissolve naturally as they arise, shutting off the physical senses, counting breaths and so forth. Most of these techniques are standard devices designed to induce a stable state of mental tranquillity, clarity and inwardly focused attention prior to meditation. In chi-gung, the easiest way to balance the mind is to focus awareness fully on balancing the body and the breath. This provides a convenient point of focus for directing attention inward during practice and sustaining it long enough for external distractions to fade into the background. Then, when the body is fully relaxed, the breath is under control, the nervous and endocrine systems are synergized to activate healing responses, and internal energies are moving in tune with the rhythmic flow of breath, the mind naturally enters the same state of balance and harmony established by body and breath. If a mental, emotional or sensory distraction arises during practice, rather than allowing it to preoccupy attention and thereby disrupt the mind, one simply shifts attention back to a particular point of balance in the body or breath, and the distraction dissolves.

The key to managing the mind's attention and thereby controlling awareness is the faculty of primordial spirit known as *yi* (intent, will). Intent is the agent that allows us to exercise volitional control over body, breath and mind, rather than letting them be controlled by other forces and factors, such as emotions, sensory perceptions, external energies, other people's expectations and so forth. In practice, however, it's much easier to use intent to control the body and balance the breath than it is to control and balance the mind – the very act of consciously balancing body and breath tends to balance the mind as well. Moreover, it doesn't really matter whether the balancing act begins with body, breath or mind, because ultimately all three must be balanced in order to practise chi-gung.

All of these schools, styles, forms and variations notwithstanding, chi-gung basically boils down to three great categories of practice in which all of the different traditions, goals and applications of chi-gung may be subsumed. These are the 'Three M's' of chi-gung: medicine, meditation and martial arts. One way or another, every style of practice may be relegated to one of these major categories, and many of them have applications in all three.

In fact, almost all great chi-gung masters in China, historically as well as today, began their training in one of these fields and then extended their practice to embrace all three. Virtually all masters of the internal schools of Chinese martial arts, for example, are also accomplished meditators and highly skilled healers, while most traditional Chinese doctors also practise martial arts for health and meditation to cultivate internal energy for healing. And ever since the time of Ta Mo, Chinese monks have practised chi-gung not only for spiritual enlightenment, but also for physical health and healing.

The common denominator that links medicine, meditation and martial arts is *chi*, the universal free energy of life that heals the body, enlightens the mind and empowers the practitioner physically as well as spiritually. Regardless of whether you enter through the gate of medicine, meditation or martial arts, once you are in the house of chi-gung you will discover that these and all other distinctions are irrelevant, because the basic energy you're working with in chi-gung is, as Lao Tze points out in the *Tao Teh Ching*, 'Without sound, without substance, dependent on nothing, unchanging, all pervading, unfailing. One may think of it as the mother of all things under Heaven.'

CHAPTER 3

Chi-Gung and the Three Powers: The Harmony of Heaven, Earth and Humanity

Heaven (*tien*), Earth (*di*) and Humanity (*ren*) are known in Taoist philosophy as the Three Powers (*san tsai*). Humanity takes form and functions in a pivotal position between the cosmic powers of *tien* and the natural forces of *di*, 'covered by Heaven above and supported by Earth below', and human life flourishes to the extent that it harmonizes itself with the forces of the cosmos and the elements of nature which shape it.

'Heaven' is the source of primordial spirit and universal awareness, the virtue of wisdom, and the volitional power of intent, as well as all the mental faculties associated with the postnatal human mind. Essentially open and empty, naturally radiant and clear, and endowed with infinite power, Heaven suffuses the human spirit with the primordial 'Virtue of Tao' (*dao-deh*), which empowers the human mind with the capacity to realize the pure primordial awareness known as 'enlightenment' in Buddhism and 'immortality' in Taoist tradition. Heaven is the abode of deities and a synonym for the divine creative power known as 'Tao' or the 'Source' in Chinese tradition, 'Brahma' in Hinduism, 'Buddha' or 'Bodhi' in Buddhist thought, and 'God' in Western religions. Heaven manifests its primordial power in human life through the mysterious forces of fate and destiny (*ming*), the universal laws of karma (*yin-guo*) and reincarnation (*lun-hui*), and the mystical gifts of divine inspiration (*ling-gan*) and spiritual communion (*tung-ling*) with divine beings.

Heaven is the penultimate expression of Yang in human life, and its most obvious visible manifestation on earth are the sun and the sky, the planets and the stars, and other celestial sources from which a constant stream of cosmic forces rain down upon Earth and Humanity. The ancient Taoist sciences of astrology and divination evolved as means to analyse, interpret and predict how the various forces of Heaven influence and guide human life on Earth. The sky is the primary symbol of Heaven in Taoist philosophy and thus the words for 'Heaven' and 'sky' are the same in Chinese – *tien*. Weather, which reflects the various conditions and transformations of energy in the sky, is therefore viewed as an earthly manifestation of Heaven's moods and is referred to in Chinese as *tien-chi*, which means 'Heaven's Temper' or simply 'Celestial energy', depending on the nuance intended.

'Earth' refers to the material world of soil and water, mountains and rivers, land and ocean, plants and animals, that constitute the concrete context of corporeal human life. It is the source of the natural forces and the basic elements and energies that compose and regulate our physical bodies and 'make the world go round'. Essentially solid and stable, rhythmic and balanced, Earth is the fountainhead of the Five Elemental Energies and the setting for the cyclic transformations of nature which shape the physiological forms and govern the biological functions of the human body. The human system extracts earthly elements and terrestrial energies from the primary postnatal sources of food, water and air, from which it produces the True Energy that fuels the physical body. Humans also derive postnatal nourishment from other supplemental sources in nature, such as herbs and minerals, sounds and colours, and the powerful energy of sex. Indeed, so important and potent is sex as a source of vital energy in human life that in written Chinese the same ideogram is used to denote the words for 'nature' and 'sex'.

Earth is thus the polar Yin counterpart to the Yang power of Heaven in human life. 'Heaven was created by the accumulation of Yang,' states the *Yellow Emperor's Classic of Internal Medicine*, 'and Earth was formed by the accumulation of Yin.' Earth expresses its power in human life through the basic instincts for survival and the primal drives to procreate and propagate the species through sexual reproduction. Its main manifestations are the planet earth itself, the moon and the lunar cycles of tide and time which its orbit around the earth governs, the myriad species of plant and animal life, the cyclic changes of season, the phases of birth, maturation, decay and death, and other basic forces and rhythms of nature. Earth is therefore the main focus of the medical and martial arts, the sciences of nutrition and physiology, geomancy and physics, and sexual yoga.

The harmony of Earth and Humanity is achieved primarily by physiological means. Chi-gung does of course enhance and support these functions by increasing the efficiency of digestion and metabolism, improving respiration and circulation, and balancing all the vital functions of the body, and therefore it plays an important role in orchestrating a healthy and harmonious relationship between Earth and Humanity and enhancing the human system's efficiency in utilizing the temporal resources of earth.

It is in the harmony of Heaven and Humanity that chi-gung plays its most direct and indispensable role as a mediator of energy. Unlike Earth, Heaven is eternal and immortal, and its power is therefore infinite and inexhaustible. The energies which humans tap from the universe through chi-gung practice bypass the physiological functions of the body and enter into the human energy system directly through the energy gates, pulsating throughout the body's meridien network as waves and currents of pure primordial energy. Unlike the food, water and air of Earth, all of which produce waste products in the body as they yield their energies – wastes which pollute the system and require a lot of energy to eliminate – the primordial energy derived from the stars and planets and other astral sources of the universe fuel the human system without polluting it, providing an unlimited supply of the highest grade energy, free of cost. That's why this energy is commonly referred to in English as 'universal free energy' – because it's freely available to any being in the universe who learns how to tap into it. Chi-gung is the only technology you'll ever need to hook your own personal energy system directly into the infinite 'Internet' of universal free energy, the very same energy that fuels the stars and planets, creates all things under Heaven, and sustains all forms of life throughout the universe. But in order to utilize this simple technology, it's important to first understand how the human equipment involved in managing energy works.

Microcosm and Macrocosm: 'The Universe Within'

The human body and its network of energy channels and power points form a microcosmic replica of the macrocosmic universe at large – 'the universe within' – complete with its own 'Heaven' and 'Earth', its internal emotional 'weather' and organ 'ecosystems', its 'rivers' of blood and 'mountains' of flesh, its mineral 'ores' of bones and its saline 'oceans' of cellular fluids. Each cell, tissue, organ and other part of the body emanates its own specific electromagnetic energy field, which pulsates at its own particular frequency and regulates its own internal energy currents, while the entire body itself radiates an auric energy field that extends about one metre around the surface. The human energy field interacts with and is influenced by the larger energy fields around it, such as those produced by the wiring in houses and buildings, by geological formations of the earth, by large groups of people, by continents and oceans, by the force field of the planet itself, and by the greater cosmic fields of the solar system, stars and galaxies. A positive empowering effect is produced when the human system and all of its parts resonate in harmony with the naturally balanced, dynamically vibrant fields of nature and the cosmos. Negative debilitating effects are created in the body when the erratic, unbalanced patterns of artificial energy fields such as those produced by high-voltage power lines and transformers, televisions and computers, cellular phones and microwave ovens, are allowed to suppress, distort and otherwise interfere with the natural oscillations of the human energy field.

The human energy field functions like a microcosm of the entire cosmos and all of its various sub-fields, such as stars and planets, sun and moon. The head is associated with the positive Yang pole of Heaven, the sacrum houses the negative Yin pole of Earth, and linking these two poles is the 'stairway to Heaven'. In the physical body, that stairway is the spine, but in the auric energy body it's the Central Channel, also known in Chinese as the 'Thrusting Channel' (*chung-mai*), along which are located the seven energy centres called 'elixir fields' (*dan-tien*), or 'chakras'. Each of these centres oscillates at a specific frequency, and each chakra, when open and balanced, resonates with specific bands of higher energy from the cosmos, thereby drawing the higher powers that ride on those frequencies directly into the human system, where they are transformed into energy pulses specific to the human body and mind.

The seven chakras function as receivers and transformers for the cosmic energies of Heaven and the natural energies of Earth that chi-gung draws into the human system through various 'energy gates' (*chi-guan*) on the body (Fig. 2). The main entry gates for the astral energies of Heaven are the *ni-wan-gung* and *bai-hui* points on top of the head, while the major gates for the forces of Earth are the *hui-yin* point at the perineum, the *lao-gung* points on the palms and the *yung-chuan* points on the soles. Cosmic energy enters the seventh chakra on the crown of the head as clear white light, which carries the full spectrum of astral energies. When this energy

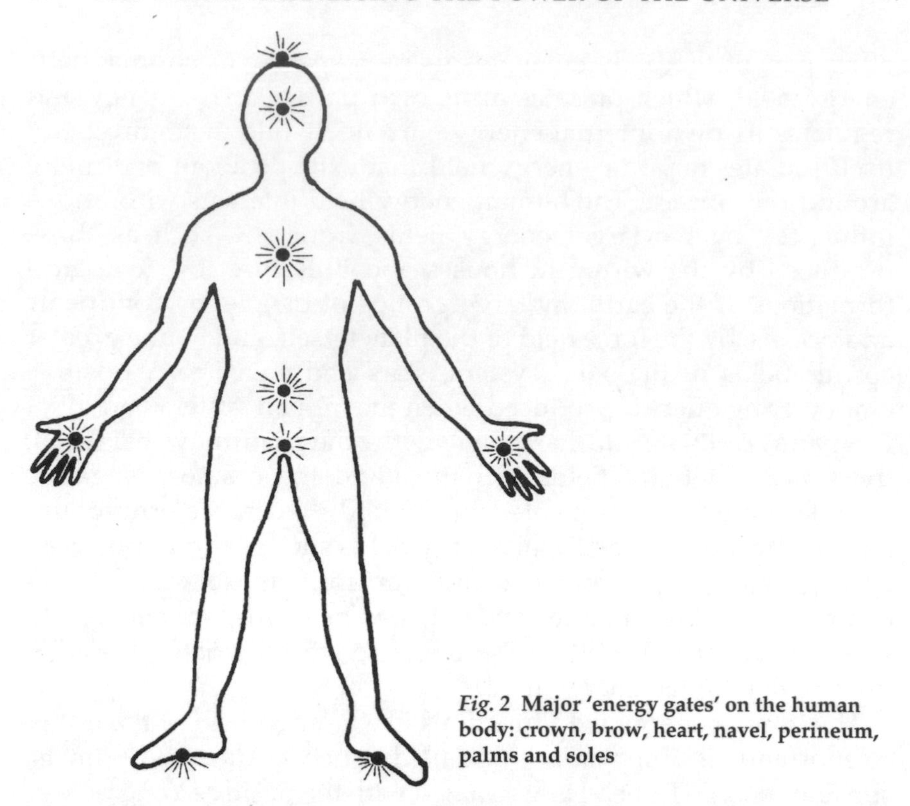

Fig. 2 **Major 'energy gates' on the human body: crown, brow, heart, navel, perineum, palms and soles**

reaches the sixth chakra, or 'upper elixir field', it is refracted into the various coloured rays associated with each of the other chakras: violet for the sixth (brain/pituitary), sky-blue for the fifth (throat, thyroid), light green for the fourth (heart/thymus), yellow-gold for the third (solar plexus/adrenal), orange for the second (navel/testes and ovaries), and red for the first (perineum/anal and sexual orifices). As this energy descends through the system, it is progressively 'stepped down' for use by the progressively lower, slower sub-systems of the human body.

Similarly, when the denser energies of earth are drawn up into the body through the feet and perineum points, they are 'stepped up' by the chakras as they ascend toward the head, from the turgid red Fire energy of the sexual and excretory organs to the pure pristine white Water energy of the brain and higher faculties of spirit. Thus the upper three of the seven chakras are related to the primordial spiritual powers and postnatal mental faculties of the mind, while the lower three are involved in the physiological functions of the body, with the central fourth chakra at the heart, which houses human consciousness (Humanity) serving as the pivotal balance between Heaven and Earth. In Taoist internal alchemy, only three of these chakras are generally involved in most practices. These are known as the 'Three Elixir Fields' (*san dan-tien*): the lower centre at the second chakra just below the navel governs vital essence and the body; the middle centre at the third chakra houses the postnatal Fire energy of emotions and ego; the upper centre in the brain is involved in spiritual practice and houses the primordial powers awakened by such practice.

The entire human energy system constitutes a 'subtle organizing energy field' (SOEF), a dynamic force field that organizes the energies and elements within it into the integrated organic systems required to sustain any form of life. In humans, for example, the SOEF organizes the atomic elements and energies into the form of the human body according to the design contained in the master template of DNA. Such energy fields are associated with all living organisms and represent the only force in the universe that resists the law of entropy, i.e., the dissolution of all compound matter. These living energy fields therefore sustain organic life in material form, but only for as long as they maintain a state of dynamic polarity and constantly recharge and rebalance themselves by resonating in synchronicity with higher force fields, such as planets, stars and galaxies. Chi-gung is a way of harmonizing the human energy field with these higher force fields, thereby recharging the microcosmic human system with the power of the macrocosmic fields of the universe. This is somewhat akin to recharging the batteries of a cordless appliance by plugging it into a constant electrical power source.

Another way in which the human system transforms the energies it assimilates through chi-gung practice is by virtue of what is known in Western science as the 'piezoelectric effect'. This refers to a unique property possessed by all crystalline structures, whereby any sort of vibratory or wave energy applied to a crystal structure is transformed into electromagnetic pulses. The human body contains a variety of tissues with crystalline structures within their matrix, particularly bone, connective tissue and the electrolytes in certain bodily fluids. These crystalline structures have the capacity to transduce various types of high-frequency wave energies to which they are exposed, such as light and sound, producing specific electromagnetic pulses that are conducted by the meridians and nerves and utilized by various organs and tissues of the body. This is the mechanism by which mantra, music and various sacred syllables may be used to balance and heal the body: as the sound waves vibrate through the body, crystalline structures within the tissues transform them into pulsed currents that are then conducted to various organs and glands, depending on the frequency and amplitude of the incoming wave signal. Chi-gung opens the human system to some of the highest bands of wave energy in the universe, which are transformed within the body to produce healing energy pulses that rebalance the whole system and can be used both to cure and prevent disease and heal specific organs. The piezoelectric effect is one of the most distinctive and important aspects of chi-gung as a method of health care and life extension.

Thus the Harmony of Heaven and Humanity is achieved by tuning the microcosm of the human energy system with the macrocosmic energy fields of ecosystems, the solar system, stellar systems, galactic systems and so forth, thereby maintaining a state of dynamic polarity that keeps all functions in the body in perfect balance. If such a state is sustained by daily practice, the imbalances that give rise to physical disease in the body cannot occur, and health and longevity are the result. This is the reason that the sages and mystics of ancient China devoted so much time and attention to the study of cosmic forces, cyclic changes of nature, planetary and stellar influences, geomantic force fields of earth, and other factors that influence the human energy system. They also developed specific practices to harness these forces and harmonize them with human energies, and among these practices, chi-gung became the primary method for achieving the Harmony of Heaven and Humanity that serves as a foundation for physical health, long life and spiritual awareness, 'on Earth as it is in Heaven'.

The Rhythmic Cycles of Nature and the Cosmos

Everything in nature and the cosmos, from the atomic to the galactic and from single cells to complex organisms, operates according to natural rhythms and regular cycles determined by the universal laws of energy. These laws, and the cyclic transformations and organic rhythms of life to which they give rise, are known as the 'Tao', the eternal 'Way' of the universe and the great 'Path' of life. 'Those who pattern their lives in accordance with the Tao, live long,' states an ancient Chinese text. 'Those who go against it, perish early.'

One of the most ancient Chinese systems for calculating the cosmic cycles and natural rhythms of Heaven and Earth in order to harmonize them with human affairs and utilize them for health and longevity is known as the 'Ten Celestial Stems and Twelve Earthly Branches'. The Ten Celestial Stems refer to radiant astral force fields that transmit rays of cosmic energy down to earth and into the human energy system from the planets of the solar system. Like the ancient cosmology of Egypt and India, the classical Taoist tradition of China cites the existence of ten rather than nine planets in our solar system, and recent astronomical observations seem to confirm the presence of the 'missing' tenth planet, which is said to orbit the sun in a broad ellipse on a different plane from the other planets. Many of the mysterious phenomena and inexplicable shifts of energy currently experienced within our solar system and on our planet are attributed by some astronomers to the imminent return of this tenth planet into closer orbit to the sun, which will also bring it into close proximity to the earth, triggering some major shifts in the earth's electromagnetic field.

The Ten Celestial Stems thus refer to the 'arteries' through which the energies of the ten planets, including the earth's own forces, enter into and influence the human energy system, and chi-gung establishes the conditions of balance and harmony that permit the human system to resonate in synchronicity with these forces, rather than conflicting with them. This synchronicity allows the chakras and crystalline structures to receive and transform these celestial frequencies into energy pulses that can be used to recharge and rebalance the human system.

The Twelve Earthly Branches refer to the twelve major organ-energy meridiens and their umbilical links to external sources of related earthly energies in nature. The Five Elemental Energies of nature flow through these branches, as do all the other types of energy harvested from the resources of earth, such as food, water, air, colour, flavour, sound and touch. The Twelve Earthly Branches manifest in all sorts of rhythmic cycles of twelve, influencing the balance and functions of the human system and the affairs of human life in many ways – twelve months in a year, the twelve two-hour periods of the day in the Chinese 'duodecimal' system of keeping time, the six solid Yin and six hollow Yang organs of the body, the twelve houses of the zodiac, and so forth. Fig. 3 shows some of the most important correlations of the Twelve Earthly Branches and how they might be used to harmonize the human system with the flux of forces represented by time and season. For example, the branch known as *chou* is related to the liver, and its energy peaks in the month of December and during the hours of one to three in the day. Therefore, if you are practising special chi-gung exercises to tonify liver energy, the best time to harvest that particular energy from the environment is between one and three o'clock in the afternoon, and the most beneficial month for this practice is December.

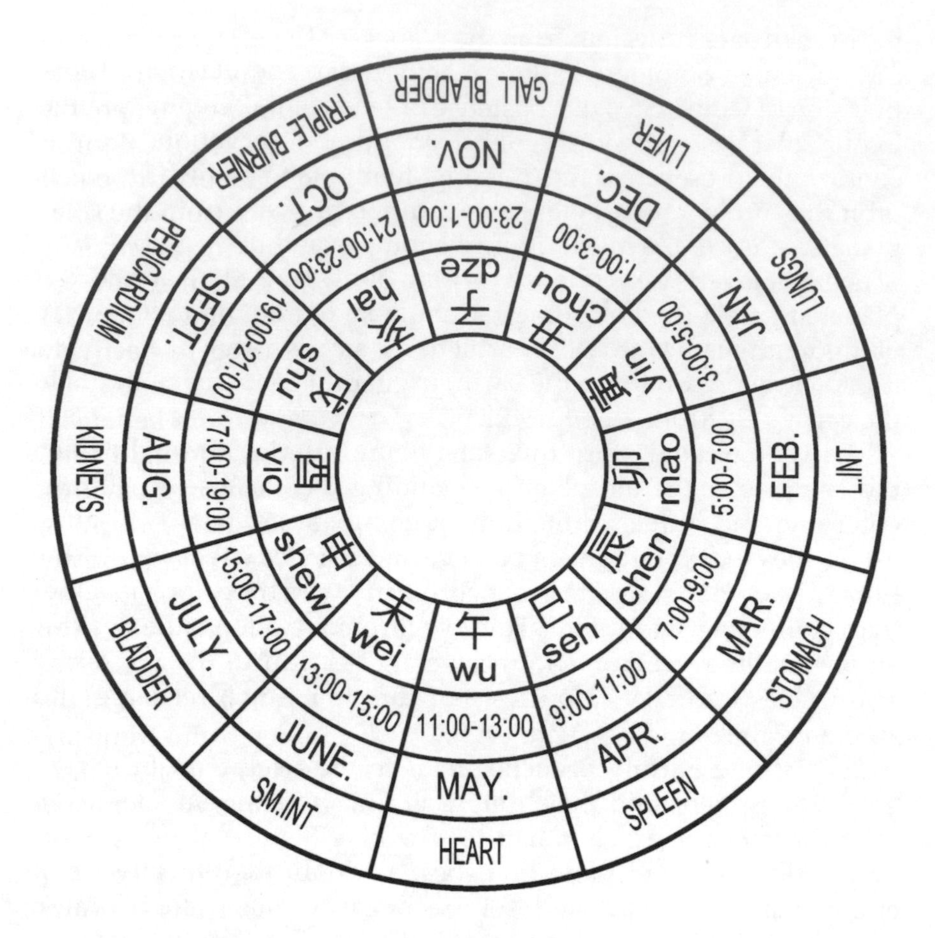

Fig. 3
The 'Twelve Earthly Branches' and their associated hours, months and internal organs

Other pivotal periods of peak energy are the summer and winter solstices, which are the longest and shortest days of the year respectively, and the spring and autumn equinoxes, when the earth's equator comes closest to the sun in its elliptical orbit through the solar system, making day and night of exactly equal length. These are excellent times to harvest energies from the solar system with chi-gung practice. The nights of the full moon and new moon are also favourite times for practitioners to meditate for prolonged periods, sometimes from midnight until dawn, in order to suffuse their systems with the Yang and Yin aspects respectively of lunar energy.

Certain hours of the day are regarded as being more beneficial than others for chi-gung practice. The hours from midnight until noon are designated as the Yang time of day, while from noon until midnight Yin prevails. In the Chinese duodecimal system of marking time, the hours from eleven p.m. until one a.m. are regarded as one of the best times for internal energy practice, for this is when the prevailing energy of the planet shifts over from waning Yin to ascending Yang. As we have seen, Yang is the active principle of light associated with Heaven, while Yin is related to the more passive, darker energies of Earth. Another prime time for practice is five a.m. to seven a.m., when Yang energy peaks before its descent toward Yin at noon. While chi-gung practice is always effective in balancing and recharging the human energy system, these two times of day provide particularly powerful results.

There are also particular times when adepts are advised not to practise chi-gung, due to adverse astral or planetary conditions or foreboding celestial phenomena. Practising chi-gung at such times imprints the aberrant patterns and negative influences of such inauspicious and unbalanced conditions on the internal energy system of the practitioner, giving rise to extreme imbalances of internal energy that can cause serious ailments and emotional disturbances. For example, Taoists regard eclipses of the sun and moon as extremely inappropriate times to practise chi-gung, because the sudden and untimely warp it causes in the natural flow of solar and lunar energies can result in a similar 'eclipse' within the human system. Similarly, Taoist masters advise against practising chi-gung when there's a comet ('broom-tail star') sweeping through the sky, because comets are maverick astral bodies that do not conform to the great cosmic rhythms of the planets and stars, and their fiery presence streaking through the sky disrupts the normal pulse of cosmic energies reaching the earth, distorting the force fields of the sun, moon and Ten Celestial Stems and transmitting their erratic energy patterns to anyone who tunes their systems into the prevailing cosmic conditions by practising chi-gung at such a time. Storms, hurricanes, sweltering heat spells, blistering cold, and any other type of extreme or freak weather conditions are also considered to be bad times for Humanity to synchronize its energies with the forces of Heaven and Earth.

In addition to particularly good and bad times for practice, there are also particularly good and bad places. Certain locations on the planet known as 'power spots' (*chi-di*) can produce remarkably powerful effects in the human energy system when chi-gung is practised there, especially when the practice is performed at particularly auspicious times of the year, month and day. The five sacred mountains of China – Omei Shan, Wu Tai Shan, Tai Shan, Hua Shan and Chung Shan – are such power spots, and for thousands of years Taoist hermits and Buddhist monks have gone to these places to perfect their practices by tapping into the powerful 'Dragon Veins' (*lung-mai*) of energy that are known to run through those hallowed peaks. Indeed, all high wind-swept mountains far from the effluvia of human civilization are regarded as superior places for practice due to the extraordinarily potent energies there, including a very high negative ion count in the air, clarity of light, purity of water, and the strong field polarity that prevails at high altitudes. Some mountains, however, are more powerful than others due to their specific locations relative to the sun, moon, planets, stars and various constellations. Mount Shasta in California and the 'Red Rock' mountain in central Australia, Mount Ararat in Iraq and many of the peaks in the Himalaya are other examples of mountains auspiciously located for internal energy work and advanced spiritual practices.

In ancient times, when these matters were much better understood than they are today, all important edifices such as temples and palaces were precisely built on locations that were known to be power spots. These locations were carefully calculated by masters of astronomy and geomancy, so that the buildings constructed on them served as focal points for the powers of Heaven and Earth that converged there. The science of geomancy, known in Chinese as *Feng Shui* ('Wind and Water'), was particularly prominent in ancient China, and even today geomancers are routinely consulted prior to constructing office buildings and private homes in places such as Taiwan and Hong Kong, in order to ensure that the flow of the earth's electromagnetic forces synchronize harmoniously rather than conflict with the energies of the people who live and work in those places. Since temples and palaces as well as imperial tombs and important monuments of the ancient world were all located at places specifically selected as vortices of auspicious astral forces and harmonious earthly energies, today these are still good places to go for practising meditation and other forms of chi-gung.

Although some of the terms and concepts discussed above may strike the uninitiated modern reader as archaic and anachronistic, in fact the principles involved here are perfectly scientific, and they apply as well today as they did when first formulated thousands of years ago. Human civilization may well have changed a lot since ancient times, but the human energy system remains much the same and so do the basic forces of Heaven and Earth. Indeed, even a cursory glance at the modern world suffices to show that humanity has definitely fallen out of synchronicity with nature and the cosmos, and this may well be one of the reasons for the decline in human health and the spiritual discontent that characterize contemporary times. Modern science and technology and the cults of materialism and consumerism have all but annihilated humanity's organic links with nature, cutting people off from the very source of the energies that sustain life. Therefore chi-gung, which restores one's links with the natural forces of Heaven and Earth, is even more important today that it was before as a means of cultivating the natural balance and harmony which has always constituted the foundation of human health and longevity, happiness and peace of mind.

Few people today are aware of the insidious effects of the 'energy pollution' that prevails throughout the world. The skies are streaked with microwaves, radio waves, radar signals and veil upon veil of artificial electromagnetic field radiation that insulate the human system from its root energy resources and have stultifying effects on human vitality. Compared with the debilitating effects of this invisible energy pollution, the smoke and smog of air pollution which most people worry about is relatively benign, for even the chemically purest air is impotent if it has been stripped of its natural wave energies, its negative ions and its dynamic field forces. Conventional modern medicine, which doesn't even recognize energy and force fields as factors in human health and disease, is clearly losing the battle against cancer, AIDS, Alzheimer's and other degenerative diseases associated with contemporary industrial lifestyles, and one of the reasons may well be its stubborn dependence on chemical and technological approaches, which only further aggravate imbalances in the human energy system. Chi-gung, which is a safe and effective form of 'energy medicine', can help the human system to resist the inhibitory influences of artificial energies and negative force fields in the environment and restore the natural balance and harmony in internal and external energies upon which human health depends.

'My life is in my own hands,' declared the sage Lao Tze 2500 years ago, 'not under the control of Heaven and Earth.' By this he meant that those who learn to practise the principles of the Tao as a way of life can take their lives into their own hands and gain control over the powers of Heaven and Earth. Such a declaration of independence from the 'powers that be' can only be made by those who learn to harness the forces of nature and the cosmos to the chariot of human life and hold the reins of power firmly in their own hands. To do this, one must first liberate one's body from unhealthy habits and self-destructive appetites instilled by society, free one's energy from the tyranny of stormy moods, egomania and emotional turmoil, and release one's mind from the shackles forged by ignorance, aggression and desire. Chi-gung unites body, energy and mind in a balanced state of harmony with the higher forces of the universe and the positive powers of nature and activates the internal alchemy of 'mind over matter', thereby allowing the practitioner to cultivate conscious command over the wild forces of animal instinct and insatiable desire that drain the energies of so many people these days. Chi-gung taps directly into the inexhaustible energy resources of the universe and channels them into the reservoirs of the human energy system, and in doing so, it also opens a spiritual gate that restores the human spirit's primordial links with the greater wisdom and compassion that guide the creative power of the universe at its source. Harmony with the wisdom and power of the universe, or 'Heaven', is the key to health and longevity on Earth and the door to peace and happiness for Humanity.

CHAPTER 4

Chi-Gung and the Three Treasures: The Alchemy of Essence, Energy and Spirit

The Three Treasures (*san bao*) are the fundamental foundations of human life and the indispensable assets of existence. They also constitute the triunal link that connects each and every human being to the infinite power and wisdom of the universe, and comprise the basic working components in the 'internal alchemy' of the *nei-gung* ('internal work') school of chi-gung.

The *Wen Tze Classic*, written about 2000 years ago, states, 'The body is the temple of life. Energy is the force of life. Spirit is the governor of life. If one of them goes off balance, all three are damaged.' As the governor of life, the spirit resides in the temple of the body and commands the life force of energy, 'and this arrangement benefits all Three Treasures'. But if the temple is not properly maintained due to negligence, or if the force of life is wasted by harmful habits, or if the governor is corrupted by worldly desires and becomes derelict in duty, then spirit loses command over energy, the body degenerates, 'and this harms all Three Treasures'. Thus the purpose of internal alchemy in chi-gung is to put spirit firmly in command as the governor of life, to restore and carefully maintain the temple of the body, and to conserve and control the vital force of energy, particularly the precious supply of power provided by *yuan-chi*, 'primordial energy'.

Prior to birth, the Three Treasures are bound in a seamless undifferentiated unity, which is known as their 'prenatal' (*sian-tien*) aspect. This is the primordial facet of life that precedes incarnate existence, the seed of life slumbering in the vast ground of the universe, like a drop of water floating in the sea (Fig. 4). This seed begins to sprout at the moment of conception, differentiating itself

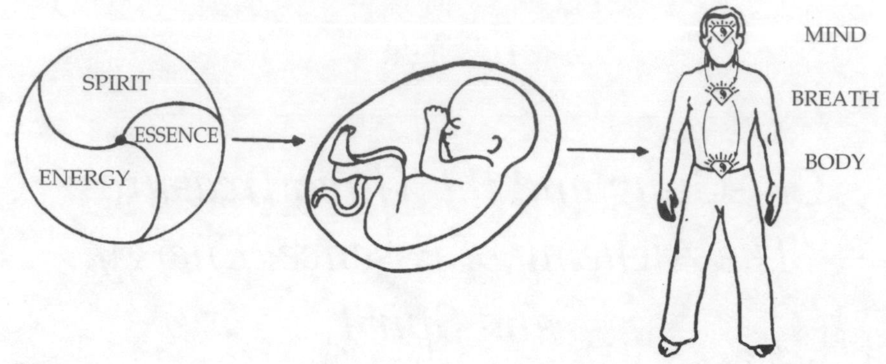

Fig. 4
Prenatal and postnatal aspects of the Three Treasures of Life: the primordial unity of essence, energy and spirit divides into the temporal functions of body, breath and mind

from the rest of the universe like a drop of water spraying loose from a wave in the sea. Although the seed for ever retains its primordial links to the universe from which it sprang, once it sprouts and takes on an individual life cycle, the Three Treasures separate into their distinctive postnatal manifestations of body, breath and mind, while their prenatal roots are held in deep reserve as primordial essence, energy and spirit.

As a prelude to our discussion of how the internal alchemy of chi-gung regulates and transforms the Three Treasures of essence/body, energy/breath, and spirit/mind to protect health, prolong life and promote awareness, let's briefly review their prenatal and postnatal aspects and see how they manifest in human life.

Prenatal essence is the primordial creative force of the universe, the primal urge to procreate and proliferate life in material form, the polar power of gender that ensures perpetual regeneration of all species of life. Every human being receives a measure of the universe's primordial essence from the fusion of sperm and ovum, and this essence manifests in life as gender and sexuality and as vitality derived from sexual hormones. It is stored in the sexual glands of male and female and in the adrenal glands of both genders, and it is transmitted perpetually from one generation to the next by sexual reproduction. This primordial spark of life, which manifests in the temporal body as sexual plasma, is therefore the only form of human essence that is truly immortal, for the sexual seed carries the genetic code of the body from generation to generation.

Postnatal essence refers to the body of flesh and bone that develops from the fusion of male and female sexual essence after conception. Synthesized from the material nutritional essence of food, water and air, its most important forms are the vital bodily fluids, such as blood and hormones, neurotransmitters and cerebrospinal fluid, enzymes and electrolytes. The seat of postnatal essence is the sacrum, and its related energy resides in the lower elixir field below the navel. In men, it is most easily damaged and depleted through excessive loss of semen in sexual activity, and in women through excessive loss of blood and bodily fluids in menstruation. In men and women, essence is also depleted by stress, fatigue, malnutrition and chronic diseases.

Prenatal energy is the primordial power of the universe, the movements and cycles of the stars and planets, the vibration of atoms and molecules, and the universal energies of the cosmos, such as light and heat, electromagnetic and nuclear forces. Its nature is constant activity and perpetual transformation. In postnatal life, prenatal energy manifests as the primordial energy of *yuan-chi*, which serves as a back-up battery of reserve energy and a basic barometer of health and vitality. It resides mainly in the adrenal cortex and the marrow and is closely associated with prenatal essence. The primordial energies of the cosmos may also be assimilated into the postnatal human system from light and other wave energies that radiate from the sky by opening the body's energy gates with chi-gung practice.

Postnatal energy refers to the energies of earth derived from natural resources, such as food, water and air, the Five Elemental Energies of the vital organ systems, breath and speech, bodily movement and cellular metabolism, and the energies of emotion. This energy is focused in the middle elixir field at the solar plexus, and it may be directly controlled and balanced by the regulated breathing methods used in chi-gung.

Prenatal spirit is the primordial 'Mind of Tao' which permeates the universe and endows every sentient being with the original light of awareness. Immortal, immaterial and luminous, primordial spirit is the infinite ocean of consciousness from which the eternal spirit of each individual springs. If the infinite space of the universe were compared to the vast expanse of an ocean, then the omnipresent awareness of primordial spirit may be compared to the wetness of the ocean's water, such is its all-pervasive, all encompassing quality throughout the entire universe. As the transcendent 'mind of the universe', primordial spirit is the source of wisdom, compassion and all spiritual virtue, the guiding light that governs the powers of creation, the master architect of every atom and molecule, star and planet in the ever-expanding temple of the manifest universe.

Prenatal spirit lies hidden like a precious pearl deep within the temporal shell of the postnatal human mind. Like a restless nomad, it wanders from lifetime to lifetime, pitching camp in this body then moving on to the next, without ever being recognized or remembered by its temporary hosts – until the day in the life of a particular being that the temporal human mind awakens to primordial spirit's subtle presence and sets it free from the delusions that bind it to mortal flesh. It is this prenatal aspect of the human mind that is immortal, and therefore recognizing it is the key to overcoming the instinctive fear of death and finding peace of mind in life. This is the ultimate goal of all spiritual practice.

Postnatal spirit manifests itself in human life as sensory perception and rational thought, personality and ego, and the dualistic delusions that separate individuals from each other. It expresses itself in the mental faculties of reason and intuition, learning and memory, and other cerebral functions. Postnatal spirit resides in the upper elixir field in the centre of the head, where it governs the body and the breath below and maintains a link with primordial spirit above. This link is the springboard for the final 'leap into space' in the highest stages of practice leading to total spiritual liberation.

There is a deep significance in the use of the term 'Three Treasures' to denote the primordial triune of essence, energy and spirit and its temporal expression in the body, breath and mind of postnatal life. It correctly implies that these three attributes are the most precious assets of life, and that they should therefore be treated, quite literally, as genuine treasures: conserved, protected, loved and valued, i.e., 'treasured'. Most people, however, take their bodies for granted and wear them out as engines of pleasure, rather than taking loving care of them as sacred temples of life. They spend their energy like money, rather than conserving it as a precious treasure of life. They apply their minds entirely to the acquisition of temporal fame and fortune and management of worldly affairs, disregarding the higher yearnings of their own spirits and paying mere lip-service to the wisdom of saints and sages. They let material concerns rule the mind and squander their precious resources just as commerce and industry squanders the resources of the planet. The purpose of the internal alchemy of the Three Treasures is to reverse this tendency by conserving and cultivating the precious treasures of life. And in the long run, the time and effort spent in such self-cultivation always proves to be a sound investment, for its reaps the rewards of health and longevity without which nothing else in life can really be enjoyed or accomplished.

Nei-Gung: The Internal Alchemy of Energy Work

When you watch someone practising chi-gung, what you see are the external facets of the practice, the *wai-gung* ('external work'). This includes rhythmic movements and balanced postures of the body designed to work on the physical body. What you don't see, but what the practitioner feels and focuses on most, are the internal aspects of the practice, the *nei-gung* ('internal work'), often referred to in English as 'internal alchemy'. While *wai-gung* establishes the physical framework for practice and helps build the body, *nei-gung* is the major focus and the primary source of benefit in chi-gung practice.

During ancient times in the Eastern as well as Western worlds, misguided alchemists spent their lives searching in vain for a way to concoct the 'Elixir of Life' or 'Philosopher's Stone' from base metals and other minerals. Many lost their lives in these experiments, which eventually discredited the entire field of alchemy, until finally the momentous discovery was made that the secret formula and all the essential ingredients and equipment required for the alchemy of physical longevity and spiritual immortality lay locked deep within the terrain of the human body, not in minerals, herbs and the alchemist's lab, and that every human being is born fully equipped to practise this alchemy. As the *Union of the Triplex Equation* states:

> Let the void be your cauldron; let nature be your furnace; for your primary ingredient, take stillness; for your reagent, use quietude; for mercury, take your vital essence; for lead, use your daily energy; for water, use restraint; for fire, take meditation.

In Taoist literature, the internal alchemy activated by chi-gung is referred to as the 'Triplex Unity' of essence, energy and spirit, while the external method of practice used to set this process in motion is called 'balancing body, breath and mind'. Like the Five Elemental Energies in nature, the internal alchemy of the Three Treasures involves two complementary cycles – the nurture cycle of transformation and the command cycle of control (Fig. 5), and each of the Three Treasures resides in one of the 'Three Elixir Fields'. In

THE INTERNAL ALCHEMY OF THE THREE TREASURES

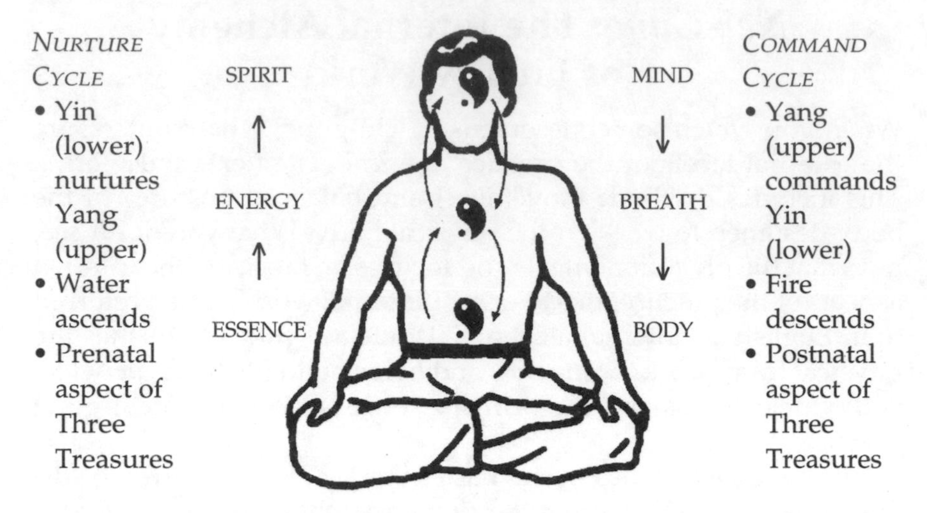

Fig. 5
The 'nurture' and 'command' cycles in the 'internal alchemy' of the Three Treasures

Taoist Yoga, Master Chao Pi-chen describes the transformation cycle of internal alchemy in relation to the elixir fields as follows:

> The lower Elixir Field under the navel is where generative force [essence] is sublimated into vitality [energy]; the middle Elixir Field in the solar plexus is where vitality is sublimated into spirit; and the upper Elixir Field in the brain is where spirit is sublimated for its flight into space.

In other words, the vital essence of hormones, particular sexual secretions, are transformed into energy in the second chakra below the navel. This energy is then raised to the third chakra, where it is transformed and refined into spiritual energy, which in turn is drawn up to the sixth chakra in the brain as fuel for the highest stage of practice – relinking the finite human mind with the infinite wisdom and power of the universe by plunging human consciousness back into the vast ocean of primordial spirit. In order to do this, the practitioner must conserve all of his or her resources of essence and energy and transform them into *ling-chi*, the highly refined energy associated with spirit. As another Taoist text puts it, 'It is *ling-chi* [spirit-energy] that reaches the top.'

The nurture cycle, which refines spiritual energy from the

essential energy of the sacrum, is the Yin aspect of internal alchemy. The command cycle, which exercises the power of 'mind over matter' through conscious control of breath and energy, is the Yang aspect. Like all polar aspects of Yin and Yang, these two cycles are interactive and interdependent. In order for spirit to gain command over the body and its energies, it must first be nurtured with energy refined from essence, and in order to conduct that subtle alchemy, spirit must exercise firm command over essence and energy. Throughout all phases in both cycles of internal alchemy, stillness, stability and concentration constitute the basic pillars of practice. As Master Chao Pi-chen states in *Taoist Yoga*:

> The generative force [essence] changes into vitality [energy] when the body is still; vitality changes into spirit when the heart is unstirred; and spirit returns to nothingness because of immutable thought.

There are eight progressive stages of practice in the internal alchemy and Triplex Unity of the Three Treasures:

1. *Conserving Essence*: for men, this mainly means conserving semen, either through periodic celibacy during times of intensive practice, or else by integrating the Dual Cultivation method of Taoist sexual yoga as part of one's practice. This involves prolonged sexual intercourse without ejaculation, preferably with a partner who understands the practice. For women, it means regulating menstrual cycles so that a minimum amount of blood is lost each month. For both genders, it also means avoiding stress, emotional turmoil, physical exhaustion and obsessive thought, all of which deplete essential hormones and neurochemicals, particularly in the adrenal/pituitary axis of the endocrine system. 'When the oil is used up,' notes an old Taoist saying, 'the lamp goes out.' Since essence constitutes the basic oil that fuels the lamp of life, the first step in the internal alchemy of the Three Treasures is to conserve essence.

2. *Restoring Essence*: Since most people have already spent many years squandering their precious supplies of sexual, endocrine and cerebral essence prior to taking up the practice of internal alchemy, it's important not only to stop wasting and start conserving this essence, but also to take steps to restore it to its original state of purity and potency. This can be done by applying supplemental *yang-sheng* (cultivating life) methods such as nutrition and dietary reform, tonic herbs, proper exercise, correct breathing and careful attention to the daily habits of life.

3. *Transforming Essence*: When essence is full and sufficiently pure and potent, it may be transformed into *jing-chi*, or 'essential energy'. This process takes place in the lower elixir field energy centre below the navel, using breath as a bellows to steam the essence and sublimate its energy in the cauldron of the abdomen, and using the mind to control the process and draw the harvested energy upward through the Governing Channel into the head.

4. *Nourishing Energy*: This stage involves the enhancement of one's overall vitality by continuously refining energy from essence and improving the efficiency of one's basic metabolic functions, so that supplies of *yuan-chi* (primordial energy) are conserved, thereby elevating the potency of one's basic life-force in preparation for the higher stages of practice. Primordial energy is further nourished by learning to tap into the energies of nature and the cosmos and drawing them into the system through the energy gates, circulating them through the meridiens, and storing them in the body's energy centres.

5. *Transforming Energy*: When the adept has accumulated sufficient supplies of energy in the lower elixir field, it is ready to be raised to the upper elixir field and transformed into the more highly refined energy associated with awareness and other spiritual faculties. This type of energy is luminous and partakes more of the wave nature of light than the pulsed electromagnetic currents associated with the physiological functions of the body. Esoteric spiritual powers such as telepathy, extra-sensory perception, clairvoyance, psychokinensis and so forth utilize this form of energy. These powers, known as *shen-tung* ('spiritual breakthroughs') in Chinese and *siddi* in Sanskrit, are regarded as signs of progress in advanced spiritual practice, not as goals in themselves, and they are only utilized with the utmost discretion when absolutely necessary for the benefit of others, never for personal profit, power or fame. Indeed, there are countless stories in China and India of practitioners who deviate from the path in order to use such powers for personal gain, then promptly lose them all and end up back at the bottom of the ladder. At this level of practice, spiritual power must always be used in close conjunction with the wisdom and compassion to which it is inextricably linked in the universal order.

6. *Nourishing Spirit*: This stage of practice concentrates energy in the upper elixir field in the centre of the head, where it awakens and illuminates the dormant primordial facets of spirit. 'Nourishing the spirit is the highest task,' states the *Yellow Emperor's Classic of Internal Medicine*. This practice requires the adept to totally still the

postnatal mind of discursive thought, tune out all sensory distractions and pacify the 'Chief Hooligan' of conflicting emotion, shrinking the role of the ego to that of a silent, passive bystander rather than the loud, demanding spoiled brat it normally plays in daily life.

7. *Transformating Spirit*: When the prevailing consciousness of the mind shifts silently and effortlessly away from the dualistic awareness spawned by words and rational thought, sensual desire and sensory perception, and subsumes itself instead in the radiant awareness, universal wisdom and infinite power of primordial spirit, then the finite awareness of the ordinary human mind transforms and expands spontaneously into the boundless transcendent awareness of the immortal 'Mind of Tao.' This transformation, known variously in English as 'enlightenment', 'transcendence', 'liberation' and 'awakening', in the Zen tradition of japan as *satori*, in Sanskrit as *nirvana*, and in Taoist parlance as *wu-dao* ('awakening to the Way'), usually occurs suddenly and unexpectedly after long and persistent practice, in a brilliant flash of universal insight that transports the mind beyond words and concepts to a higher place of awareness that answers all questions and resolves all doubts with a singular luminous vision. Emerging from this experience, the adept is forever transformed, still in the world but no longer of it, with nothing to do in life but help others reach the same sublime state.

8. *Returning to the Source*: This is the ultimate and final stage of practice, the proverbial 'flight into space'. When an adept who has already dissolved the ego and experienced enlightened awareness feels that it is time to shed the material body, he or she prepares to leave the world consciously in a pure adamantine vehicle of energy and spirit sometimes referred to as a 'Rainbow body'. Known in Taoist tradition as *ling-tai* ('spiritual embryo'), its gestation may be fostered through specific practices, which include techniques such as projecting consciousness into space in order to let spirit roam free and 'rehearse' for its final departure from the body, and to familiarize the adept's awareness with the terrain of primordial spirit. As a fusion of luminous light and pure awareness forged from the adept's essence, energy and spirit, the Rainbow Body restores the primordial unity of the Three Treasures and returns them to the universal source of all creation, 'like a drop of water slipping into the shining sea'.

However, unlike the dissolution of a drop of water when it slides back into the sea, the spirit of an enlightened individual expands to embrace the universal awareness, infinite space and boundless energy of the source to which it returns. The spirit becomes one with the universe rather than being dissolved by it, and remains there for ever in a luminous state of exalted universal awareness rather than tumbling blindly through it in the fear, anger and other karmic hangovers of life – only to be reborn once again on the same old merry-go-round of reincarnation. Very few practitioners complete this stage of practice, but those who do become 'immortals' (*shian*), forever free from the ceaseless rounds of birth and death that characterize incarnate existence, although some choose to return to the suffering of corporeal life of their own accord to help others attain the same state of self-liberation.

Thus the only true 'elixir of life' is energy, and the only immortality a human being can achieve is purely spiritual. Cultivating the primordial energy of life and achieving the enlightened state of primordial awareness are the ultimate goals of the 'internal family' (*nei-jia*) of chi-gung practitioners. However, cultivating primordial energy (*yuan-chi*) also has practical benefits for the more immediate, less lofty goals of protecting the health and prolonging the life of the physical body.

Most people are not even aware that they possess such a thing as primordial energy and that it plays such a decisive role in their physical well-being. Consequently, they carelessly squander this precious asset without even realizing it. Every time you lose your temper, subject yourself to stress, overwork your body, neglect your health and let your system get run down, you overtax your normal metabolic sources of postnatal True Energy derived from food, water and air, thereby forcing your system to dip into precious and irreplaceable reserves of primordial energy, most of which is stored in the adrenal, pituitary and other glands. If this happened only rarely in life, it wouldn't have much negative impact on health and longevity, but for most people this sort of 'deficit spending' has become par for the course in daily life, both at work and at play, and the endocrine system and our immune response are the first to malfunction as a result of such overdrive. This is the light in which traditional Chinese physicians view the condition currently known as 'acquired immune deficiency syndrome'.

The quality and quantity of primordial energy that one receives at birth depend on three main factors: the purity and potency of the parents' genetic plasma; the condition of the parents' health and vitality and the state of their emotional relationship at the time of conception; and the spiritual factors such as karma that are brought into this life by the incoming spirit. Karma, which refers to specific conditions that arise in this life as a cumulative result of the activities and habits cultivated in former lives, and reincarnation – the cyclic transmigration of the immortal spiritual seed from life to life, body to body – are taken as basic facts of life in traditional Eastern thought, not as doctrinaire tenets of any particular religion, and therefore they are also regarded as fundamental factors in health, longevity and spiritual development. Indeed, until they were erased from the scriptures by church decree during the ninth century AD, karma and reincarnation were also integral elements in Christian thought. Since these factors often unravel the little mysteries and explain the persistent problems in life that defy any other explanation, including matters of health, it behoves one to at least keep an open mind on the subject of karma and reincarnation, particularly when it comes to energy, which is closely associated with spirit.

Yuan-chi is thus the basic life-force that every human being brings into this world at birth. It is something that cannot be replaced, traded or purchased, nor can it be obtained from supplements or transplanted from other sources. It can, however, be conserved, cultivated and controlled, and its purity and potency may be enhanced through the practice of chi-gung and other *yang-sheng* regimes, such as diet and supplements, exercise and sexual yoga, relaxation and meditation. These practices ensure that there is always a sufficient supply of postnatal True Energy to support the daily energy requirements of body and mind, while also counteracting the effects of stress, malnutrition and exhaustion that so quickly deplete True Energy, thereby conserving reserve supplies of primordial energy to support the higher stages of internal alchemy. Whenever *yuan-chi* is borrowed to support physiological functions in times of stress, illness and other conditions of deficiency, it is irretrievably lost, but when it is incorporated into the internal alchemy of the Three Treasures, it is reinforced, refined and recirculated throughout the system, thereby preserving it.

The conservation and cultivation of primordial energy through internal chi-gung amplifies the power of the entire human energy system, like stepping up the current in an electrical circuit so that all the lights suddenly get brighter. This is the proverbial 'glow of good health' – the rosy cheeks and sparkling eyes, the spring in the step and the radiant clarity of spirit. When conserved and amplified through practice, primordial energy has a bright radiant quality that it imparts to the whole system, suffusing every organ, tissue and cell with the protective aura of its force field and enveloping the whole body with a luminous shield of energy that guards against invasion by aberrant environmental energies and harmful electromagnetic fields and wards off the negative influences of malevolent spirits, ill intentions and demonic forces. The latter benefit, known in Chinese as *bi-shieh* ('to repel evil'), may strike Western readers as arcane and superfluous, but in Asia, protecting oneself from hostile energy and spiritual malice projected unconsciously or deliberately by others and from the parasitic influence of malignant entities are regarded as highly important dividends of chi-gung practice. Like karma and reincarnation, unless you've seen conclusive evidence that such forces do *not* exist, it might be a good idea to give the benefit of the doubt to the experience of spiritual masters who say that they do, and therefore take them into account as factors in your life and practice.

Now let's take a quick look at some of the practical benefits of practising chi-gung and the internal alchemy of the Three Treasures in terms of human health, longevity and awareness.

Chi-Gung and Essence

As we have seen, essence manifests itself in postnatal life as the physical body in general, and its various vital fluids in particular, while energy manifests as breath. According to the principles of internal alchemy, 'energy commands essence', so it follows that breath controls the secretion and circulation of vital fluids in the body. The deep, diaphragmic breathing used in chi-gung gives a powerful boost to the circulation of blood throughout the body by alternately compressing and releasing pressures in the abdominal and chest cavities, with the diaphragm acting as a 'second heart' to pump blood through the vessels. Every deep abdominal breath you take helps pumps blood through the system and takes a big load off the heart. When this sort of breathing is practised throughout the day, it serves as a highly effective preventive against heart disease and helps prolong life.

The long, rhythmic extensions of the limbs and torso performed in moving chi-gung exercises stimulate the movement of lymph throughout the body. Since lymph helps purify the blood and intercellular fluids, chi-gung exercises promote detoxification of the entire body, right down to the individual cells.

Another way that chi-gung breathing stimulates bodily fluids is by massaging the abdominal organs. As the diaphragm descends on inhalation, it squeezes stale blood, bile and other stagnant fluids from the liver and other organs, and when the pressure is released on exhalation as the diaphragm ascends, fresh blood rushes into the organs and replenishes them with oxygen and nutrients. This internal diaphragmic pressure also stimulates secretions of vital hormones from the glands located in the abdomen and sacrum, particularly the adrenal cortex on top of the kidneys.

Deep breathing greatly enhances the oxygenation of the blood and the elimination of carbon dioxide in the lungs by increasing the surface area of the alveoli involved in gas exchange with the bloodstream. In conjunction with the enhanced circulation and distribution of blood provided by the pumping of the diaphragm, the net result of this improvement in respiratory efficiency is a significant increase in the oxygenation and detoxification of tissues and cells throughout the body.

The importance of this effect today cannot be overemphasised. Two hundred years ago, the air we breathed contained 38 per cent oxygen and only 1 per cent carbon dioxide. Today, due to factors such as deforestation, burning fossil fuels and industrial pollution, the level of oxygen in the air has dropped by half to only 19 per cent, while the carbon dioxide level has risen to a dizzying 25 per cent. This means that every breath we take today delivers only half the oxygen to our bodies that it did for our ancestors and contains twenty-five times more carbon dioxide, which is a metabolic waste product that we are supposed to expel through breathing. Thus the enhanced assimilation of oxygen and elimination of carbon dioxide which chi-gung causes in the body is more important to human health today than ever, and this factor alone more than justifies the time and effort required to practise chi-gung every day.

In 1931, Dr Otto Warburg received the Nobel Prize in medicine for his discovery that the primary condition associated with all forms of cancer is severe deprivation of oxygen to the cells of the affected tissues, and that cancer cannot occur in tissues that are sufficiently oxygenated. This finding, which has been ignored by the medical establishment, is further supported by the fact that the worldwide increase in the incidence of cancer has closely paralleled the concurrent decrease in oxygen levels, and that cancer is spreading fastest in the most industrialized regions of the world, where oxygen levels are lowest. The obvious conclusion here is that the best preventive measure against cancer is to make sure that all of the cells and tissues of the body receive sufficient supplies of oxygen, and the simplest, most effective way to do that is by daily practice of chi-gung, which not only increases oxygenation of the blood but also ensures its complete distribution to every cell in the body, while also eliminating the toxic wastes whose accumulation in the tissues further predispose them to the development of cancer.

When people in the Western world think of 'exercise', what usually comes to mind is gruelling workouts in the gym 'pumping iron', jogging till you 'hit the wall' from exhaustion, and other physically demanding sports that fulfil the axiom, 'no pain, no gain'. In fact, however, this sort of exercise usually does more damage to the body than it does good, particularly when performed sporadically, without stretching and loosening the body first and reoxygenating the blood and tissues afterward with deep breathing. After the age of thirty, this type of strenuous exercise is even more harmful.

This kind of exercise tends to compress muscles, tighten tendons, stiffen joints, and acidify the blood and tissues with excess lactic acid, carbon dioxide and other metabolic wastes. While professional athletes take elaborate measures to counteract such deficits, very few amateurs bother to do so, and most people are not even aware of the cumulative damage caused by such activity.

By contrast, chi-gung exercises, which involve soft, slow, gentle flowing movements harmonized with deep diaphragmic breathing, stretch and tone the muscles and tendons, loosen and limber the joints and ligaments, increase the flexibility of the body's moving parts, and stimulate all of the internal organs and glands with the deep therapeutic massage provided by the contraction and expansion of the diaphragm. At the same time, the blood and intercellular fluids are oxygenated and alkalized rather than carbonated and acidified, the endocrine system is balanced rather than excessively flooded with adrenaline, the nervous system is relaxed rather than overworked, and energy is accumulated and stored rather than scattered and depleted. The bottom line in chi-gung may be summed up by the Taoist axiom, 'less strain, more gain'.

Moreover, chi-gung requires no expensive equipment and exclusive club memberships, no competition and score-keeping, hardly any training and very little effort, and a lot less time and trouble than sports and games, delivering a maximum dividend in health for a minimum investment of effort. Such are the bodily benefits of practising chi-gung for physical fitness at home.

Chi-Gung and Energy

Breathing is the primary method of controlling the balance and flow of energies in the human system, but only when we take conscious command of our breath and train it to regulate energy.

When we breathe unconsciously on 'automatic pilot', as most people do twenty-four hours a day throughout their lives, our breathing patterns are determined by various internal and external energy factors, such as thoughts and emotions, tension and stress, weather and environment, and the unnatural forces and fields produced by power lines, broadcasting towers, televisions, electrical appliances and other gadgetry. In this passive mode of breathing, energy is not regulated and balanced by breath; instead, it takes on the erratic patterns of the breath and is subject to the same disruptive factors.

On the other hand, when we learn how to breathe consciously and correctly, as in chi-gung practice, breath becomes the master regulator of every energy in the human system, balancing emotional and cerebral energies, controlling the Five Elemental Energies of the organ systems, and harmonizing the human energy system with the powerful force fields of nature and the cosmos. This is done through the command cycle of internal alchemy, whereby the mind controls the body through its command over breath.

One of the most important benefits of chi-gung in terms of energy is emotional equilibrium. TCM views the emotions as forms of errant energy moving uncontrolled through the system rather than as mental phenomena, as in Western medicine. In this view, emotion is nothing more than 'e-motion', or 'energy-in-motion'. When allowed to run rampant through the system, emotions are regarded as the primary internal causes of disease in TCM. Thus, the *Yellow Emperor's Classic of Internal Medicine* states:

> Anger causes energy to rise, joy causes energy to slow down, grief causes energy to dissipate, fear causes energy to descend, fright causes energy to scatter, exhaustion causes energy to wither, worry causes energy to stagnate.

Rather than dismissing emotional disturbances as mental aberrations and sending emotionally disturbed patients to see psychiatrists or psychologists, as in modern medical practice, TCM diagnoses emotional imbalance more in terms of organic dis-functions in the body, nutritional deficiencies, environmental factors, and the disruptive effects of external forces and energy fields on the human system. In this analysis, the mental dis-turbances associated with emotional imbalance are usually symptoms rather than causes of the problem. Schizophrenia, for example, has recently been found to respond very well to megadoses of niacin (vitamin B3), an essential nutrient involved in producing vital neurotransmitters in the brain, and this sort of nutritional therapy has demonstrated a far better cure rate than conventional psychotherapy. In this case, the emotional energy imbalance associated with schizophrenia is caused by a simple nutritional deficiency, not by a mental problem, and no amount of 'counselling' can ever correct such a condition.

As we have seen, each of the Five Elemental Energies governs the functions of a particular pair of internal organs, and each is also associated with a particular emotional response (see page 15). When an emotional response becomes extreme or habitual and is allowed to erupt and run its course without control, it invariably comes to rest in the related organ, where it disrupts that organ's functions and, if allowed to continue, damages the cellular matrix. Extreme anger, for example, inflames the liver, making you feel 'livid'. If anger becomes a habitual response in life, it can easily lead to chronic liver disease, and such disease in turn further predisposes one to frequent anger, creating a vicious cycle of self-destruction. Fear impairs kidney function, and as we all know, when fear grows extreme and becomes fright, it can cause such a radical shift in kidney energy that the bladder spontaneously evacuates itself. Emotion, therefore, can be a major factor in the development of chronic disease in the body, although it is not recognized as such in modern conventional medicine.

If you observe your own or others' breathing patterns during moments of emotional imbalance, you will note that each type of uncontrolled emotional response causes a specific imbalance in the breath. Anxiety causes the breath to grow short, shallow and fast, like a panting dog, and to rise to the top of the lungs. Anger brings on an erratic huffing and puffing and shifts the breath from nostrils, where it belongs, to mouth. Fear causes a gulping, swallowing, withholding pattern of breath, with long retention and short, tentative exhalation. Grief grinds the breath down to a very short, slow, shallow sigh and sometimes draws it to a complete halt. Therefore, not only do emotional imbalances cause damage to the associated organs, they also suppress breathing, thereby depriving the body of sufficient supplies of oxygen while allowing toxic cellular wastes to accumulate, inhibiting the circulation of blood and energy, and stagnating the entire energy system.

Regardless of what causes a particular emotional imbalance and where it comes to rest in the body, in the final analysis it is nothing more than a runaway 'energy-in-motion', and therefore it can always be easily controlled and rebalanced with a few minutes of deep diaphragmic breathing. It's important, however, to do this as soon as the emotional response arises, before it has a chance to cause damage and upset the whole system. This sort of timely 'damage control' requires conscious recognition of extreme emotions for what they really are – runaway energies triggered by external stimuli – rather than confusing them with 'feelings', which are intuitive forms of thoughts that can be quite useful. By being vigilant and catching emotional outbursts in the bud, you can prevent a lot of health problems and save a lot of precious energy. You can easily demonstrate the efficacy of breath control as a means of emotional control for yourself simply by doing a few minutes of deep abdominal breathing next time you feel anger, anxiety, fear or grief arising in your system. It works immediately and without fail to calm the emotion and rebalance the entire energy system. Furthermore, if chi-gung is practised daily, it serves as a preventative against emotional outbursts because after a round of practice, one tends to breathe properly throughout the day, precluding radical swings in emotional energy.

Another beneficial effect of chi-gung practice on energy is that it establishes harmonic resonance between the human energy system and the ambient energy pulse of the planet. The prevailing frequency of the earth's electromagnetic field pulses at a rate of 7.8 herz (cycles per second), and numerous studies have shown that this frequency is highly conductive to the activation of healing responses in the human body. Known as the Schumann Resonance, 7.8 herz is the precise frequency at which the human energy system activates the body's own innate immune responses. By tuning the microcosmic human energy field into synchronicity with the macrocosmic field of the earth, chi-gung clears the entire human energy system of all negative energies and aberrant energy patterns and establishes the ideal conditions for internal healing and repair work. This effect is also a very good antidote for the constant influx of imbalanced energies and harmful force fields to which the human body is exposed by power lines, transformers, microwave radiation, electrical appliances, broadcasting towers and other forms of 'energy pollution' produced by modern technology.

The physical relaxation, mental tranquillity, emotional equilibrium and deep abdominal breathing that prevail during chi-gung practice allow the opening of the Twelve Organ-Energy Meridiens and the Eight Extraordinary Channels and permit energy to flow freely through the entire system. This serves as a general tune-up for all of the body's vital functions, balances all energies, and draws supplemental energy supplies into the system from nature and the cosmos, while clearing the channels of stagnant energy. Since energy is the foundation of both physical and mental health, chi-gung recharges and rebalances body as well as mind and harmonizes them both with the rejuvenating powers of Heaven and Earth.

Chi-Gung and Spirit

The great advantage of practising chi-gung as a form of daily exercise and preventive healthcare is that it works on so many different levels. While protecting the body from disease and degeneration and keeping the whole energy system in balance, it also enhances all the faculties of spirit, improving the postnatal cerebral functions of the brain and awakening the inherent link between the human mind and the primordial spirit of the universe. Every human being is born with the 'precious pearl' of primordial awareness – a 'Wish-Fulfilling Gem' of infinite power and wisdom – but very few have the time or inclination for the rigorous spiritual disciplines traditionally employed to awaken this insight and power. Chi-gung offers a viable compromise, paving a gradual and far less demanding path to the same goal, while still permitting the practitioner to pursue worldly life. While chi-gung alone may not carry you all the way to spiritual enlightenment, it certainly will propel you strongly in that direction. Furthermore, while chi-gung cultivates the energy required for practical goals such as health and longevity, productivity and pleasure, it simultaneously provides the energy needed for spiritual purposes, because energy is the basic fuel for body as well as mind.

First, let's see how chi-gung enhances the practical cerebral functions of the brain. The brain is irrigated by thousands of metres of minuscule capillaries that pump hundreds of litres of blood to and from millions of neurons. Of all the body's tissues, the brain suffers the most damage from the chronic deficiency of oxygen that has become such a common condition throughout the world today, particularly in industrially developed regions. The brain normally consumes about 25 per cent of the body's total metabolic energy, all of which depends upon adequate supplies of oxygen. Therefore, it is the brain that realizes the most dramatic improvement in function that results from the increased oxygenation of blood and tissues and the improvement in microcirculation produced by chi-gung practice. Studies at several universities in China have shown marked improvement in memory and recall, learning and concentration, and other basic cerebral functions after only a few weeks of daily chi-gung practice, and these benefits continue to accumulate with long-term practice. Attention disorders in children, which in America are often treated with amphetamines, have also responded well to chi-gung therapy.

When the autonomous nervous system switches over to the restorative parasympathetic circuit during chi-gung practice, the brain begins to synthesize and secrete fresh supplies of the essential neurotransmitters required for normal brain functions and proper cerebral balance. When the brain is kept running non-stop on the active sympathetic circuit, as most people do these days, it soon uses up all reserves of vital neurochemicals, resulting in such symptoms as fatigue, irritability, memory loss, confusion, depression, insomnia and other cerebral malfunctions. Many people resort to drugs such as Prozac, amphetamines and barbiturates, or stimulants like caffeine and nicotine, to counteract these symptoms of cerebral imbalance, but this approach provides only temporary relief, leads to addiction, and ultimately makes the situation worse by further suppressing normal secretions of vital neurotransmitters. In fact, recent evidence indicates that the real reason why some people use so-called 'recreational drugs', such as cocaine, heroin and cannabis, is not for their intoxicating effects but rather as a way to counteract inherent or acquired imbalances in neurotransmitters. Half an hour of chi-gung practice every morning and evening supplies the brain with all the oxygen and nutrients, as well as the cerebral energy, it requires to replenish supplies and rebalance secretions of the full spectrum of neurotransmitters it needs to function properly. This effect is even more pronounced in conjunction with a properly balanced diet and synergistic nutritional supplements.

Another way in which chi-gung promotes mental clarity, cerebral balance, and spiritual awareness is by drawing energy up the spinal channels into the upper elixir field centre in the head. Even if you are not consciously aware of this process as it occurs during practice, you can always feel the results quite clearly after the session is over. As long as the exercises are correctly practised in terms of posture, breath control and mental focus, the internal alchemy they activate takes its course through the system whether you're aware of it or not, refining and raising energy from the sacral region and feeding it into the higher centres in the head. This is why breath control is a central pillar in the higher practices of all spiritual and mystical traditions. But even for ordinary practitioners with more modest goals, the basic mechanism of internal alchemy works in the same way to enhance the quality and increase the quantity of energy available to the spirit. Whether one uses this energy to enhance the postnatal cerebral functions of the brain for daily life or to awaken the higher awareness of primordial spirit in preparation for what comes after life is up to the individual.

Most people take up chi-gung in order to improve their health, enhance vitality and prolong life, but almost everyone who continues to practise eventually begins to realize the spiritual benefits of chi-gung as well. Slowly but surely, as latent spiritual powers such as intuition, insight and intent begin to awaken, one discovers a growing interest and appreciation for the spiritual aspects of existence. One also begins to realize the power of 'mind over matter', and to understand that many of our physical ailments are caused by negative thoughts and 'bad attitudes'. This alone usually suffices to focus our attention more fully on how the mind works, because no one wants to create unnecessary discomfort, or even fatal illnesses, within their own bodies. All of these insights and inspirations arise from the personal experience of working with one's own energies. It's unlikely that playing tennis or lifting weights or jogging will set you on the path of spiritual discovery, but chi-gung, due to the way in which it activates the internal alchemy of essence, energy and spirit and balances body, breath and mind, does just that, even without any particular effort in that direction. In this pragmatic age of convenience and cost-effective considerations, this makes chi-gung a 'great deal'.

Chi-Gung and Psychoneuroimmunology

When reading books like this, readers who are unfamiliar with the theory and practice of chi-gung and TCM sometimes wonder what things like essence, energy and spirit, internal alchemy and breath control, and other Taoist ideas have to do with the 'nuts and bolts' of modern medical science. Recent research on the innate human healing response known in Western medicine as 'psychoneuroimmunology' (PNI) has now revealed some very interesting parallels between traditional Chinese paradigms of human health and healing and the latest findings of modern medical science. The discovery of the PNI healing mechanism offers clear scientific evidence which validates the internal alchemy of the Three Treasures as a basis for human health and longevity.

The most celebrated case of PNI was that of Norman Cousins. After enduring the extreme discomfort and debilitating effects of a long and losing battle against a crippling spinal disorder with conventional modern medical therapies, Cousins suddenly decided to switch tactics and literally laughed himself to a complete cure and full recovery by watching all the old Marx Brothers and Laurel and Hardy films that he could find. He also insisted on moving from the hospital room to a comfortable hotel room, thereby freeing his system from the immunosuppressive effects of the unhealthy energies – and notoriously unhealthy food – to which patients in large medical institutions are subjected. Before long, Western medical science began to realize what TCM has known for thousands of years – that a patient's state of mind can make the crucial difference between illness and recovery, life and death, and that the mind has the power to heal the body by rebalancing its energies without any assistance from drugs and doctors. As Cousins notes in the book he wrote about his experience, 'The will to live is not a theoretical abstraction, but a physiological reality with therapeutic characteristics.'

An article in the May 1992 issue of the American magazine *Omni* describes the PNI response as follows:

> Over the past ten years, there's been an explosion of evidence linking the power of the mind [spirit] to the health of the body [essence], and experts in the new field of psychoneuroimmunology, or PNI, are gaining a greater understanding of how the brain and the body can cooperate to fight off illness. It's been discovered, for one thing, that there are nerve fibres in the thymus, the immune system's master gland, as well as in the spleen, the lymph nodes, and the bone marrow – all vital parts of the immune system. Some immune system cells have receptors for neuropeptides, chemicals that are produced within the brain itself . . . suggest[ing] that the brain talks directly to the immune system . . .

The question is: what exactly triggers the brain to secrete the specific neurochemicals responsible for activating the healing responses of the immune system? As Norman Cousins' case indicates, one way to achieve this is by creating a happy, carefree, positive state of mind, and this indeed is the only approach so far recognized in modern medical circles. Unfortunately not everyone is able to control their minds and balance their emotions sufficiently to activate the PNI response solely through the 'power of positive thinking', and many patients, particularly those who are emotionally disturbed or mentally impaired, are therefore unable to switch on their own immune systems in this way.

Virtually anyone – including those suffering from senile dementia – can learn the basic postures and breathing exercises used in chi-gung, or at least be treated with emitted chi by master healers. This activates the PNI response in a way not yet understood by mainstream modern medicine – through the avenue of the human energy system, which links body and mind and can be directly regulated by breath. In other words, chi-gung, whether practised by a patient or applied by a healer, switches the brain and central nervous system over to the mode of operation in which the neurotransmitters responsible for activating the immune system are produced. Since it is a lot easier to control your breathing than your mind, chi-gung provides an easy and effective way to activate the innate healing mechanisms involved in the PNI response. As Lo Te-hsiou, a chi-gung master from Taiwan, puts it,

> When properly practised, chi-gung activates the parasympathetic circuit of the central nervous system, thereby stimulating the production of neurochemicals which cause the endocrine system to secrete hormones that enhance vitality and boost immunity.
>
> These healing hormones in turn help sustain continued production of calming parasympathetic neurotransmitters, establishing a cycle of biofeedback that enables the body to heal itself naturally.

In terms of internal alchemy, spirit/mind commands energy/breath, and energy/breath commands essence/body. In terms of Western medicine, the neurotransmitters secreted by the brain when the nervous system operates on the parasympathetic circuit, represent the factor of mind in internal alchemy. The healing hormones which these neurotransmitters cause to be secreted in the glands of the immune system represent the vital essence of the body. The breath, which is not yet recognized in Western medicine as a pivotal control mechanism for activating the healing powers of PNI, represents and regulates the human energy system, which is also not recognized in Western medicine. Nevertheless, it is the breath and the energies it governs that mediates the power of 'mind over matter' by causing the brain to secrete the neurochemicals that activate the immune system to heal the body. This is the command cycle of internal alchemy.

The complementary nurture cycle of essence to energy and energy to spirit also comes into play in PNI. Once the positive biofeedback between the nervous and immune systems has been established, the calming neurochemicals and healing hormones (i.e., 'essence') secreted in the body have a powerful pacifying effect on the mind (i.e., 'spirit') and a balancing influence on the emotions (i.e., 'energy'). This effect reinforces the entire PNI response by sustaining the conditions of mental calm and emotional equilibrium, allowing the healing process to continue even after the actual practice of chi-gung is over. If the mind gets agitated or the emotions upset, thereby interrupting the healing response, all the patient needs to do to reactivate PNI is simply practise another round of chi-gung and re-establish the requisite conditions through the interaction of body, breath and mind.

Thus the ancient Chinese medical maxim that mind is the master healer of the body and that the elixir of health and longevity lies within the human system, not in a pill, is beginning to emerge as a fact of modern medical science. Two thousand years ago, the *Yellow Emperor's Classic of Internal Medicine* declared, 'If one maintains an undisturbed spirit within, no disease will occur.' In *Maximum Immunity*, Dr Weiner virtually paraphrases this statement when he writes, 'By learning how to control our mind, subtle hormone changes emerge that then control our biochemical reality.' Chi-gung is a simple and effective way to control the mind and balance the emotions and thereby create the subtle hormonal changes that produce the biochemical reality of health and longevity.

Chi-gung engages the Three Treasures of the body, energy and mind in a whole, harmonious healing process that integrates the physical, emotional and mental aspects of health. Modern medicine splits mental and physical diseases into two separate categories, relegating the former to psychology and the latter to physiology, then further fragments both fields into specialized branches of therapy based on symptomology, without even taking into consideration the energy system that links the two in an inseparable, interdependent phenomena. Complete healing of the whole system can never be achieved this way, for it never deals with the basic imbalances of energy that lie at the root of and intersect both the physical and the mental symptoms of disease.

In chi-gung healing, the patient's mental and emotional states are every bit as important in the diagnosis and treatment of disease as the results of blood tests and X-rays, a point that modern allopathic medicine finds difficult to swallow. The so-called 'miraculous' and 'impossible' cures achieved by chi-gung in recent years for cancer, cerebral palsy, Parkinson's disease and other conditions regarded as 'incurable' by Western medicine have succeeded because the therapist diagnosed and treated the case on the invisible but ultimately decisive level of energy, rather than just the superficial physical symptoms that appear in the body. When the root causes of such diseases are traced to energy imbalances and those imbalances are then corrected, the physical symptoms they cause, such as tumours or paralysis, simply dissolve or disappear. Many such cures have recently been witnessed in China by visiting Western doctors, who no longer regard them as miracles once they learn how the human energy system functions and see how chi-gung works. 'Seeing is believing', and these are the doctors who are beginning to bring the benefits of chi-gung and the 'internal alchemy' of healing that it activates to the attention of their peers and patients in the West.

CHAPTER 5

Chi-Gung and Health: Healing with Energy

'One way of looking at illness,' writes Jack Schwartz in *Human Energy Systems*, 'is to characterize it as stagnant energy that is not being transformed.' In TCM, all disease, physical as well as mental and emotional, is diagnosed and treated as a basic imbalance in the vital energies of the human system. Today, so-called 'energy medicine' is the newest development in modern Western medical science, but in China, 'energy work' (i.e., chi-gung) has been used to prevent and cure disease for thousands of years, and recent research has begun to validate the therapeutic efficacy of this approach in human health and healing. Numerous studies conducted in China as well as America have established a solid scientific foundation for chi-gung as a primary means of preventing and curing disease.

Chi-gung may be utilized with equal efficacy for preventing as well as curing disease. For preventive healthcare, a regular regimen of daily practice, such as the one recommended in Chapter 10, protects the practitioner from both acute disease as well as chronic degenerative conditions by strengthening immunity and resistance, regulating vital functions, enhancing vitality, and keeping the human energy system in perfect balance. For curing disease and correcting degenerative conditions that have already developed, self-therapy through intensive practice of chi-gung is supplemented with transmission of healing energy from healer to patient. In both preventive and curative care, self-therapy through practice as well as transmission of energy from healer to patient, the basic healing agent is the ambient free energy of the universe, and the delivery system for this medicine is the mind.

About four hundred years ago, the Taoist healer and chi-gung master Shih Chien-wu wrote, 'Energy is a medicine that prolongs your life. Mind is the aspect of spirit that controls energy. Therefore, if you can learn how to use your mind to control energy, you can become a wizard.' Chi-gung masters in China have been using their minds to control energy and energy to cure disease and prolong life for thousands of years, but until recently, incredulous Western observers have dismissed such healers as wily 'wizards' who obtain results through some sort of hypnotic suggestion or faith healing. Now, however, in light of irrefutable scientific evidence, Western physicians are taking a closer look at chi-gung healing. Instead of seeing wizards they now see healers, and where they once saw magic they now see science.

Chi-Gung as Preventive Healthcare

Since time immemorial, chi-gung has been known in China as 'the method for preventing disease and prolonging life'. Modern medicine finally seems to have come full circle regarding human health and healing. After several centuries of trying to 'conquer' disease with chemical drugs, radiation, radical surgery and other technological solutions, and trying to prevent disease with vaccinations, synthetic additives to 'fortify' food, and all-out chemical warfare against germs, medical science is beginning to realize that 'the best offence is a good defence', and that the best defence is a strong, well-balanced energy system. When all is said and done, daily practice of chi-gung is the best preventive health measure against acute disease, the development of chronic degenerative conditions, the debilitating effects of stress, and the dangers posed by environmental pollution – including the less obvious but equally damaging factors of 'energy pollution', such as artificial electromagnetic fields, microwave radiation, emanations from power lines, computers and appliances, and so forth. Let's take a look at some of the ways that chi-gung practice protects health and prolongs life by reviewing the most important benefits it has on various aspects of the human system.

Brain and Central Nervous System

As we have already seen, chi-gung switches the autonomous nervous system from the stress-related 'fight or flight' mode of the sympathetic branch over to the restorative healing mode of the parasympathetic branch. When this happens on a daily basis due to regular practice, the body has a chance to heal itself and restore balance day by day, long before serious physiological damage has a chance to develop. In order for the nervous system to function in the healing mode of the parasympathetic branch, the cerebral cortex, where the constant chatter of the 'internal dialogue' arises, must be stilled. Electroencephalographic (EEG) monitoring of people practising chi-gung has shown that during and after a session of chi-gung practice, the cerebral cortex enters a state of calm and quiet that very few people experience even in sleep.

It's a well-known fact that the average person uses only five to ten per cent of his or her 15 billion brain cells. That's like trying to operate a computer with only five to ten per cent of its software loaded: many basic functions simply cannot operate properly under such conditions. Small wonder then that so many people's immune functions fail to respond successfully to the challenges of disease and environmental pollution, and that by the time they reach old age, so many experience memory failure, senility and other symptoms of cerebral deficiency. EEG tests have demonstrated that chi-gung activates the dormant 90 per cent of the human brain by suffusing even the deepest layers of the cerebrum with stimulating bioelectric currents that activate long-dormant functions and cause measurable electrical excitation of brain cells that previously showed no activity. The practical results of this effect include significant improvement in memory, learning and other intelligence factors, enhancement in physiological functions controlled by the brain, and the awakening of latent psychic powers, such as extrasensory perception. Of particular interest here is the fact that the EEG brain scans of adults and elderly people who practise chi-gung regularly show a peak value and a frequency that are characteristic of the patterns in children. This sheds scientific light on the frequent references in Chinese medical literature to the 'youth-restoring' (*huan-tung*) effects of chi-gung practice.

As we know from the basic axioms of internal alchemy, 'energy commands essence'. In terms of brain function, the enhancement and balance of the bioelectrical energies associated with brain activity observed in those who practise chi-gung should in turn result in a significant improvement in brain chemistry; i.e., in the synthesis and secretion of vital neurotransmitters, and this indeed proves to be the case. Numerous studies in China and America have shown that after a session of chi-gung practice, there is a significant rise in the level of essential neurotransmitters in the blood, brain and cerebrospinal fluids, particularly norepinephrine, acetycholine, serotonin and dopamine. Deficiencies and imbalances in these neurochemicals are causal factors in such increasingly common conditions as Parkinson's disease, Alzheimer's disease, chronic depression, insomnia and drug addiction. By maintaining a constant supply and proper balance of essential neurotransmitters, chi-gung not only prevents cerebral deficiency diseases but also eliminates the need for the recreational and prescription drugs which so many people use today in an effort to balance their brain chemistry.

One of the most potent classes of neurochemicals in the human brain is the endorphin group. Endorphins have a molecular structure analogous to morphine, but their analgesic effects are about two hundred times stronger than morphine. One of these natural pain-killing neurochemicals is called enkephalin, and tests have shown that chi-gung stimulates the brain to produce large amounts of enkephalin, while also enhancing the capacity of the endorphin receptors to receive and hold enkephalin. No doubt this accounts for some of the astonishing feats that some adepts perform under the influence of chi-gung, such as walking on red-hot bricks, running knives through their cheeks, and so forth. This effect accounts for the well-known analgesic effects of chi-gung, and further explains why most chi-gung practitioners have no need of addictive substances.

Immune Response

Closely related to the improvement in cerebral function is the significant enhancement in immunity and resistance that results from chi-gung practice. As we have seen, the innate healing mechanisms known as psychoneuroimmunology are mediated by positive biofeedback between the nervous system and the endocrine system, and chi-gung activates this response by stimulating production of the neurotransmitters, hormones and other immune factors required for healing.

One of the primary factors in immunity is the activity of white blood cells, which are produced in bone marrow. Chi-gung not only enhances white blood cell production by stimulating the marrow, it has also been shown to increase the phagocytic activity of these scavenger cells in the blood. Recall that the title of one of the two classic bibles of chi-gung attributed to Ta Mo (Bodhidharma) is the *Marrow-Cleansing Classic*. That's because one of the most important benefits chi-gung has for human health is the revitalization of bone marrow. TCM has known for thousands of years that bone marrow is a primary source of immune factors in the body, but it was less than a hundred years ago that Western medicine discovered this fact.

Blood tests on practitioners have demonstrated that chi-gung also increases the production of T-cells in the thymus gland. T-cells are another pillar of human immune response, and their virtual disappearance from blood serum is one of the primary indications of AIDS. Chi-gung stimulates pituitary, adrenal and other glandular secretions as well, thereby keeping the entire endocrine system in proper balance. A major study in China shows that just thirty minutes of chi-gung practice also results in a big increase in red blood cell count, which enhances the bloodstream's capacity to carry and deliver oxygen to the cells and further improves immune response.

Another way that chi-gung boosts immunity is by inhibiting the secretion of adrenaline and cortisole, both of which are released in response to stress, over-excitement and hyperactivity, and are well known for their immunosuppressive effects. Chronic stress has become increasingly recognized in Western medicine as a primary causal factor in immune deficiency, chronic degenerative conditions, and cancer. By counteracting the physiological effects of stress, chi-gung serves as a powerful protector of immune response and a preventive against disease and degeneration.

Chi-gung's well-documented benefits for those who suffer from arthritis are due to the enhancement of natural steroid production in the body. The synthetic steroids commonly used to treat arthritis in allopathic medicine have dangerous side-effects, including suppression of normal immune response, but daily practice of chi-gung relieves and corrects the condition both by activating natural steroid production in the body and by lubricating and loosening stiff joints with gentle rhythmic exercise. As the old Chinese chi-gung proverb says, 'The hinges of a moving door will not rust.'

In addition to these biochemical factors of 'essence', chi-gung also strengthens resistance directly on the level of energy by increasing the field force and enhancing the protective power of the natural shield of Guardian Energy (*wei-chi*) that envelopes the human body. The existence of this shield has been scientifically verified by Kirlian photography, a method of visually recording energy auras, invented in Russia. Kirlian photographs of people before and after chi-gung practice clearly reveal the enhanced brightness, power and field circumference of this protective energy shield after practice.

Heart and Circulatory System

One of the most pronounced effects of chi-gung in the human system is a dramatic improvement in blood circulation throughout the body, particularly microcirculation in the brain, extremities, and deep tissues of the vital organs. As another axiom of internal alchemy states, 'blood goes where energy leads'. By driving energy to every tissue and cell of the body, chi-gung ensures adequate circulation of blood, which in turn guarantees delivery of sufficient supplies of the oxygen and nutrients required to sustain health.

Chi-gung takes a tremendous workload off the heart by turning the diaphragm into a 'second heart' to support circulation, thereby preventing exhaustion of the heart muscle and prolonging life. Studies in China have shown that twenty to thirty minutes of chi-gung practice reduces the pulse by an average of 15 per cent and that this effect continues for several hours after practice. This reduction in heart pulse is accompanied by an overall increase in circulation, proving that chi-gung shifts much of the body's circulatory duty from the heart to the breath.

High blood pressure is easily prevented, and can also be cured, by daily practice of chi-gung. High blood pressure has become one of the biggest banes of human health today, and the conventional approach to this problem is to prescribe drugs that may have dangerous side-effects, and to recommend a reduction of dietary salt intake. The drugs prescribed for high blood pressure today actually aggravate the root causes of the condition by robbing the blood of the very minerals required to regulate blood pressure, thereby making it a permanent condition. Furthermore, it is not salt that causes high blood pressure, but rather the denatured, mineral-deficient industrial type of salt produced by the food industry. Whole sea salt in fact helps regulate blood pressure by ensuring a proper balance of essential minerals in the bloodstream.

The entire problem of high blood pressure can be readily prevented simply by practising chi-gung, which balances blood pressure throughout the circulatory system. A study conducted on 100 cases of chronic hypertension at the Shanghai Research Institute for Hypertension showed that after only five minutes of chi-gung practice, blood pressure in every patient began to drop, and after twenty minutes, their blood pressure was reduced to the same level it reached three hours after taking the drugs normally prescribed for high blood pressure. Ninety-seven of these patients were able to prevent a recurrence of hypertension by practising chi-gung, thereby effectively curing themselves, while three of them suffered relapses when they stopped practising.

Since various forms of heart and circulatory disease have

become the leading cause of premature death in the USA and many parts of Europe, chi-gung could prevent millions of unnecessary deaths at no cost to the consumer and without any negative side-effects.

Respiratory System

Chi-gung, particularly the deep diaphragmic breathing it involves, greatly improves respiratory functions and protects the lungs from damage due to airborne pollution. Chi-gung breathing increases the oxygenation of the blood in the lungs, while chi-gung movement improves delivery of oxygen to the cells, resulting in a significant enhancement in overall respiratory efficiency. With oxygen levels in the air today reduced to only half of what they were two hundred years ago, this oxygenating effect alone represents an enormous step forward in preventive healthcare, particularly against cancer.

A study on deep breathing in India revealed that after fifteen minutes of practice, the average volume of air taken into the lungs on inhalation rose from 482ml before practice to 740ml afterward, while the average number of breaths per minute dropped from fifteen down to only five. This represents a huge improvement in respiratory efficiency. These benefits are due to the important role which the diaphragm plays in breath control. Chi-gung, which engages the diaphragm as a pump to regulate breath and circulation, strengthens this powerful muscle and restores its natural role in breathing, resulting in a cumulative improvement in respiratory efficiency the longer chi-gung is practised. For example, a recent study in China demonstrated that after only two months of daily practice, the average flex of the diaphragm, which is only about 1 inch (3cm) in people who do not practice diaphragmic breathing, rose to between 2½ and 3½ inches (6 and 9cm), a two- to three-fold increase.

Su Tung-po, one of China's most beloved poets, who took up chi-gung as a health practice in mid-life during the twelfth century, praised the salutary benefits of deep breathing exercises as follows:

> At first, one feels little effect, but after practising breathing exercises regularly for one hundred days or so, the efficacy of this method is beyond measure, and its benefits are a hundred times greater than any medicine . . .
>
> The method is actually quite simple . . . If you try it for just twenty days, already your spirit will feel different . . .

your waist and legs will feel light and limber, and your eyes and complexion will grow bright and lustrous.

These benefits are permanent for as long as one continues to practise.

Digestive System

Another clear manifestation of the 'energy controls essence' axiom of internal alchemy is the remarkable enhancement in digestive secretions observed in chi-gung practitioners. Chi-gung stimulates an immediate increase in the secretion of saliva in the mouth, digestive secretions in the stomach, and essential digestive fluids in the intestines. Just fifteen minutes of practice has been shown to produce a major elevation in the secretion of pepsin, one of the most important digestive enzymes in the stomach. Besides increasing the amount of digestive enzymes in saliva, chi-gung has also been shown to enhance the production of salivary lysozyme, an enzyme with potent anti-bacterial properties. Indeed, traditional Taoist literature refers to the saliva secreted from the ducts below the tongue during chi-gung practice as 'sweet dew' (*gan-lu*) and 'jade fluid' (*yu-yi*), and emphasizes the importance of swallowing this saliva as a sort of preventive medicine.

It has also been scientifically demonstrated that chi-gung balances the pH level of digestive fluids, which is absolutely essential to proper digestion of food and assimilation of nutrients. 'Acid indigestion' has become such a common condition in the West that many people never leave the house without a pocketful of antacid remedies. pH balance is one of the most important aspects of Yin/Yang balance in human health, and here again chi-gung regulates this vital form of 'essence' by balancing the energy that governs it.

The movement of the diaphragm in chi-gung breathing, in conjunction with the movements of the body in chi-gung exercise, provide a highly stimulating massage to all the digestive organs, thereby helping to regulate their functions and balance their secretions. This therapeutic massage effect also enhances peristalsis throughout the alimentary canal, improving digestion, enhancing assimilation, and preventing constipation and flatulence.

A lesser known but equally important benefit of chi-gung for the digestive system is that it greatly improves the body's ability to extract and assimilate nutrients and transform them into energy. As we know from our discussion of internal alchemy, 'essence transforms into energy', and chi-gung results in a manifold increase in the energy the body derives from essential nutrients. It also enables the body to tap the abundant supplies of nutrients stored in the body. This is the basis of the *bi-gu* fasting regimen practised by some chi-gung adepts: every time an adept fasts for a period of three to thirty days, or longer, the body's digestive power and efficiency take quantum leaps, and the amount of food required thereafter decreases proportionately. During periods of food abstention, chi-gung triggers the transfer of stored nutrients from various tissues into the digestive fluids, which deliver them directly into the stomach and duodenum in highly refined and concentrated form for quick and easy assimilation. Here again we see the 'essence transforms into energy' axiom of internal alchemy at work in scientifically verifiable terms.

Acid/Alkaline Balance (pH)

Among the most important preventive health care benefits of chi-gung is the way it immediately balances the pH level of the blood, digestive juices and other bodily fluids. Chronic excess acidity gives rise to a condition of pH imbalance known as 'acidosis', which has become a primary causal factor in many common degenerative conditions today. This is due to the extremely acid-forming properties of modern diets, particularly meat, dairy products and refined starches and sugars. Stress and physical exhaustion also produce a lot of excess acid in the blood and muscles.

Chi-gung, particularly the deep-breathing aspect, restores normal pH balance to the blood every time you practise. This effect is related to oxygenation: proper pH balance can only be maintained when sufficient oxygen is present in the blood. Conversely, oxygen deficiency predisposes the blood and other bodily fluids to excess acidity. Recall that excess acidity and insufficient oxygen are the two primary conditions of imbalance that predispose tissues to the development of cancer. Thus, chi-gung helps prevent cancer by correcting the two main imbalances associated with its development.

The French physicians Dr Peschier and Walter Michel make note of the preventive health benefits of deep breathing as follows:

> Every organic or functional disorder leading to conditions of illness is susceptible to the influence, if not always the cure, of controlled breathing.
>
> Controlled breathing is the most outstanding method

> known to us for increasing organic resistance . . . There is always a natural immunity attributed to ionic balance in the blood, and dependent on breathing . . . It confers on the balance of the acid/base a regularity which is re-established with each breath.

Free Radical Scavenger

Modern Western medical science now accepts the thesis that the main mechanism involved in ageing and deterioration of the human body is cumulative damage from the activity of 'free radicals'. Free radicals are unstable, highly reactive molecules that are produced naturally as by-products of metabolism, but today they also enter the human system with pollutants in air and water, pesticides and chemical additives, junk foods and convenience foods, and many other unnatural factors in modern lifestyle. The result is the saturation of the tissues with free radicals, which constantly bombard healthy cells and thereby produce more free radicals, setting in motion a chain reaction that gradually destroys the cellular matrix, inhibits vital functions and prematurely ages the whole body.

Free radicals are controlled in the body by free radical 'scavengers', also known as 'antioxidants', which neutralize free radicals by balancing their electrical charge. Most antioxidants are either basic nutrients such as vitamins A, C and E and various minerals and trace elements, such as selenium, or else particular enzymes that are specifically designed and secreted for this purpose. The most important free radical scavenger in the body is the enzyme called 'superoxide dismutase' (SOD). Laboratory analysis of blood samples taken from elderly chi-gung practitioners shows that after a session of chi-gung, the level of SOD in their bloodstreams rises to double that of those who do not practise, indicating a major enhancement of antioxidant activity as a direct result of chi-gung practice. Chi-gung also seems to increase the bioavailability of certain minerals and trace elements, particularly zinc and selenium, which are essential factors for the production of SOD, peroxidase and other antioxidant enzymes.

Enhanced antioxidant activity in the body has been scientifically proven to retard the ageing process and prevent the degenerative conditions associated with old age, so here we see another modern scientific validation of one of the most ancient claims regarding chi-gung – that it slows down the ageing process, 'restores youth' and prolongs life.

Curative Applications of Chi-Gung

'Breathing and related exercises are one hundred times more effective as medical therapy than any drug,' wrote the Ching dynasty Tao master Shen Chia-shu. 'This knowledge is indispensable to man, and every physician should study it thoroughly.' Indeed, if every physician thoroughly studied the therapeutic powers of 'breathing and related exercises' (i.e., chi-gung) and applied them as medical therapy, before long there would be such a dramatic improvement in public health that the conventional medical industry would probably shrink to a small percentage of its current size.

When used for curative purposes, chi-gung is most effective when an intensive programme of self-practice is combined with healing energy therapy by emitted *chi* from a qualified chi-gung master. The sort of chi-gung exercises practised for curing disease are much the same as those used for daily preventive healthcare, but when used for curative therapy, a lot more time is devoted to practice each day than in preventive chi-gung. For mild diseases, for example, a person might practise his or her chi-gung regimen for three or four hours per day until cured. For serious ailments, such as cancer, patients in China often practise for eight to twelve hours per day.

An effective set of chi-gung exercises developed specifically for healing is the Six Syllable Secret, which is discussed in Chapter 6. This is basically a standard 'moving meditation' style of practice; except on exhalation, one aspirates a particular syllable in the top of the throat, thereby modulating energy in a way that guides it to a particular organ. The entire Six Syllable healing set with detailed instructions on how to practise it is presented in the author's previous work *Guarding the Three Treasures*.

Emitted Chi (fa-chi)

This is the aspect of healing energy that is exciting so much popular as well as scientific interest in chi-gung today. If even half of the claims regarding the cures achieved in China with emitted *chi* are true, and evidence seems to indicate that they are, then curing disease with emitted *chi*, in conjunction with intensive practice by the patient, represents the greatest revolution in human healthcare in medical history. Many Western physicians remain sceptical about curing disease in this way, but those who have taken the time and trouble to go to China and witness this method with their own eyes, and to speak with the patients and the therapists involved, have returned to the West with their views on human health and healing totally transformed.

The irony here is that chi-gung was the very first form of curative therapy ever recorded anywhere in the world. Five millennia later, after having dabbled with virtually every conceivable variety of herb, drug, chemical nostrum, blood-letting, surgery, radiation and other techniques to cure disease, healers as well as patients are finally realizing that both the problem and the solution lie not in germs, physical symptoms and other external factors of disease, nor in the chemical and mechanical warfare modern medicine wages against the human body to battle disease, but rather in the invisible template of the human energy system and the natural balance of internal energies.

Extensive scientific research has been conducted in China on chi-gung masters who have the ability to emit *chi* to heal disease. For one thing, it has been shown by technological means (through machines which can measure energy vibrations) that these healers emit a beam of energy from the *lao-gung* points in their palms, with properties and penetrating powers similar to that of laser beams. These beams are able to penetrate several centimetres of wood, leather and metal. The same research showed that when a healer beams emitted *chi* at a patient, the patient's energy field patterns become identical to that of the healer. In other words, the healer literally 'plugs' his or her energy into the patient's system, and in doing so, any imbalances, deviations, deficiencies and other abnormalities in the patient's energy patterns are immediately corrected. This makes scientific sense, because it is a well-known fact of physics that a high-energy field always prevails over a low-energy field, imposing its patterns on the lesser field. This effect may also be achieved by practising chi-gung exercises: by tuning the human system into the energy field of the earth, which is always perfectly balanced, chi-gung induces the earth's power to naturally straighten out any kinks and wrinkles, supplement any deficiencies, correct any imbalances, and normalize any abnormal patterns in the practitioner's energy system. In the case of emitted *chi*, the perfectly balanced patterns of the healer's powerful field are super-imposed over the patient's weak imbalanced system, immediately rebalancing and recharging it. When that happens, any problems that have developed in the patient's body as a result of the imbalance in the energy system simply disappear and normal physiological health is naturally restored.

These studies also showed that emitted *chi* could kill powerful bacterias that have grown resistant to drugs, such as staphylococcus, and dangerous viruses such as hepatitis B, but that this only happened when the healer was told in advance that this was the purpose of the treatment, so that he or she could consciously modulate the emitted energy to produce 'killer *chi*'. Here again we find sound scientific confirmation of an ancient axiom of internal alchemy: 'spirit commands energy'. What this means is that the energy emitted by the healer will perform precisely the healing functions which the healer imprints on it with his mind. Hence, emitted *chi* carries healing power as well as healing information from healer to patient, and heals the patient's body in exactly the way the healer's mind commands it to do.

It has also been shown that after treating several patients, a healer's own energy reserves become depleted. Some healers' bodies actually take on some of the physical symptoms of the diseases they have just finished clearing from their patients, such as yellow eyes when treating hepatitis, diarrhoea after treating gastrointestinal ailments, headaches and so forth. Sometimes a foul sour smell exudes from the healer's body after a treatment. This indicates that while the healer was treating the patient, during which time the healer's energy gates are wide open, some of the patient's 'muddy energy' (*juo-chi*) seeped into the healer's system. It is therefore of utmost importance that chi-gung healers take careful measures to clear their systems each and every time after treating patients with emitted *chi*. Special breathing exercises, body movements, visualizations and sounds have been specifically developed for this purpose.

The most accomplished healers, who learn how to work entirely with universal free energy channelled through their systems and transmitted onward to the patient, without getting their own personal emotional energy or ego involved, do not experience as much contamination from their patients' polluted energies, but very few masters have reached this level of practice, because it requires a very high degree of spiritual development and complete withdrawal of the personal ego from the healing process.

Curative therapy with emitted *chi* usually begins with a brief diagnostic scan by the healer, who passes his or her hands slowly over the surface of the patient's body, without touching, to detect areas where energy is out of balance, blocked, toxic or otherwise abnormal. Sometimes the diagnostic methods of TCM are also used, such as looking at the patient's tongue fur, eyes and skin, sniffing the breath and body, and palpating the organs, but the best chi-gung healers can simply feel a patient's condition instantly just by scanning the body with their sensitive hands. The patient is then told to either lie down or sit comfortably, while the healer beams energy into the patient from a distance of six inches (15cm) up to six feet (170cm) away. A session may last anywhere from twenty minutes to an hour, and the treatment is repeated several times a week for as long as the condition requires.

Let's take a look at some of the conditions which are currently being successfully cured in China with emitted *chi*. If you or any of your friends or family suffer from any of these conditions and are not getting positive results from conventional modern medicine, you might consider taking a 'health holiday' in China to try this approach, or contacting some of the chi-gung associations listed in the Appendix to see if you can locate a qualified healing energy master in the West.

Parkinson's, Alzheimer's, Senile Dementia

In China, emitted *chi* has been used for several decades now to treat people with degenerative conditions of the brain, such as Parkinson's and Alzheimer's. Several of modern China's top leaders, including Deng Xiao-ping, were treated in this manner with great success.

In 1985, a controlled study was conducted on patients in the Columbia Lutheran Home, a nursing home in Seattle, to test chi-gung as therapy for Parkinson's, Alzheimer's and other forms of senile dementia. The healer who provided the emitted *chi* therapy was Dr Effie Chow from San Francisco. The improvement in these patients was so dramatic that the staff at the nursing home were moved to tears. In almost all cases, major symptoms either disappeared entirely or were significantly reduced, and some patients were able to terminate heavy drug therapy on which they had depended for years. The results of these tests were later presented in testimony to the House Select Committee on Ageing in the US Congress.

As we have seen, when healing energy is transmitted into the systems of people suffering from severe imbalances in brain chemistry, the enhanced infusions of cerebral energy stimulate production of vital neurochemicals, such as dopamine, deficiencies of which are associated with Parkinson's and other cerebral diseases. After these imbalances have been corrected with emitted *chi*, daily practice of chi-gung at home prevents them from recurring. A very significant point here is the remarkable finding that the EEG brain wave patterns of elderly patients treated with emitted *chi* become identical to those found in children, a clear indication that a genuine 'rejuvenation' effect has occurred. If ever there were a 'fountain of youth' in medicine, then *chi* is most certainly the water.

Paralysis, Stroke

Emitted *chi* has established a very strong track record as therapy for paralysis due to stroke, spinal injuries or other conditions. In 1991, a chi-gung master in China by the name of Wang Heng treated three totally paralysed stroke victims who had been under conventional medical therapy for several years. The treatment was monitored under close scientific scrutiny by sceptical observers at a modern hospital, under the supervision of several licensed Western physicians. After three days of treatment, two of the patients got up out of bed and started walking!

The attending doctors were so amazed by these results that they immediately set up another controlled study at a larger hospital, this time with one hundred paralysed stroke patients. After only three days of treatment from Master Wang, 85 of these patients were able to walk. One of them got up out of bed after the first treatment and walked down three flights of stairs, unassisted, to get a breath of fresh air.

Similar results have been obtained treating children with partial paralysis and limb deformities due to cerebral palsy. Dr Effie Chow, who is trained in both Western medicine and TCM, treated an eight-year-old cerebral palsy victim named Eric at her medical institute, witnessed by seventy-five Western health professionals. Within twenty minutes, the boy was able to move his formerly useless arms and hands, straighten out an ankle that had never taken a normal step, and walk normally across the room by himself. The same sort of results have been observed in countless other cases, and yet chi-gung is still not recognized as valid therapy for these conditions in any Western countries, despite the spectacular results it has achieved for those fortunate enough to encounter qualified therapists.

Spinal Fractures

Emitted *chi* therapy has been used in China to rehabilitate patients suffering from disabilities due to severe fractures of the spine. Dr Yan Xin, a chi-gung master who has recently established a following in the USA, cured several such cases under close scrutiny in China during the late 1980s and early 1990s. In one case, the patient had a fractured skull, a fractured L-2 vertebrae in the lower back, and severe injury to the spinal cord. He was paralysed in both legs, unable to sit or turn over in bed, and virtually helpless. While the patient lay in bed in a hospital, Dr Yan sat in a temple about ten miles away and spent the entire night beaming healing energy to the patient, who later reported that he felt a soothing warm sensation wash over his body all that night and could smell a faint trace of sandalwood on the air in his room. Lo and behold! After sleeping soundly for nine consecutive hours after the treatment, the patient was able to get out of bed and walk again.

Dr Yan subsequently treated about a dozen more similar cases, all with equally successful results. These are not cases of 'anecdotal evidence', but documented cases of patients hospitalized in serious condition, complete with X-rays, blood tests, EEG scans and other modern medical technology to monitor the results. When such patients get up and walk again, after years of being bedridden under conventional medical care, the evidence is rather difficult to refute.

AIDS

One of the first observable benefits of chi-gung, both from personal practice as well as treatment with emitted *chi*, is an immediate enhancement in immune response. This is due partly to effects on the nervous system and partly the endocrine system. When internal energy is brought back into proper balance, the innate healing responses in both systems are activated and sustained by establishing a cycle of positive feedback between neurotransmitters and hormones. Every test ever conducted on the blood of chi-gung practitioners has shown enhanced levels of T-cells, white blood cells, antioxidant enzymes and other immune factors after a session of practice.

Patients with AIDS have been successfully treated with chi-gung in China as well as in the USA, but only if they refrain from taking AZT and the other toxic drugs currently used to treat people with HIV. The causal link between HIV and AIDS has never been scientifically proven, and many medical scientists are beginning to suspect that the extremely toxic drugs used to treat HIV themselves contribute to the patient's immune deficiency, due to their immunosuppressive side-effects. Therefore, in order to treat an AIDS patient with chi-gung, regardless of whether he or she also has HIV or not, it's important to do so before any toxic drugs have been administered. Unfortunately, the medical establishment has become so entrenched in the HIV/AIDS hypothesis and so convinced that the cure is to be found in chemicals, that they have, in the vast majority of cases, refused to consider the results of chi-gung therapy for this condition. Nevertheless, the fact remains that chi-gung has been proven to significantly enhance every aspect of human immune response, so it stands to reason that it would be an effective treatment for any sort of acquired immune deficiency, as long as no drugs are used to counteract its benefits and the patient agrees to alter the lifestyle factors which caused his or her immune deficient condition.

Eradicating 'Super-Bugs' with Chi

Studies conducted at the Microbiology Department at Shandgong University in China demonstrated that emitted *chi* destroys staphylococcus bacteria more effectively than carbolic acid, a disinfectant commonly used for this purpose. Eight minutes of exposure to emitted *chi* resulted in a 76 per cent kill rate. Other microbes were eradicated with equal efficacy under similar conditions.

Similar results are also observed on a wide range of bacteria and viruses when infected patients are treated with emitted *chi*. Many serious viral ailments that often do not respond to drug therapy, such as hepatitis B, have been successfully cured by treatment with 'killer *chi*'. In America and Canada, it has been discovered in recent years that intensive care units have become breeding grounds for drug-resistant strains of staphylococcus and other germs, and that many patients in these hospitals end up dying of diseases contracted as a result of exposure to these 'super-bugs'. In light of the proven efficacy of *chi* in destroying such microbes, it would seem advisable to conduct some studies by having qualified chi-gung masters come in and 'clean the house' in contaminated hospitals to eliminate these dangerous health hazards. It would certainly be a lot cheaper and much safer than continuously developing ever stronger chemicals and antibiotics, which in the end only breed ever more resistant strains of germs.

Cancer

It is in the field of cancer that emitted *chi* is having the most dramatic results as a cure. First of all, the incidence and mortality rate for cancer have been steadily rising over the past thirty years, while the treatments developed for it by modern medical science have not proven successful as cures. In America, over $40 billion has been funnelled into cancer research since the mid-1960s, and half that figure in the UK, and the treatments have grown almost prohibitively expensive, but still more and more develop cancer and continue to die from it, sometimes as a direct result of the therapy itself.

In addition to the regular chi-gung exercises used for prevention, there are also special sets which have been developed especially to cure particular diseases. In China, there is a form of curative chi-gung called 'Guo Lin Chi-Gung', which was developed as a specific cure for cancer by a woman of that name about thirty years ago. Not only did she cure herself of a serious case of uterine cancer with her practice, she also taught the same set to other cancer patients, most of whom experienced similarly effective results. Eventually the Guo Lin Research Society was established to study and teach this form of chi-gung practice to cancer patients all over China, and it is estimated that over one million cancer patients in China and elsewhere in Asia are now practising this cure in preference to conventional cancer therapy. A significant number of these practising patients report that their tumours have either stopped growing, gone into remission, or disappeared entirely, and the long-term survival rate for cancer patients who cure themselves this way is proving to be far higher than that achieved by conventional modern treatments such as chemotherapy and radiation. Sceptical Western doctors who doubt this claim need only contact the Gou Lin Research Society in China and arrange to go and see for themselves, or request copies of the copious scientifically documented records now being kept in China regarding cancer cures with chi-gung. The real question here is not whether chi-gung works as a cure for cancer and other supposedly 'incurable' diseases, but rather whether the Western medical establishment is willing to consider a form of treatment that in effect would eliminate the need for expensive doctors, drugs and hospitals.

There are so many case histories of successful cancer cures with chi-gung that it would take several volumes just to categorize them, so we will discuss only two here. Those interested in finding out more about curing cancer with chi-gung can do so by contacting some of the organizations and institutes listed in the Appendix (see page 308).

One of the most celebrated cancer cases in China was that of Feng Jian, a national badminton champion and popular hero. At the age of only twenty-one, he was diagnosed with lung cancer, which is almost always fatal. His doctors suggested immediate surgery, to be followed by chemotherapy and radiation – the conventional 'cut, poison and burn' approach. However, Feng Jian declined to accept their advice. Instead, he found a teacher and started practising Guo Lin Chi-Gung, the special practice set developed specifically for cancer, in conjunction with careful attention to diet, regular exercise, plenty of rest and other related *yang-sheng* health regimes. He practised chi-gung every day for ten months, sometimes up to twelve hours a day, and when he went back to the hospital to have his condition checked, his doctors were astounded to discover that the cancer had completely disappeared. Two decades later he is still alive and well.

While doing a story on Chi-Lel Chi-Gung in China, health writer Luke Chan was invited to sit in front of an ultrasound machine monitor and watch a patient's bladder cancer literally dissolve before his eyes. Prior to the treatment, the tumour could be plainly seen attached to the wall of the bladder. While Chan kept his eyes riveted on the image on the screen, the patient was treated with emitted *chi* by four therapists. Within minutes, the tumour began to dissolve, and by the end of the treatment, it could barely be detected. Ten days later, after several more treatments and daily self-practice, the patient was checked again, and the cancer had completely disappeared.

Scores of such cases, all of them documented, were presented at the Medical Conference for Academic Exchange on Medical Chi-gung, held in China in 1988, and again in 1993, with health professionals from all over the world in attendance. Case studies of successful treatments for virtually every known type of cancer were included in the papers presented. Patients were not only cured of their cancers, but they also recovered their overall health and vitality, a far cry from the debilitated condition in which most patients are left by conventional cancer therapy, which virtually destroys human immune response, decimates the liver, causes impotence and digestive problems, and weakens the whole system. Chi-gung therapy, in addition to dissolving cancerous tumours, also rebuilds the whole immune system, rebalances the blood, oxygenates the entire body, normalizes all vital functions, and enhances vitality, permitting patients to recover total health and enjoy the remaining years of their lives. Unfortunately, conventional doctors these days scare their patients into submitting to immediate surgery, chemotherapy and/or radiation treatment, before they ever have an opportunity to consider alternative approaches. Many of these patients end up trying alternative therapy such as chi-gung after conventional therapy fails to cure them, but by that time there has been so much damage done to their bodies that it is far more difficult, and sometimes impossible, to effect a cure.

The precise mechanism whereby chi-gung cures cancer has not been fully established, but it probably has a lot to do with oxygen and alkalinity. If the tissues in which a tumour is growing can be saturated with oxygen and kept in an alkaline state, the cancer will shrink and dissolve. Oxygenation and alkalization of blood and tissues are two of chi-gung's most prominent effects. Other factors involved in chi-gung therapy for cancer might be the overall enhancement of immune response, which would allow the body to fight and destroy malignant cells, the great improvement in microcirculation, and the rebalancing and recharging of biolectric currents in each and every cell in the body. Obviously, cancer does not occur in a properly balanced body, and since chi-gung's overall effect is to properly balance the body, what chi-gung seems to be doing is creating conditions in which cancer simply cannot exist. Sufficient oxygen and alkalinity are two basic parameters of balance that can be easily measured, but no doubt there are also many other factors, some of them as yet unknown, involved in the optimum balance which chi-gung establishes in the human system.

Chi-Gung Hospitals and Research Centres

Due to the popular as well as academic interest sparked by publicity surrounding some of the more spectacular cures achieved by chi-gung, a number of special hospitals and research centres have been established in China and elsewhere around the world to conduct further studies and make treatment more widely available to those who wish to try it.

One such hospital is the Wahzhan Zhineng Chigong Clinic and Training Centre, located in an old navy hospital in Qinhuadao, a five-hour train ride from Beijing. Founded in 1988 by Dr Pang Ming, the hospital uses no drugs, no herbs, no special diets and no surgery of any kind. Instead, it offers only one kind of medicine and one kind of treatment, and that is *chi*. Over the past ten years the hospital has treated hundreds of thousands of patients for nearly two hundred types of disease, posting an amazing 95 per cent success rate. The diseases treated and cured here include diabetes, arthritis, coronary disease, paralysis, lupus and cancer.

The type of chi-gung used at this hospital is called 'Chi Lel', and it was developed specifically for curing disease by Dr Pang. The programme consists of four parts:

1. Strong understanding of the healing powers of *chi* in the mind of the patient. Patients are first taught how and why *chi* works to cure the human body, so that there are no doubts in their minds to counteract the effects of the healing energy. Remember the basic axiom, of internal alchemy: 'spirit commands energy'.
2. Group healing sessions. Large groups of patients are treated together in order to amplify the power of universal free energy as it flows through the group.
3. Individual treatment with emitted *chi*. Patients are treated on an individual basis by qualified masters, according to their requirements.
4. Individual practice. Patients are taught various chi-gung sets, and they spend the entire day, and much of the night, practising.

According to medical records kept at the hospital on approximately 10,000 specific cases selected for study, an overall success rate of 95 per cent was achieved in these cases as follows: 15.20 per cent experienced total cures, with all functions returning to normal; 37.68 per cent experienced 'very effective' results, which means that symptoms almost completely disappeared and tests indicated great improvement in vital functions; 42.09 per cent experienced 'effective' results, meaning there was noticeable improvement, and the patient was able to eat, sleep and function normally again. Only 5 per cent of the people treated in this study experienced no improvement whatsoever. Anyone who has ever been treated in a modern Western hospital, or who has gone to visit friends and family in such places, knows that this is a far better record than drugs, surgery and other high-tech therapies have posted, and at far less expense, discomfort and risk. Today, a significant number of people treated at great expense in modern hospitals end up contracting serious diseases there that they did not have when they entered.

Average cost of treatment with Chi-Lel Chi-Gung at this hospital in China amounts to about £50 per month. Compare that with medical costs in any big Western hospital, and we find yet another major advantage to treating disease with chi-gung. The only medicine used in chi-gung healing is universal free energy, which costs nothing and is readily available to anyone in unlimited supply. The only equipment required to administer healing energy therapy is the human body and mind, so the only real costs involved for treatment at this sort of hospital are room and board.

The Guo Lin Research Society is another well-known organization that studies and teaches curative chi-gung in China. Developed as a specific cure for cancer, Guo Lin Chi-Gung has been used by millions of cancer patients to cure themselves. Those who opt for conventional cancer therapy, such as radiation or chemotherapy, sometimes practise Guo Lin Chi-Gung to relieve the unpleasant side-effects of those therapies.

The World Academic Society of Medical Chi-Gung in Beijing organizes international conferences to present the results on medical chi-gung to health professionals from around the world, and to exchange information with similar organizations elsewhere. In addition, there are hundreds of individual chi-gung masters practising chi-gung as medical therapy in China, and anyone who makes the effort to go there and find one will certainly succeed in doing so.

Similar organizations are beginning to crop up in America, Australia and elsewhere in the Western world. In San Francisco and Vancouver, there's the East West Academy of Healing Arts and the Qigong Institute, which offer personal consultations, professional references, and documented information on medical chi-gung. Chi-gung master Dr Yan Xin has recently established training centres for his school of healing chi-gung in the USA, as have other noteworthy masters, such as Dr Yang Jwing-ming from Taiwan and Master Hyunmoon Kim from Korea. In the UK, The British Council for Chinese Martial Arts and the Qigong Institute in Manchester offer courses, workshops and personal consultations. The infrastructure for healing chi-gung therapy is already in place in the Western world, but you must still take the initiative to find a qualified master and a style that suits you, because it's highly unlikely that you'll get a reference from your local family doctor or city hospital. Some of the addresses listed in the Appendix should be helpful in guiding anyone who's interested in practising chi-gung for preventive healthcare, or finding a master healer to receive treatment by emitted *chi*, to the right place.

CHAPTER 6

Elemental Energies: Ways of Working with Chi

Since *chi* means 'breath' as well as 'energy', what usually comes to mind when we think of chi-gung is breathing exercises. And, in fact, breath control is the primary means of working with energy, particularly for purposes of health and longevity. In *Precious Recipes*, his great tome on healthcare and self-cultivation, the Tang dynasty physician Sun Ssu-miao, who lived to the age of 101 by following his own advice, extolled the virtues of proper breathing:

> When correct breathing is practised, the myriad ailments will not occur. When breathing is depressed or strained, all sorts of diseases will arise. Those who wish to nurture their lives must first learn the correct methods of controlling breath and balancing energy. These breathing methods can cure all ailments great and small.

The functions of proper breathing in chi-gung exercises are to replenish, balance and circulate energy throughout the human energy system, to synchronize the human energy field with greater fields of nature and the cosmos, and to harmonize body and mind with breath. As the temporal manifestation of primordial energy in the human body, breath provides an effective tool for managing the various internal and external energies that fuel vital functions and influence health, but the efficiency of breath as a regulator of energy depends entirely on how well we exercise the skill of breath control. Most people go through life without ever drawing a consciously regulated breath, and without realizing that each and every breath they take has the potential capacity to harness the power of the universe to the chariot of human life. The only time most people breathe in a manner that rebalances their energy system is when they yawn (a spontaneous Yin recharge breath) and when they sigh (a spontaneous Yang discharge breath).

Just as energy is the universal medium through which primordial spirit (God, Brahma, Tao, the Creator, the Great Spirit . . .) expresses itself in material form in the primal alchemy of creation, so breath is the agent through which mind may learn to control and cure the body in temporal life on earth. Significantly, breathing is the only autonomous vital function of the body over which our minds can exert direct volitional control. Once you learn how to control your breath, you may use it to regulate all of the other vital bodily functions, such as pulse and circulation, digestion and elimination, the endocrine and nervous systems, immunity and resistance, and sexual and emotional response.

Although breath is the supreme regulator of energy in the body, there are also other ways of working with energy to protect health and prolong life, heal the body and enhance the mind. Energy takes many forms in the universe – light and colour, sound and tone, aroma and flavour, pressure and vibration, electric and magnetic forces – and all of them may be harnessed for the benefit of human life by applying the various faculties and functions of the human body and mind. Since breath control is by far the most important and effective way of harvesting energy from the universe, guiding it through the human system, and storing it in the energy reservoirs of the body, we'll begin our discussion by looking into the art and science of breathing, then move on to some other basic methods of working with energy.

The Art and Science of Breathing

In the spiritual traditions of Asia, breathing has always been regarded as a very precise science of energy management and an important branch of the healing arts. Since Western medicine doesn't even recognize breath and energy as decisive factors in human health and healing, Western notions about breathing are limited to the basic exchange of gases in the lungs. But there's a lot more to breathing than just 'hot air'.

In Chinese medicine, oxygen is regarded as an essential nutrient of postnatal life, like vitamins and minerals and proteins, and therefore air, which supplies this nutrient, is viewed as a sort of 'food'. The True Energy that fuels postnatal functions of the body is thus a synthesis of the nutrients extracted from food and water by digestion and the oxygen extracted by respiration from air. However, air contains more than just a chemical cocktail of elemental gases: it also contains potent energy and possesses strong electromagnetic polarity. This is the atmospheric form of energy assimilated through breathing, the *chi* in Chinese chi-gung and the *prana* in the *pranayama* practice of India, and it's every bit as important as oxygen in human health and healing.

Chi rides on the air in tiny, hyperactive molecular fragments that carry a negative charge equivalent to that of one electron. Known in Western science as 'negative ions', these vibrant electromagnetically charged particles are naturally produced in the air by the action of short-wave rays radiated into the atmosphere from the sun and other astral bodies; over oceans, lakes and rivers by evaporation and agitation of water; and by the movement of wind over large open spaces, such as mountains and deserts. Known as 'ionization', this process splits air molecules into fragments and imparts energy to the resulting particles in the form of a negative charge.

Negative ions are the factor that give fresh air its characteristic vitality, and this is why the Chinese refer to air as *chi* – energy. The most potent atmospheric *chi* is found at high altitudes in the mountains, where the ionizing radiation from the sun and stars is strongest and combines with the ionizing effects of free-blowing wind and fast-flowing streams. This is one reason why hermits and yogis in Asia have traditionally preferred to live and practise in high mountains, where the *chi* is always strong, stable and pure. The negative ion energy of atmospheric *chi* also accounts for the revitalizing effects experienced at the beach or sailing on the open water, where the action of wind and water produce an abundant supply of negative ions in the air.

On the other hand, atmospheric pollutants such as smoke, dust, automobile exhaust, and the toxic chemical effluvia of industry enter the air as large, heavy, sluggish molecules carrying a positive charge, and their presence depletes air of its natural *chi*. Such pollutants inhibit the free oscillation of negative ions, trapping them and robbing them of their vibrant energy. Fresh air in the mountains or open countryside contains an average ratio of three negative ions to one positive, and this sort of air imparts a potent vitality to the body with every breath. By contrast, the air in a typically polluted big city has only one negative ion for every five hundred positive, drastically reducing the atmospheric vitality by a factor of 1500 times. Air conditioning and central heating also deplete air of its vital force by neutralizing the energy of negative ions.

The other energy factor in air is its field polarity, or 'potential gradient'. This refers to the potential difference in voltage between two points, a factor which determines the overall strength of the electromagnetic field in a given area. The strength of this field in turn determines how actively the negative ions within it vibrate and how strongly energy flows between points within the field. In the mountains, for example, the potential gradient can reach several hundred volts per metre, which means that in a person two metres tall, energy will flow with a potential force of 400 to 500 volts from head to foot. In big cities enclosed by high-rise buildings, as well as in closed spaces within those buildings, the air has virtually no gradient whatsoever, leaving the air 'flat'.

In Taoist terms, this atmospheric polarity boils back down to the positive Yang charge of the sky (Heaven) and the negative Yin charge of the ground (Earth). Between these poles stand people (Humanity) and other living organisms, which serve as conductors for the flow of energy between sky and ground. This is an important facet in the Harmony of Heaven, Earth and Humanity discussed earlier. A potential gradient of several hundred volts per metre greatly facilitates the free flow of energy through the human system, ensuring that every tissue and cell in the body is fully charged with *chi*. A report by a firm that manufactures negative ion generators for the modules in which astronauts travel in the US space programme states:

> The electric current caused by the presence of an electric field passes through all the cells, organs, and the whole of the nervous system, and stimulates the metabolism as well as all other physiological functions of living organisms . . .
>
> If the field is too weak, tiredness, indolence, and lack of vitality will be manifest. This is the main cause of tiredness and numbness felt in cars, planes, tanks, submarines, and trains, and now in space capsules.

If airlines were to install negative ion generators in airplanes, as all space capsules are equipped, it would greatly relieve the 'jet lag' passengers experience on long-haul flights by charging the air in the cabin with energy and field polarity. It would also sanitize the air in the cabin, thereby protecting passengers from infection by bacteria and other pollutants trapped in the stale recirculated air they're all required to share for so long. A unique trait of negative ion generators is that in addition to recharging flat air with *chi*, the constant stream of negative ions they generate overwhelm and neutralize the positive ions of dust, chemicals, viruses and other air-borne pollutants, precipitating them out of the air and on to the floor. Furthermore, these devices consume less electricity than lightbulbs, making them highly economical. In Japan, where the power of *chi* is understood, high-rise office buildings are routinely equipped with negative ion generators, which may well be one of the secrets to Japan's renowned productivity.

Unlike oxygen and carbon dioxide, which pass to and from the bloodstream through the lungs, the negative ion energy of *chi* is absorbed into the human system mainly through highly sensitive receptors located along the nasal passages and sinus cavities of the nose. That's why air is always inhaled through the nose in chi-gung practice, never the mouth. As air is drawn through the convoluted passages, or 'turbinates', of the nose, its ionic energy is absorbed through these receptors and transmitted directly into the meridiens as well as the nerves and bloodstream, travelling swiftly into the brain, nervous system, organs and other tissues. This energy recharges each and every cell in the body, balances the polarity of all cells and tissues, and dissolves toxins in the blood and other bodily fluids by neutralizing their positive charge with its own negative charge.

The size, shape and convolution of the nasal passages are designed to extract maximum energy from air by making it take a long winding road across a large surface area before reaching the lungs. These passages, which are lined with *chi* receptors, are automatically regulated by spongy erectile tissue in the nose, similar in function to the erectile tissue in sexual organs and breasts. These tissues control air flow through the nose by alternately opening and closing the right and left passages. Known as the 'infradian rhythm', this cyclic switching of nasal passages occurs naturally about every two hours, in accordance with the traditional Chinese duodecimal system of keeping time, and it is closely connected with the left and right hemisphere functions of the brain, as well as the Yin and Yang balance of the entire energy system. If either nostril becomes chronically blocked, the natural rhythmic balance of breath is disrupted, resulting in a critical imbalance of energy flow throughout the system and upsetting the normal balance of cerebral functions. If such an imbalance continues for long without correction, it can lead to serious malfunctions and physiological disease. That's why both chi-gung and *pranayama* include special exercises, such as the alternate nostril breath, designed to open up clogged nostrils and rebalance the flow of air through both sides of the nose. Flaring the nostrils on inhalation also helps keep air flowing freely through both sides, thereby promoting balance throughout the energy system during practice.

Flushing the nose with warm salt water, as in the 'neti' nasal douche prescribed in Indian yoga, is another effective way to keep the nostrils clear and clean so that air may flow freely through both sides and the infradian rhythm may function normally day and night. This is a particularly important practice in areas where the air is contaminated with dust, smoke, grease, chemicals and other particulate matter. Such atmospheric pollution clogs the nostrils by adhering to the nasal cilia and leaves a sticky film on the delicate membranes through which *chi* is absorbed, thereby desensitizing them to negative ion energy. Swimming in clean ocean water, or simply inhaling fresh ocean mist, has similar cleansing effects on the nasal membranes, which is another reason that people feel energized after spending a day at the beach or on the sea.

While the 'nose knows best' when it comes to detecting and collecting *chi* in the air, the diaphragm is the ideal workhorse in the art of proper breathing. It's truly amazing what a difference it makes to health and overall vitality when you learn how to breath deeply from the diaphragm, as nature intended, rather than shallowly with the ribs and clavicles, as most adults tend to breathe. Take a look at the belly of a baby sleeping in a crib, or a dog snoozing on the floor, and you will see that nature designed our breathing apparatus to function from the diaphragm, not the chest. When the diaphragm is used, it's the lower abdomen that expands and contracts with every breath, not the chest. A tough, tensile muscle that separates the chest from the abdominal cavity, the diaphragm is designed to drive the breath like a suction pump, but in most sedentary adults it has become 'frozen' with disuse, forcing the breath upward to the ribs and clavicles, where only a small fraction of the lungs' capacity is engaged in breathing.

Breathing with the diaphragm is the key technique in all forms of chi-gung, as well as in yoga, *pranayama*, and all practices where breathing plays a central role. The benefits of diaphragmic breathing extend far beyond the respiratory system, greatly enhancing the power of the circulatory system, balancing the nervous system, regulating the endocrine system, and providing a deep stimulating massage to all of the organs of the digestive system. In fact, chi-gung is sometimes referred to as 'internal organ exercise' due to the therapeutic benefits of this internal massage. Dr A Salmanoff extols the virtues of the diaphragm as follows:

> It is the most powerful muscle in the body; it acts like a perfect force-pump, compressing the liver, the spleen, the intestines, and stimulating the whole abdominal and portal circulation.
>
> The number of movements of the diaphragm per minute is a quarter of the those of the heart. But its haemodynamic power is much greater than that of cardiac contractions because the surface of the force-pump is much greater and because its propelling power is superior to that of the heart. We have only to visualize the surface of the diaphragm to accept the fact that *it acts like a second heart*.

The deep, soothing compression of the abdominal organs and glands combined with the enhancement of oxygen delivery to the brain, the slowing of the pulse, and the total relaxation of the body which result from deep diaphragmic breathing cause the autonomous nervous system to switch over from the 'action' or 'fight or flight' circuit of the sympathetic branch to the calming, restorative mode of the parasympathetic branch, and this in turn signals the immune system to activate the body's natural healing responses. Healing yourself is as simple as that. Yet most people don't even know they have such a thing as a diaphragm, much less how to use it properly to drive the breath, pump the blood and regulate the nervous and endocrine systems. In order to clarify the matter, let's review the four stages, three locks and two modes of breathing used in chi-gung to control breath and energy, regulate the vital functions and stimulate the internal organs.

The Four Stages

The four stages of breath control are inhalation, compression, exhalation and intermission (Fig. 6). In practice, these four stages are strung together in a smooth continuous sequence, like the rise and fall of waves on the sea, with each one playing a particular role and all of them orchestrated by the diaphragm.

• *Inhalation*. With empty lungs and nostrils flared, relax the diaphragm and commence a soft, slow, smooth inhalation through the nose, deliberately drawing the air deep down into the bottom of the lungs so that the diaphragm descends and the abdominal wall expands. As the lower lobes of the lungs fill up with air and the abdomen swells, continue breathing in slowly and deeply so that the mid-sections of the lungs begin to fill next, causing the ribcage

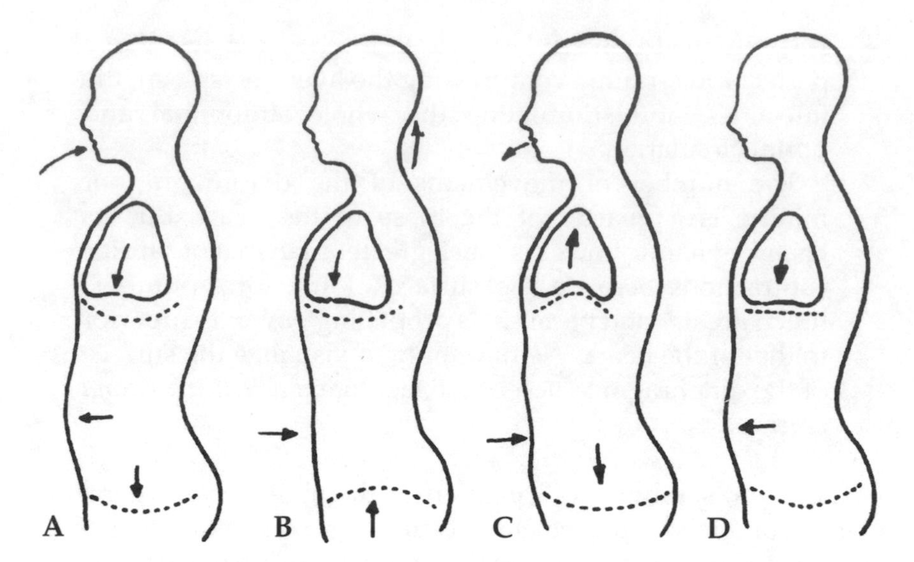

Fig. 6 **The four stages of breath control:**
A. Inhalation: diaphragm and pelvic floor descend; abdominal wall expands
B. Compression: anal lock raises pelvic floor; abdominal lock draws abdomen slightly inward; neck lock straightens back of neck
C. Exhalation: diaphragm rises; pelvic floor relaxes; abdominal wall contracts
D. Intermission: diaphragm and abdominal wall relax and return to normal position for the next breath

to expand. When the lungs feel comfortably full and both the abdomen and ribs have expanded, draw the inhalation to a halt. Do not try to 'top off' the upper lungs by taking an extra gulp of air, for this will make you hunch up your shoulders and tense your neck and also cause the diaphragm to rise. A 'full' breath in chi-gung means that the lungs are about two-thirds to three-quarters filled, with most of the air packed down into the lower and middle sections. In shallow chest breathing, only the narrow upper pockets of the lungs get filled, which represent only about a quarter of the lungs' capacity, but due to years of shallow breathing, people tend to feel that they must fill up these pockets to get a 'full' breath. Practice will eliminate this tendency.

• *Compression*. This phase is quite brief – usually only three to five seconds – but its benefits are deep and manifold. Longer retentions of breath should only be practised under the personal supervision of a qualified teacher. The first step in the compression phase is to press the diaphragm firmly downward to settle the air into the bottom of the lungs and compress the abdominal cavity. As you do this, apply the 'three locks', which are described in the next section.

When properly performed, this brief retention of breath provides several important benefits. It slows down and deepens the pulse of the heart and balances blood pressure throughout the circulatory system. By increasing the pressure of the air against the surface of the lungs and holding it briefly, this compression greatly enhances the exchange of gases, enriching the blood with extra supplies of oxygen and allowing more elimination of carbon dioxide. It also improves gas exchange between the bloodstream and cells throughout the body because this compression in the lungs extends throughout the entire circulatory system, increasing the partial pressure of oxygen against the walls of the capillaries.

Even the briefest breath retention triggers cellular respiration, an innate response that cause cells to 'breathe' by themselves whenever breath is held in the lungs. When this happens, blood sugar is spontaneously broken down by the cells to release oxygen and produce body heat. This is the basis of the so-called 'dive response' that allows seals to dive deep into ice-cold water for prolonged periods without breathing and young children who fall into frozen rivers and lakes to survive underwater for up to two hours and revive without brain damage when rescued. In most adults, this response has atrophied, but a few years of deep breathing practice usually suffices to restore it.

The compression phase of breathing also helps keep the autonomous nervous system in the healing mode of the parasympathetic circuit. The excessive overstimulation of the sympathetic 'action' circuit in modern lifestyles leads to a condition known as 'sympathetic syndrome', or 'Fire-energy excess' in TCM, which gives rise to such conditions as chronic indigestion, constipation, hypertension, insomnia, heart palpitations, shortness of breath and sexual dysfunction. Every moment spent in the parasympathetic mode allows the body to correct these imbalances, and this is one of the main ways that deep breathing heals the body.

Never hold the compression phase of breath beyond what feels comfortable. If you feel compelled to gasp or burst out on exhalation, it means that you've held the compression too long and lost control of your breath.

• *Exhalation*. When you're ready to exhale, release the three locks (see next section), relax the diaphragm and ribs, and begin exhaling slowly and evenly in a steady continuous stream through the nostrils or lips, depending on the exercise. While all chi-gung exercises involve nasal inhalation, some call for oral exhalation, which facilitates elimination of stagnant air and energy.

Empty the lungs in reverse order of inhalation, starting from the top of the lungs, then the middle, and finally the bottom. Continue exhaling until the lungs are empty, letting the abdominal wall collapse and contract inward and the diaphragm ascend upward into the chest, then expel the last residues of air from the lungs by drawing the abdominal wall further inward. The entire exhalation should be performed in a long, slow, even stream, not in a sudden explosive burst. If the latter occurs, shorten the compression phase on the next round.

• *Intermission*. When the lungs are empty and exhalation is complete, do not immediately start drawing in the next inhalation. Instead, pause briefly to let your diaphragm and abdominal wall relax and fall back into place in preparation for the next breath. If you start inhaling while the diaphragm and abdominal wall are still drawn in, the breath will tend to rise up in the lungs, making it more difficult to sink the air down to the bottom. The intermission phase should also be used to check that shoulders and neck are fully relaxed and posture is correct, but do not pause too long, or you'll find yourself sucking in the next inhalation in a short sharp gulp.

The Three Locks

The three locks are used to create a therapeutic compression within the abdominal cavity. This compression gives a strong boost to venal circulation, opens the meridien system, and helps activate the pneumogastric nerves of the parasympathetic branch of the autonomous nervous system. The locks are applied at or toward the end of inhalation, held in place briefly during compression, and released on exhalation. At first it may seem difficult or awkward to apply them without interrupting your breathing, but with practice they will become an integral part of your natural breathing patterns. Like the four stages, the three locks should be performed smoothly and without excessive effort.

• *The Anal Lock*. Known as *mula bhanda* in *pranayama* and *ti-gang* ('lifting the anus') in chi-gung, the anal lock is designed to raise the entire pelvic floor in order to lock in and enhance the compression created in the abdominal cavity by the diaphragm as it descends from above during inhalation. The resulting increase in abdominal pressure has profound therapeutic benefits for all of the internal organs and glands, driving stale blood and cellular wastes from the tissues and stimulating the secretion of essential hormones.

The pelvic floor, also known as the 'urogenital diaphragm', consists of a flexible web of muscle and tendon that supports the colon, prostrate, uterus and sacral glands. By flexing this lower diaphragm, the anal lock massages all of the organs and glands within the sacrum, strengthens the tissues of the pelvic floor, and gives a stimulating tug to the sacral roots of the pneumogastric nerve endings, which helps activate the immune responses of the parasympathetic nervous system. It also pulls on the nerves of a small gland, known as the 'Luschka gland', that hangs from the tip of the coccyx, stimulating secretions that further enhance neuro-immunological healing responses.

As inhalation approaches completion, the anal lock is applied by contracting the outer ring of the anal sphincter, a tough band of muscle that controls the external aperture of the anus. This manoeuvre lifts the anus and contracts the webbing of the entire urogenital diaphragm. For the more powerful effect, the contraction may be extended deeper to the inner ring of the anal sphincter, located about one inch above the external ring. This raises the entire perineum between the anus and sexual organs and deepens the compression throughout the sacrum. However, for regular practice, contracting the external ring is sufficient, while the internal ring may be used when stronger stimulation of the sacrum is desired.

The anal lock is also effective preventive and curative therapy for haemorrhoids, a condition caused by clogged capillaries in the anal sphincter. Rhythmic contraction and relaxation of the anal sphincter flushes stagnant blood from the tiny vessels of this muscle and suffuses them with freshly oxygenated blood, while also toning sluggish capillary walls to facilitate free circulation. The anal lock also stretches and tones the tissues of the urogenital canal from bladder to external orifice, making it an excellent exercise for men who wish to develop ejaculation control and for women who are prone to cystitis. In addition, the flexing, flushing and toning effects of this exercise are beneficial therapy for inflammations of the prostrate and uterus. For these purposes, the anal lock may be practised as an exercise by itself for a few minutes any time of day or night.

• *The Abdominal Lock.* The purpose of the abdominal lock is to seal in the therapeutic compression in the abdominal cavity when the diaphragm descends and the pelvic floor is raised with the anal lock on completion of inhalation. If the abdominal wall is simply allowed to expand outward, much of this compression is lost, diminishing the stimulating massage effect on the internal organs and glands. Furthermore, the powerful boost that the diaphragm gives to circulation depends largely on enhanced abdominal pressure against the vena cava, a major vein that draws stale blood up from the abdominal organs for replenishment in the lungs. The increase in abdominal pressure exerts a powerful propulsive force on the vena cava, pushing blood up into the chest like a pump and thereby taking a huge workload off the heart. This effect is particularly beneficial early in the morning, when up to half the body's blood supply lies dormant in the liver and pancreas. Try doing just a few deep diaphragmic breaths with the three locks while sitting up in bed the moment you wake up in the morning, and you can feel this propulsive power on circulation from head to foot.

When inhalation is complete with the anal lock in place, the abdominal wall will be fully expanded. To apply the abdominal lock, simply pull the lower part of the abdominal wall inward toward the spine. It is neither necessary nor desirable to pull it in very far or with excessive effort. Just draw it slightly inward with a light contraction of the abdominal muscles, hold it briefly, then relax it completely as you commence exhalation. That brief moment of enhanced abdominal pressure saves your heart at least twenty beats of work, so if you practise this sort of breathing throughout the day, you can well imagine how much it extends the working life of your heart.

• *The Neck Lock*. The neck lock serves several functions. By partially constricting the carotid arteries in the throat, it prevents excess blood from rushing straight up into the brain due to enhanced circulatory pressure from below, instead diverting some of it out to the extremities for more balanced distribution. Carotid compression also slows and deepens the pulse, thereby further benefiting heart function. The neck lock seals the breath down inside the lungs after inhalation, so that it doesn't rise up and cause uncomfortable pressure in the throat, nostrils and Eustachian tubes during compression. It also stretches the entire spinal cord from skull to sacrum, stimulating all the nerves and ganglia along its entire length and opening the energy channels that run along the spine. The latter effect draws energy up from the sacral region to the head, activating the energy circuit of the Microcosmic Orbit. The slight pressure it puts on the carotid sinus nerve is known to facilitate mental calm and the internalization of awareness, which are helpful factors in breath control, particularly during meditation.

To apply the neck lock, wait until the anal and abdominal locks are in place, then contract the throat muscles and clamp the glottis over the trachea. (If you're wondering how to do this, try taking several short inhalations one on top of the other. As you 'pack' each one into the lungs, what prevents it from coming out before you draw in the next one is clamping the glottis over the trachea.) Some practitioners find it helpful to swallow first, which facilitates the neck lock and helps pack air and energy into the chest cavity, but this is not an essential step. When the throat is closed and contracted, tuck the chin slightly in toward the chest and stretch the back of the neck, but without actually bending the neck forward. Be sure to keep the shoulders relaxed so that they do not hunch up and cause tension in the neck and shoulder muscles, blocking energy flow from the spine into the head. When you're ready to exhale, simply raise your chin a bit, relax the throat, and let the air stream out.

Regarding the four phases and three locks, please bear in mind that they are stages in a smooth continuous breathing process, not separate steps. When you first take up chi-gung practice, it's helpful to practise them with great deliberation for five to ten minutes several times a day, focusing carefully on each phase, as a way of training the breath, loosening the diaphragm, and growing accustomed to correct breathing techniques. It is also a good way to balance the breath in preparation for a session of still sitting or moving meditation chi-gung practice. However, during your main practice, try not to focus too much attention on the individual phases and locks; instead, try to incorporate them all in a smooth continuous process that feels natural and comfortable. You'll find that after a while your diaphragm will naturally take command of your breathing, and that your body will automatically apply the locks in a way that is most appropriate to each type of exercise. Indeed, in some of the still sitting meditation practices in which internal energy is regulated mainly with the mind, breath can become so fine that it grows almost imperceptible, in which case phases and locks do not apply. On the other hand, if you wish to give a strong boost to the circulation of blood and energy throughout the body and recharge your brain and other tissues with oxygen, such as early in the morning, practising a round of deep diaphragmic breathing with deliberate attention to the four phases and strong application of the three locks provides very effective results. There are as many different ways to breathe as there are to dance, each with its own rhythm and beat, but just as all dancing is done with the feet, so all breathing should be done with the diaphragm. The rest depends on the mood and music of the moment.

The Two Modes

The two basic modes of breathing are known as the 'Scholar's Breath' (*wen-shi*) and the 'Warrior's Breath' (*wu-shi*). These are not breathing exercises in themselves, but rather two different ways of performing any breathing exercise.

The Scholar's Breath is soft, gentle, silent and requires minimal effort. It tends to calm and balance the whole system and activate the rejuvenating parasympathetic branch of the autonomous nervous system. This is the mode employed in meditation, internal alchemy and ordinary daily activity.

The Warrior's Breath is forceful, deliberate and usually audible, driven by deep, strong contractions of the diaphragm and abdominal muscles. It provides a powerful stimulation to the circulation of blood and a swift surge of energy. This is the mode of breathing utilized in the 'hard' forms of martial arts, such as many of the Shao Lin forms, and in the 'external' styles of chi-gung exercise. It may be used therapeutically to quickly purge the blood and tissues of toxic wastes and replenish the whole system with fresh supplies of oxygen and energy, but it is not conducive to cultivating a state of spiritual quietude.

Most of the chi-gung forms discussed in this book employ the gentle, natural Scholar's Breath, although some of the breathing exercises introduced in the next chapter, such as the 'Bellows', may also be performed with the more dynamic Warrior's Breath for more powerful effects. The Warrior's Breath is also useful as a means of balancing the breath and stimulating the energy system in preparation for a session of still or moving chi-gung with the Scholar's Breath. The only real difference between the two is the magnitude of force involved in performing them and the degree of deliberation required. The two may be intermingled within any particular set of exercises, depending on the results you wish to achieve, and practice will quickly acquaint you with the relative qualities of both modes.

Guiding Energy with the Body

There are basically two styles of chi-gung practice: slow-motion moving exercises, sometimes referred to as 'moving meditation', and still forms, or 'meditation'. In the latter forms, the body is kept still externally, while the mind 'moves' internally to guide energy through the channels and gates. In the former, the mind is kept still internally, while the body moves externally as a means of guiding energy through the system. In both styles, deep, rhythmically regulated breathing with the diaphragm is used to mobilize and balance internal energy within the system, and to link it with external energy sources outside.

The slow rhythmic movements of arms, legs and torso employed in 'moving meditation' chi-gung are designed to guide the energy mobilized by breath to flow freely through particular movements and travel to specific tissues and organs. Thus there are special bodily movements to guide energy to the liver, the kidneys, the heart and other organs, movements to raise energy up the spine and into the head or draw it down the front of the body into the abdomen. There are other movements to spread energy out to the arms and legs, or collect it into the central energy centres, and so forth. When deciding which particular combination of exercises to practise in a particular session, the practitioner bases his or her selection on the specific organs and tissues targeted for energy work in that session.

This style of practice is known in chi-gung as *dao-yin*, literally 'to induce and guide', and it is one of the oldest methods of energy work on record in China, with written references dating back more than 2500 years. The late Han dynasty physician Hua To prescribed *dao-yin* exercises for respiratory and digestive ailments, arthritis and rheumatism, circulatory and heart problems, depression and fatigue, and the great Tang doctor, Sun Ssu-miao, recommended it as supplementary therapy for virtually all conditions, including impotence and infertility.

The key to *dao-yin* practice is to harmonize the prescribed movements of the body with the rhythmic rise and fall of breath, which is why these exercises are always performed very slowly and deliberately, with the body following the pace set by the breath. It's also very important to keep the whole body relaxed and the joints loose throughout the exercises, because any sort of tension in the muscles or tightness in the joints obstructs the free flow of energy.

As for the mind, it must remain calm, quiet and clear during the course of the exercises, with attention focused on the attunement of body and breath. If the mind wavers and wanders off into idle thought, or attention is distracted by external things, body and breath lose synchronicity, and energy follows the mind in an uncharted course of mental and emotional digression. That's why in chi-gung the physical senses are called the 'Five Thieves' of energy, and emotion is called the 'Chief Hooligan', for they disrupt the mental tranquillity and internal focus of attention required to perform the practice, and steal the energy which the practice is designed to regulate. As in all forms of chi-gung, moving meditation exercises require a triunal effort of body, breath and mind focused on the flux and flow of internal energy.

Another way of guiding energy with the body is to use the palm of the hand as a '*chi* brush' to sweep energy from one part of the body to another. The *lao-gung* point is located in the centre of the upper surface of the palms, exactly one inch (2.5cm) down from the slot between the third (middle) and fourth (ring) fingers. This point is one of the most powerful transmitters of energy in the body, and it's the point that master chi-gung healers usually use to emit healing energy into the bodies of ailing patients. Sensitive scientific equipment can detect and measure the energy that streams from this point, indicating the presence of infrared waves, alpha waves and energies very similar in nature to laser beams. In master healers, the magnitude of these energy emissions is over one hundred times stronger than in ordinary people.

The palm points may be used to move energy away from parts of the body where it has accumulated to excess or become blocked, or to draw it into areas where it has grown deficient. For examples, when excess energy collects in the head during chi-gung practice or as a result of intensive cerebral activity, the palms may be used to sweep it from the crown down the back of the neck, from the back of the neck down along the sides of the neck to the chest and on down into the abdomen. If the shoulders feel tense, use the palms to brush blocked energy down the arms and out through the fingers. When feeling weak or fatigued, energy may be swept in towards the centre of the chest and torso from the ribs and waist, or brushed away from the centre off to the sides when feeling overstimulated. The '*chi* brush' can be used to soothe and balance any part of the body that feels tense or painful, to relieve inflammation in the joints, to warm up cold spots, and so forth, by placing the palm over the affected area and rubbing gently in circular motions. This is particularly effective for tired or aching eyes. To move energy away from a spot, sweep repeatedly in one direction away from that point. To soothe, relieve pain and restore balance, rub in circles.

Before using the palms to brush and balance energy, first rub them together briskly until they feel warm, to charge them with extra *chi* and increase their polarity. Sweeping may be done either with light contact on the body, or else about one inch from the surface, whichever works best for you. Rubbing should always be done with light contact. To test the field strength of your own '*chi* brush', rub the palms briskly together, then hold them up in front of you at chest level with the *lao-gung* points facing each other a few inches apart, and the fingers lightly curled, as though holding a ball. As you inhale, bring the palms slowly closer together, and as you exhale, draw them slowly further apart, like an accordion. You should be able to feel the *chi* expanding and contracting like a balloon between your palms, perhaps some tingling or pressure at the fingertips, heat and various other sensations in the hands, arms and sometimes in other parts of the body as well.

Guiding Energy with the Mind

One of the first 'wonders' you will learn to appreciate after practising chi-gung for a while is the incredible power – especially the healing power – of the mind. Most people seem to take the mind for granted as a mere extension of the brain and an agent in service of the body, until they discover the existence of energy and begin to experience what amazing things the mind can accomplish as commander-in-chief of energy.

Guiding energy with the mind is best accomplished while keeping the body motionless; i.e., in still meditation, which may be done in sitting, standing or reclining postures. The *Yellow Emperor's Classic of Internal Medicine* states, 'When the mind is quiet and empty, energy will rise to its command, and the danger of disease will turn to safety.' This is essentially another way of stating the basic principle of psychoneuroimmunology, whereby a calm and quiet mind free of worry sets in motion the natural self-healing mechanisms of the body through positive biofeedback between the nervous and immune systems. In order to achieve the state of internal tranquillity that allows energy to rise to the command of the mind and heal the body, one must learn how to shut off the incessant chatter that spouts from the cerebral cortex. This is the mental roost of the ego and the perpetrator of all the worry and mental machinations that keep the nervous system perpetually locked into the restless 'fight or flight' mode of the sympathetic branch.

Note, however, that the mind never really stands still. When we speak of 'stilling the mind', we mean stilling the discursive thoughts of the postnatal human mind and turning off the shrill high-frequency static produced by the cerebral cortex. This permits the more subtle, deeper faculties of prenatal spirit, such as intent, intuition and visualization – and at higher stages of practice, telepathy, clairvoyance and other psychic powers – which operate at lower frequencies and express themselves in images rather than word-thoughts, to rise to the fore of the mind and manifest their powers. These are the faculties which may be used to modulate and guide energy.

Visualization

Visualization is a way of using the 'mind's eye' to view energy as luminous light and apply intent to guide it. While the temporal vision of the body's eyes perceives objects by virtue of light reflected from the sun or other external sources, the primordial vision of the mind's eye perceives things by virtue of their internal radiant energy. All primordial energy is self-luminous by nature, and therefore it can be seen either directly through the gift of physic vision, such as clairvoyants do, or else 'virtually' by visualizing it as radiant light with the mind's eye, which anyone can do. Furthermore, since 'spirit commands energy', as soon as the mind's eye has focused attention on energy by visualization, intent may then be invoked to guide it wherever the mind intends it to go.

Whether you are consciously aware of it or not, energy is constantly streaming in, out and through your system on its own accord, but the moment you focus your mind on it, 'energy will rise to its command', and you may then control it. Here's one way to do that: when body, breath and mind are resting stably in a balanced state of stillness during meditation, shift your attention from the flow of air through the nostrils over to the flow of energy through the *ni-wan-gung* point on the crown of your head (Fig. 7), visualizing it as a stream of luminous white light that enters the crown and travels down the central channel to the lower elixir field below the navel on inhalation, then rises back up the same path and exits through the same gate on exhalation. After only a few days of practice, you should start feeling a tingling or throbbing sensation at that point as the energy enters and exits. You can also do this through the 'Celestial Eye' point between the eyebrows, the *lao-gung* points on the palms, and other energy gates. Simply visualizing energy immediately amplifies its magnitude. If you

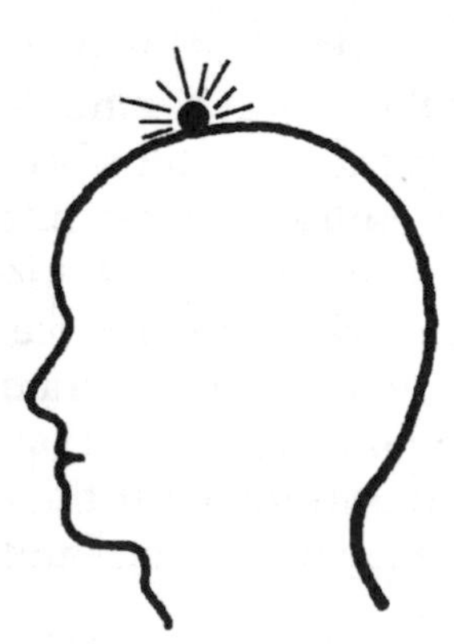

Fig. 7 **The *ni-wan-gung* ('Medicine Palace') point on the crown of the head: the major energy gate linking the powers of heaven and humanity**

then exercise a bit of creative intent, you can guide it to any organ or tissue you wish, draw it in or drive it out, make it hot or make it cold, and so forth.

Guided Imagery

Guided imagery is a more precise type of visualization used to achieve more precise effects, such as healing particular injuries, clearing specific organs, stimulating sexual potency, and so forth. For example, if a particular part of your body has become contaminated with toxic residues, such as your lungs or liver, or if you have a tumour somewhere in your body, you may visualize the polluted energy surrounding those tissues as dark clouds, dense smoke, dry dust or whatever image works best for you; then use intent to mentally lift the negative energy away from the ailing area and guide it completely out of your body, letting it dissolve into the atmosphere and literally 'disappear into thin air'. Next, visualize pure, vibrant energy in the form of clear light, pastel colour, sparkling water, a soft breeze, or whatever image you prefer, stream into the injured tissues and bathe each and every cell, healing your body with the creative power of the universe. You can do this with the mind alone, or further reinforce the effect by synchronizing the outflow of dark energy with exhalation and the inflow of clear energy with inhalation. This should be continued until you can actually feel the quality of the images you're working with moving in your body, not just see them in your mind, and the practice should be repeated until the condition is corrected. With persistent practice, you can use this method to actually repair damaged tissues of the body in the image visualized by the mind, using energy as a medium.

The Power of Positive Thinking

This is not just an uplifting slogan but also a basic axiom of internal alchemy with very real therapeutic powers. A good example of how the power of positive thinking may be enlisted to heal the body is the placebo effect. Patients given plain sugar pills are told that the pills are powerful new drugs with amazing healing powers, and because they now believe they will be cured, their minds activate their own innate responses, and they make a full recovery. Meanwhile other patients who are given the real drug but do not have such a positive outlook fail to realize any therapeutic benefits and remain sick. Pharmaceutical companies operating 'double-blind' studies to test new drugs regard the placebo effect as a real nuisance and an unfortunate quirk of nature, but actually they are missing the real point, which is the fact that the body heals itself only when the mind fully intends it to, with or without drugs, whereas no drug in itself can ever generate a healing effect without the mind's active cooperation.

The well-known correlation between health and happiness is another reflection of the power of positive thinking and the alchemical command of mind over matter. A happy heart generates wholesome thoughts and feelings, which in turn produces the sort of healthy energy that heals and balances the body and protects it from harmful energies. Conversely, negative thoughts and ill feelings, malice and resentment, anger and envy, all pollute the human system with the sort of destructive energies associated with that state of mind, thereby giving rise to physical disease and degeneration. Habitual anger, for example, invariably leads to liver dysfunction, because its crude abrasive energy comes to rest in the liver and pollutes it just as surely as alcohol and drugs do. Habitual negative attitudes and emotions can therefore become direct contributing factors in the acquisition of immune deficiency because they generate energies that inhibit the body's natural healing mechanisms in a sort of reverse PNI response that we might call 'psychoneuroimmunodeficiency'. Not only do negative states of mind generate negative energies, they have also been scientifically proven to impede secretion of the hormones and neurotransmitters associated with healing and to stimulate secretions of 'fight or flight' hormones and neurochemicals that suppress immune response and stress the entire system. As Dr Cass Igram puts it:

> The role played by stress in the causation of cancer is so great that it would not be an exaggeration to say that 80 per cent or more cancer cases have their immediate origin in some form of mental pressure or strain. Grief, distress, fear, worry and anger are emotions which have horrible effects on the body's functions. Researchers have discovered that these emotions cause the release of chemicals from the brain called neuropeptides. These potent compounds have a profound immune-suppressive action. Scientists have traced pathways from the brain to the immune cells proving that negative emotions can stop the immune cells dead in their tracks.

In today's world of chronic stress, spiritual doubt and violent emotions, the power of negative thinking has become one of the biggest, albeit unrecognized, causes of chronic disease, degeneration and acquired immune deficiency.

Positive thinking and the affirmation of happy feelings are very effective ways of using the mind to generate the type of energy associated with health and healing. Numerous scientific studies have demonstrated that whenever patients in hospitals and nursing homes are able to express heartfelt feelings of happiness, there is an immediate rise in their white blood cell count, endorphin and serotonin secretions, hormone balance, enzyme activity and other measures of active immune response. Norman Cousins refers to the therapeutic power of positive thinking as 'the full exercise of the affirmative emotions as a factor in enhancing body chemistry'.

Unfortunately, affirmative emotions are extremely difficult to engender and express in the impersonal atmosphere of huge hospitals, surgical wards, radiation clinics, nursing homes and other citadels of modern medicine. Consequently, modern medical therapies often work directly against the human body's own innate healing mechanisms, giving rise to so much stress, fear and discomfort that the patient's entire system becomes saturated with self-destructive immunosuppressive responses.

Love Heals

The most powerful healing energy of all is triggered when the mind experiences the radiant warmth of love. 'Love conquers all' is a maxim that applies as much to human health and healing as it does to romance, war and peace, and other human relationships. There have been countless cases of miraculous recoveries from the very brink of death due to the timely ministration of love. This is not mere 'anecdotal evidence', but a very real force with therapeutic applications in healthcare. As Yale University cancer surgeon Dr Bernie Seigel writes:

> If I told patients to raise their blood levels of immune globulins or killer T-cells, no one would know how. But if I can teach them to love themselves and others fully, the same changes happen automatically. The truth is, 'Love heals'.

The specific energy frequencies and wave patterns that arise in the human system under the influence of love have extremely powerful healing properties. A simple hug can set in motion a whole healing response by 'injecting' a dose of love energy from hugger to huggee, and this effect can be scientifically verified in the clinic by testing the huggee's blood for the presence of antibodies, hormones and neurochemicals associated with the PNI healing response, both before and immediately after the hug has been administered. Here again we can see another largely unrecognized factor in the drastic decline in human health throughout the industrialized world today, where loneliness and alienation, anger and hostility, have displaced communal feelings of love in the hearts of so many people. Nor is it any coincidence that immune deficiency diseases, such as AIDS and cancer, have become most rampant in the most technologically advanced societies, where 'old-fashioned' love has become rather unfashionable and science is regarded as a know-all and cure-all for everything.

Fashionable or not, love is still the keynote that awakens the healing power of mind, because love motivates the fundamental force of creation throughout the universe. When it comes to healing the body, a little bit of love goes a long way, for it mobilizes the energies and stimulates the secretions involved in the body's own innate healing responses. When those energies are further amplified and guided with such tried-and-true techniques as visualization, guided imagery, positive thinking and emotional equilibrium, the body's capacity to heal itself under guidance from the mind approaches the level of a true panacea.

Working with Sound

Sound is one of the most potent forms of energy in the universe and therefore it's also a very effective way of working with energy in chi-gung. The Bible states that the world was created with the power generated by a single word: 'In the beginning there was the word', and Eastern spiritual traditions attribute similar creative power to the energy of sound. Hindu scriptures cite 'Om', or more precisely 'Aum', as the sacred syllable from which the entire universe sprang into manifest existence, and many scholars believe that 'Amen' uttered at the end of Christian prayers is a direct derivative of this ancient Sanskrit syllable.

Mantra and music are examples of sounds as forms of energy endowed with healing as well as spiritual powers. In Hindu and Buddhist tradition, mantra is used not only to invoke particular deities and awaken primordial spiritual awareness, but also to heal the body and balance the energy system with specific frequencies and wave patterns produced by particular sounds. The universal appeal of music is based on the way its melodious tunes and dulcet tones harmonize and soothe the human energy system through the vibratory energy of sound. Scientific studies have shown that plants grow faster, trees bear sweeter fruit, cows produce more milk, prisoners behave better, and patients recover more quickly when they are exposed to mellifluous music. Since trees don't have ears and cows don't share human culture, it's obviously not the particular melody or lyrics in music that produce the salutary effects it has on living things. It's the harmonious vibrations it creates and the way these vibrations influence the energies of living organisms.

As we have seen, vibratory wave energy is transformed in the human body by the piezoelectric properties of tissues with crystalline structures, such as bones and connective tissue. The resulting electromagnetic energy pulses are then utilized by the human system for specific purposes, such as healing. Particular frequencies and wave patterns in sound produce particular pulses of electromagnetic current, each with its own natural affinity for particular glands, organs and tissues in the body. Therefore, certain sounds may be used to heal the liver, stimulate the heart, balance the adrenals, and so forth.

In chi-gung, there is an ancient healing practice known as the 'Six Syllable Secret' that employs specific sounds to cure specific organs, balance their energies, and stimulate their related functions. In a text entitled *The Maintenance and Extension of Life*, written during the fifth century AD, the physician Tao Hung-ching describes this healing method as follows:

> One should take air in through the nose and let it out slowly through the mouth . . . There is one way of drawing breath in and six ways of expelling breath out. The six ways of expelling breath are represented by the syllables *shü, he, hoo, sss, chway* and *shee*. The six ways of exhalation can cure illness: to expel heat, one uses *chway*; to expel cold, one uses *hoo*; to relieve tension, use *shee*; to release anger, use *he*; to dispel malaise, use *shü*; and to regain equilibrium, use *sss*.

These syllables provide a convenient and effective way to modulate the energy of sound for healing purposes. When combined with deep diaphragmic breathing and slow rhythmic movements of the body, their effects are even more powerful. In *Guarding the Three Treasures*, this author gives a detailed presentation of the entire Six Syllable healing system, including all six sounds, the accompanying exercises, and the most important points of practice. To avoid repetition, only one of these exercises is introduced in this book, for the benefit of those who are unfamiliar with the practice. Readers who wish to learn the entire practice may refer to the author's previous work (see page 145). The exercise introduced below (Fig. 8) is the third in the series, which uses the syllable *hoo* to balance and heal the spleen, pancreas and stomach and regulate the Earth energy associated with these organs:

Syllable: hoo (pronounced 'who', with lips rounded and tongue suspended in mid-mouth, as though blowing out a candle)

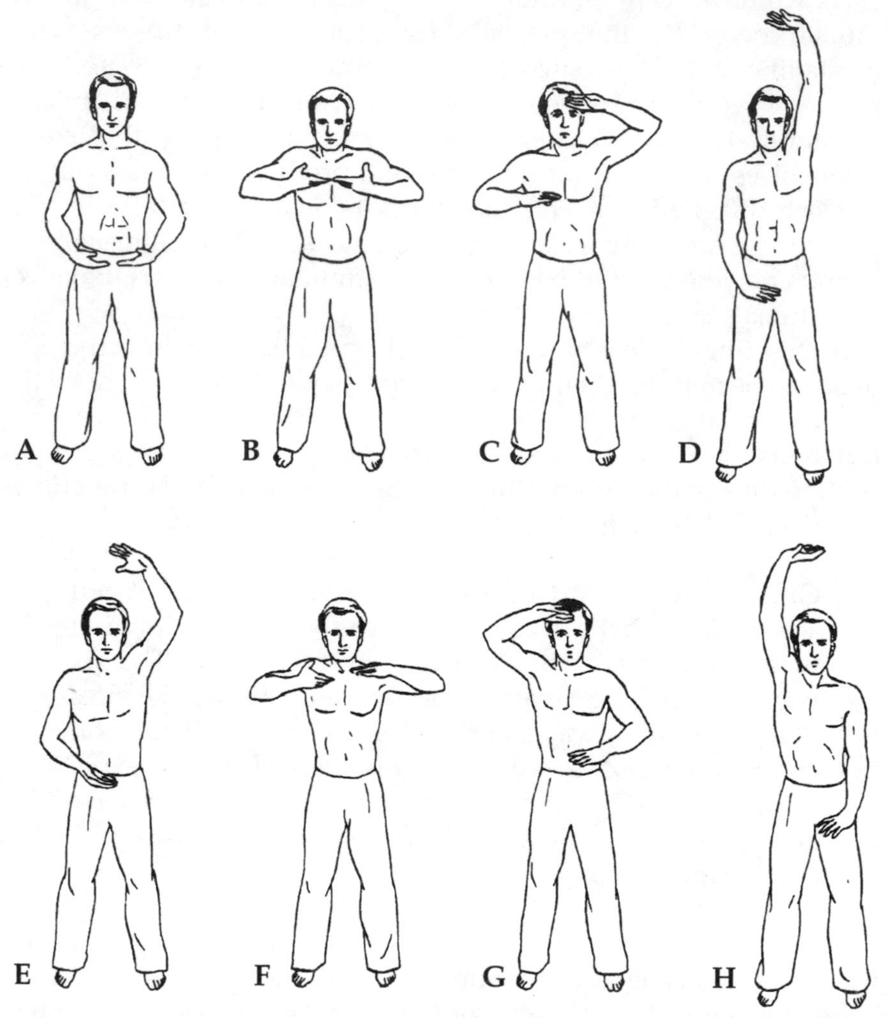

Fig. 8
The 'Six Syllable Secret' exercise for healing and balancing the spleen/stomach (Earth) organ-energy system

Element: Earth
Season: Late Summer
Organ: Spleen and pancreas/stomach

Method: 1. Stand in Horse posture (see page 161). Bring hands out to front, just below the navel, with palms facing up to the sky and fingers aligned. Start inhaling slowly through the nose while raising both hands together up the centre of the torso.

2. When hands reach the heart and breath is full, start exhaling through the mouth aspirating the syllable *hoo*. At the same time, turn one palm out and around 360 degrees so that it faces the sky and continue raising it upwards, and turn the other palm in and around 180 degrees so that it faces the ground and bring it back down the front.

3. When breath is empty, one palm will be extended up towards the sky above the head, while the other is extended down towards the ground at the groin. Turn both palms around so they face one another, and slowly bring them toward one another on the next inhalation. Palms should reach heart level just as inhalation is complete.

4. Start the next exhalation and aspirate the syllable *hoo*, while continuing to move the descending palm downward and turning the ascending palm around 360 degrees and continuing to push it upward, reaching full extension above and below just as exhalation is completed. The syllable need not be sounded out loud; the important point is to form the mouth and throat as though pronouncing that specific syllable.

5. Turn palms and bring them slowly together at the heart as you start a new inhalation. Repeat 6 to 12 times.

Benefits: Improves digestive functions of spleen, pancreas and stomach. Promotes secretions of digestive enzymes. Helps heal ulcers. Eliminates bad breath caused by incomplete digestion in the stomach.

Another way of working with energy through sound is by voicing tones (*fa-yin*) to vibrate the chakras, opening them to the inflow of the higher energies of the universe and balancing the flow and transformation of these energies as they move through the chakras. Unlike bones and other tissues with crystalline structures that transform sound energy into electromagnetic pulses by the piezoelectric effect, the chakras are immaterial energy centres which belong to the invisible grid of points and channels that constitute the human energy system. The First Chakra is at the perineum (also sometimes described as at the genitals; Second

Chakra ('Lower Elixir Field') is just below the navel; Third Chakra ('Middle Elixir Field') is at the solar plexus; Fourth Chakra is at the heart; Fifth Chakra is at the throat; Sixth Chakra is in the middle of the brain ('Upper Elixir Field'), and Seventh Chakra is at the crown of the head.

This system serves as a master template for the cellular matrix of the physical body and a functional bridge between body and mind. The tones used to stimulate the chakras increase the energy that flows through them, which in turn enhances the spiritual faculties associated with each chakra, such as compassion, wisdom, creativity and so forth. Thus, while the six healing syllables work by virtue of the piezoelectric properties of crystalline structures within the tissues and primarily influence the physical body, the seven chakra tones open and balance the major energy centres and awaken the spiritual faculties and psychic powers associated with each one.

In the case of chakra tones, it is not only the syllabic structure of the sound that counts, but also the pitch in which the sound is toned, with the higher chakras responding to higher pitched tones and the lower chakras to lower pitches. The precise tones used to open each chakra should be learned from a qualified teacher in accordance with each individual's unique requirements, because not all pitches work in the same way for all people. Although the syllables used for each chakra are the same for everyone, different people have slightly different requirements in pitch, depending on the condition of their chakras and the nature of their personal energy systems.

However, the fifth chakra tone is fairly standard to everyone and may therefore be introduced for practice here. The throat chakra governs speech, invokes truth, and promotes honesty. It also controls the breathing apparatus and helps expel toxic and stagnant energies from the system. The tone for opening and balancing this chakra is a medium-pitched *ahhhhh*, which should be intoned loudly and strongly, with mouth and throat wide open, so that the vibrations may be felt deeply throughout the bronchial system from the palate down into the lungs and diaphragm. First draw a deep breath in through the nose, compress it, then open your mouth wide and sound the syllable *ahh* from the back of the throat, in a pitch that feels natural and comfortable to your voice, not too high or too low. Continue steadily and evenly without pause until your breath is completely expelled. You may enhance the effects by also visualizing the associated colour of this chakra – light blue – bathing the entire throat and upper chest with luminous light. Repeat three to ten times. This is a very good way to balance the breath and stimulate the respiratory system prior to a period of meditation. It may also be used to harmonize the energy of speech with the spirit of truth prior to important speaking engagements.

Just say, 'Ahhhhh!'

Working with Light and Colour

Light is another fundamental form of energy that pervades the universe, and like sound, light may utilized to balance the human energy system, stimulate vital functions and heal the body. Heliotherapy, referred to in the ancient Taoist canon as 'the method of administering sunbeams', has been used in human health and healing for thousands of years in China, and modern science is beginning to rediscover the potent therapeutic benefits of sunlight for a wide range of ailments and degenerative conditions. Traditional Chinese sources suggest direct exposure of skin and eyes to sunlight as the best way to obtain the healing benefits of solar energy, and contemporary studies confirm the efficacy of this method.

It has been scientifically proven that sunlight is the primary nutrient upon which the pituitary gland depends for normal function. As the master gland of the endocrine system, the pituitary regulates a wide range of vital functions, including growth and repair, metabolism, sexual potency and immunity. The specific energy in sunlight that stimulates the pituitary gland is contained in the invisible ultraviolet band. When sunlight enters the eyes, UV rays act upon a layer of highly sensitive neuro-active cells in the retina called epithelial cells, which transmit the UV stimulus via the optic nerve directly to the pituitary gland. Known as the 'oculo-endocrine' system, this mechanism is absolutely essential for normal physiological functions throughout the body, particularly immune responses, because the pituitary gland controls hormone balance throughout the endocrine system.

The oculo-endocrine system is activated by direct exposure of the eyes to sunlight or to full-spectrum electrical light, which contains all the natural bands found in sunlight and is now commercially available. Since glass blocks out UV rays from sunlight, people who wear eye-glasses and/or spend most of the daylight hours in buildings and cars risk developing a chronic deficiency in pituitary function due to insufficient UV exposure to their retinas. Ideally, one should spend at least an hour or two out in the sunlight every day. For people whose jobs and general lifestyles deprive them of sufficient exposure to the sun, the following simple sun-blinking exercise may be used as a way of 'administering sunbeams' to harvest the essential pituitary nutrient of UV energy from sunlight:

> Pick a time before nine a.m. or after four p.m., when the sun is bright but low in the sky. Stand or sit comfortably facing the sun with eyes closed and head held at an angle that aims the eyes ten to fifteen degrees above the sun, not directly at it. Open your eyes and blink very rapidly for about three seconds, then close them again. Rest briefly, then tilt your head so that your eyes are aimed ten to fifteen degrees below the sun, open them and blink rapidly for three seconds and close them again. Repeat this procedure to the left and right as well, thereby ensuring complete and even exposure of the retina to UV rays. Another way to perform this exercise is to aim your eyes off to any side of the sun, then open them and roll your eyeballs rapidly around in the sockets, so that your line of vision inscribes circles around the sun, for three to five seconds. Repeat three times, making sure that the pupils are never aimed directly at the sun.

Conventional medicine tells us that ultraviolet radiation is harmful to health and that we should therefore avoid exposure to it. So how does this accord with the scientific fact that UV rays are essential for normal pituitary function? First of all, it is short-wave UV rays that are harmful to the body, not long-wave, and the short-wave band is almost entirely filtered out of sunlight by the atmosphere long before it reaches the earth. The long-wave UV rays, which are not harmful, are the ones that nourish the pituitary, and these are the ones that reach the earth, just as nature intended. Secondly, due to global air pollution and the 'greenhouse effect' caused by rising carbon dioxide levels, there has been a nearly 30 per cent reduction in the level of beneficial long-wave UV radiation reaching the earth throughout the world, making it even more important than ever to take measures to increase exposure to sunlight (though not the midday summer sun). The reduction in long-wave UV levels is cited by many scientists as a major factor in the drastic decline in crop yields and greater vulnerability of plants to pests observed in farmlands throughout the world in recent years. If it's having this effect on plants, one can well imagine the inhibitory effect it's having on human health, particularly immune response. Due to the importance of beneficial UV rays on endocrine balance and overall health and vitality, heliotherapy is a highly beneficial practice in any preventive healthcare programme.

In fact, there is no conclusive evidence that short- or long-wave UV causes cancer. It is the Western obsession with getting a tan (in itself an emergency response by the skin to protect itself from damage) thereby exposing ourselves to strong sunlight that does the damage.

The other tissue through which the body assimilates beneficial solar energy is the skin. It is a well-known fact that our primary source of vitamin D is solar energy, which stimulates synthesis of this vital nutrient in the fatty tissue just below the surface of the skin. A lesser known fact is that vitamin D is absolutely essential for the assimilation of calcium in the intestinal tract. Without sufficient supplies of vitamin D present, it is simply impossible to absorb calcium from food or supplements, no matter how rich your diet may be in calcium. Besides its essential role in the structure of bones and teeth, calcium is also essential for proper nerve transmissions, the transfer of nutrients and wastes in and out of the cells, maintenance of proper pH levels in the blood and other bodily fluids, and many other vital functions, and all of this in turn depends on sufficient exposure to sunlight. At a meeting of the International Committee on Illumination in Washington DC, Russian scientists, who have always taken a keen interest in energy work as a basis for human health, reported:

> If human skin is not exposed to solar radiation (direct or scattered) for long periods of time, disturbances will occur in the physiological equilibrium of the human system. The result will be functional disorders of the nervous system and a vitamin D deficiency, a weakening of the body's defences, and an aggravation of chronic diseases.

Colour is another element of light that can be used to enhance and balance the energies involved in human health. For example, acquired or constitutional imbalances in Yin and Yang may be at least partly corrected by utilizing the energy of colours. People with hot, over-active Yang constitutions can help rebalance their systems by wearing clothes with Yin colours, such as blue, black and silver, which have cooling, calming effects, and by using these colours in bedding, furnishings, jewellery and so forth. Similarly, those who require a boost in warming, stimulating Yang energy may use more red, white and gold in their daily lives.

Imbalances in the Five Elemental Energies of the vital organs systems and their related functions and faculties may also be corrected by the judicious use or avoidance of their related colours. People with weak liver functions, for example, can help boost the Wood energy of the liver system by wearing green clothes and jewellery, eating green food, practising chi-gung amid the grass and greenery of a garden, and so forth. On the other hand, someone with high blood pressure, hypertension and other symptoms of an overstimulated heart would be wise to avoid the colour red, which stimulates the Fire energy of the heart. The same principle applies to all of the Five Elemental Energies and their associated organs.

A particularly potent way of using colour to channel the cosmic energies of the sun, moon and planets into the human system is by using precious gems. Precious gems such as rubies, emeralds and diamonds are among the most powerful conductors of energy on earth. As crystals, they possess the capacity to receive the subtle wave energies that rain down on the earth from the sun and moon, stars and planets, and to transform them by the piezoelectric effect into pulsed electromagnetic currents that may be used to heal and balance the human system. Wearing a ruby, for example, will bring the hot Fire energy of the sun into your system, while a pearl or moonstone transmits the cool Water energy of the moon, a green emerald tunes into the energy of Mercury, and so forth. Similarly, wearing precious gems that channel planetary energies which conflict with your astrological energy requirements or further aggravate constitutional imbalances can have serious negative impacts on health and longevity.

When using precious gems to receive and transduce beneficial cosmic energies of planets and other astral sources, it is of utmost importance to use only flawless gems. If there are any defects in the crystal surface, the energies the gem transmits will be warped and have adverse rather than beneficial effects on your system. Therefore, when using gemstones as energy transmitters, it's important to consult a gemologist in the ancient science of planetary astrology to ensure that you select a gem which suits your individual constitution and has a flawless structure.

Working with Aroma

Aromatic essences extracted from flowers and medicinal herbs have been used for millennia to cure disease and balance human energies. The volatile aroma extracted by a flower or the essential oil of a plant carries the essential energy of that plant in the air in a way similar to negative ion energy, and this energy is assimilated into the human system through the same sensitive olfactory receptors in the nasal passages. Depending on their natural affinities for various organs and tissues, different aromatic essences may be used to cure specific diseases, balance particular energies, and stimulate various functions. This is the basic principle involved in aromatherapy, but it only works when using aromas derived from natural sources, such as plants, minerals and animals. Artificial fragrances have smell but no *chi*.

Writing in the French medical journal *L'Hôpital*, Dr J. Valent explains the way plant aromas affect human energies:

> Carried by the bloodstream, the ionized plant aroma impregnates every corner of the body, powerfully revitalizes the polarized and discharged cells, replenishes electronic shortages by recharging the bioelectromagnetic batteries, and disperses cellular residue by dissolving the viscous and diseased substances of the body fluids. It oxidizes poisonous metabolic waste products, increases energy balance, frees the mechanism of organic oxidation and of self-regulation, and reaches the lungs and kidneys, whence it is excreted or exhaled without trace.

Meditators throughout the world use incense to enhance their practice due to the balancing effects it has on human energies. Sandalwood in particular is well known among meditators in Asia for its power to pacify emotions and settle energy down into the lower elixir field (second chakra) below the navel, thereby establishing the ideal conditions for entering a stable state of spiritual tranquillity. The smoke produced by burning white sage, used by native tribes of North America for purification, sublimates the dense, heavy energies generated by negative thoughts and conflicting emotions and lifts them away from the body, thereby clearing the human energy system.

It's interesting to note that during medieval times in the Middle East, medical texts took note of the fact that people who worked in perfume and incense shops were the only ones who never succumbed to the various contagious plagues that periodically swept through the ancient world, and even today it is often noted that clerks who work in fresh flower shops rarely seem to catch the flu and other infectious ailments. 'Flower Power' is more than just a catchy phrase: it reflects the potent healing properties of aromatic essence.

Working with Touch

The human energy system may be stimulated and balanced by various forms of physical contact, including tapping, rubbing and acupressure. Let's take a quick look at each of these methods.

- *Tapping*. Rhythmically tapping various parts of the body transmits a vibrational wave into the tissues that causes stagnant energy to scatter, drives surface energy deeper, stimulates blood circulation and glandular secretions, and balances energy flow in the meridiens. For example, after practising a round of chi-gung exercises, the inside and outside surfaces of the arms and legs may be vigorously tapped with a fist or open palm to drive energy accumulated on the surface deep into the bones and marrow for storage and to stimulate production of white blood cells in the marrow. If a particular organ feels sluggish, you may trace the path of the associated meridien along the surface of the body and tap it from one end to the other. The tapping activates the flow of energy in the meridien, which then channels energy into the related organ, clearing out stagnant residual energy and rebalancing its functions.

A popular tapping set in chi-gung is the 'Three Taps' (Fig. 9), which involves rhythmic tapping of three parts of the body that house glands of central importance to immunity and overall vitality: the head and neck (pituitary and pineal glands); the chest (thymus gland); and the kidney area (adrenal glands). This is an excellent exercise for stimulating and balancing endocrine functions and boosting immunity. For the head and neck tap, first rub the palms together till warm, then roll the fingers into fists, with thumbs clenched against the outsides of the index fingers, and use the first row of knuckles and the base of the palms to vigorously tap the back of the neck along both sides of the cervical vertebrae, moving from the top of the shoulders up the neck to the base of the skull, then continuing up the skull over the crown to the top of the forehead, and back down the neck again. In addition to directly stimulating the pituitary and pineal glands by vibrating the skull, this exercise also draws energy into the head, helps relax tense neck muscles, and stimulates microcirculation in the brain.

For the thymus tap, use the middle row of knuckles of one hand to rhythmically tap the chest at the point between the nipples, using the beat of one heavy followed by two lighter taps (ONE two three), ONE two three, etc.). This vibratory pattern stimulates secretions of the thymus gland, which are extremely important for normal immune response and which are often deficient in adults due to shrinkage of this gland. Daily tapping helps restore the size of the

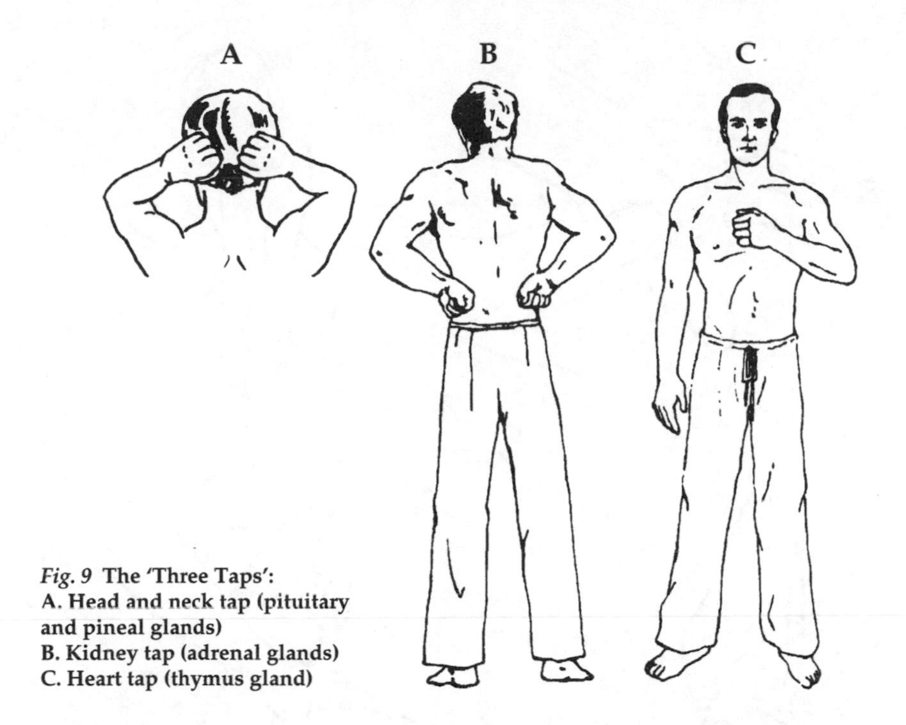

Fig. 9 **The 'Three Taps':**
A. Head and neck tap (pituitary and pineal glands)
B. Kidney tap (adrenal glands)
C. Heart tap (thymus gland)

thymus and activates its secretions of immune factors. The thymus tap also stimulates the heart and helps loosen toxins impacted in the lungs.

To tap the kidneys and adrenal glands, use the back of the hands to gently tap the left and right kidneys, alternately, from top to bottom. The vibrations are carried into the adrenals, where they stimulate secretions of beneficial hormones. They also draw energy into the kidneys and help to clear them of residual toxins. About two minutes of tapping for each of these areas suffices for a general 'tune-up'. If you're trying to build up your immune system during or after a period of illness, then five or six minutes each is better.

• *Rubbing*. Rubbing various parts of the body with the palms, after first charging them up, has been discussed earlier in this chapter. Suffice to say here that this technique may be used to relieve pain, clear congestion, soothe inflammation, warm, and balance energy almost anywhere on the body. The eyes respond particularly well to this method. Rubbing the testicles or ovaries with *chi*-charged palms helps promote fertility, while rubbing the thyroid glands on the throat is a good way to balance metabolism.

• *Acupressure* (Fig. 10). Acupressure involves the application of deep-tissue pressure at specific energy points along the body's surface. These points are major relay terminals for the various organ-energy meridiens, and pressure applied to them stimulates

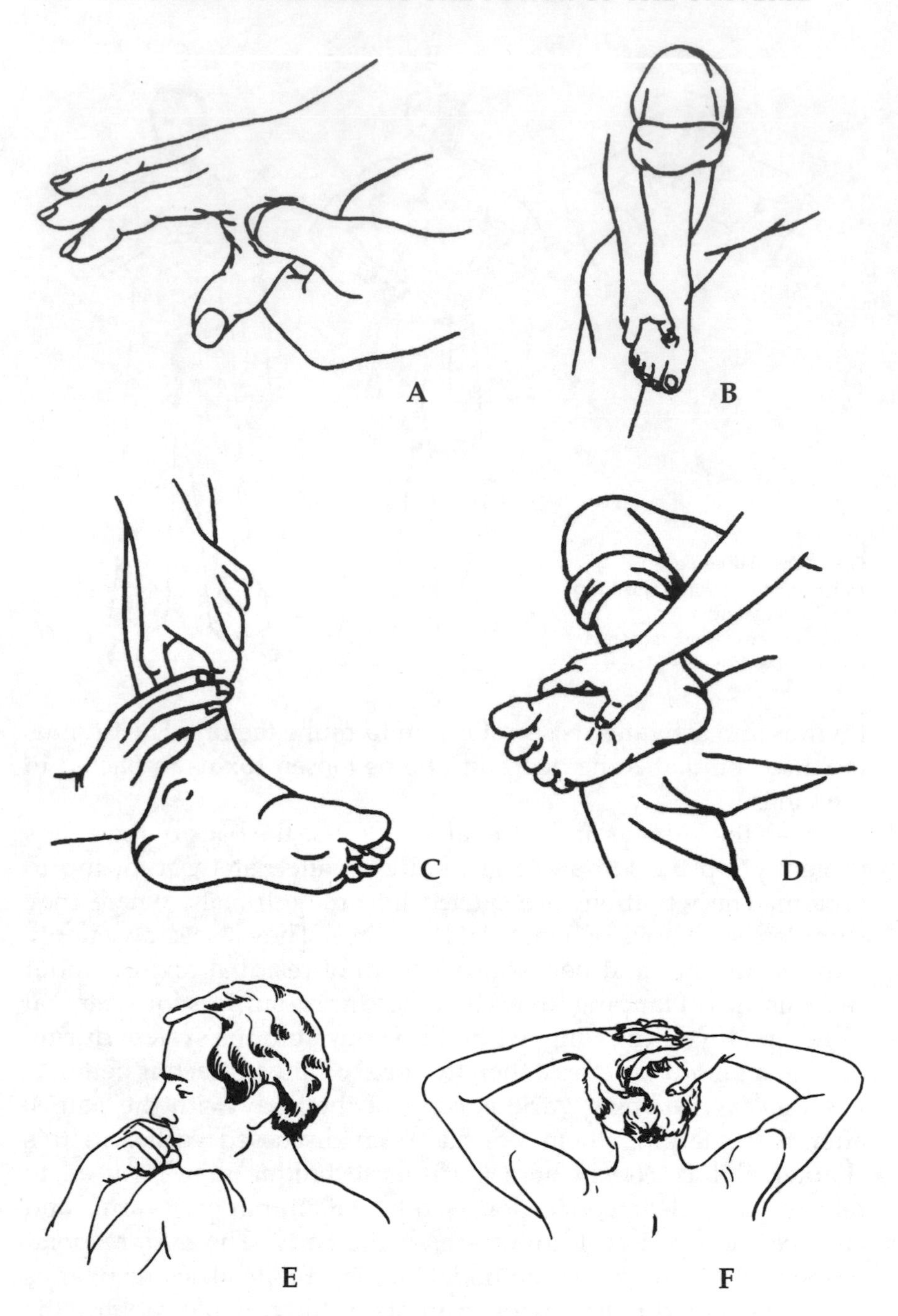

Fig. 10 **Major acupressure points for self-therapy:**
A. 'Valley of Harmony' (*ho-gu*)
B. 'Supreme Thrust' (*tai-chung*)
C. 'Triple Yin Intersection' (*san-yin-jiao*)
D. 'Bubbling Spring' (*yung-chuan*)
E. 'Human Centre' (*ren-chung*)
F. 'Wind Pond' (*feng-chih*)

and balances the flow of energy through the related meridiens. Pressure may be applied either with the tip of the thumb or index finger, or else with a knuckle. Acupressure should always be practised in conjunction with deep abdominal breathing to further enhance its effects. The following are some of the major points that may be readily utilized to balance energy by self-application of acupressure:

– *Ho-gu* ('Valley of Harmony'). This is one of the body's major power points, located along the large intestine meridian, in the depression at the base of the webbing between the outstretched thumb and index finger. Probe deeply into the fleshy 'valley' between the base of these bones until you find a sensitive point, then press it deeply, hold for about ten seconds, release, and repeat 3 to 6 times. Pressure here improves circulation throughout the body, relieves headaches and toothache on the side pressed, eases tension in the neck and shoulders, and improves respiration.

– *Tai-chung* ('Supreme Thrust'). This is the point on the foot equivalent to the Valley of Harmony on the hand. It's located along the liver meridian, on top of the foot, between the tendons of the big and second toes, about 2 inches (5cm) up from the slot between these toes. Use the thumb to probe deeply until you find it, then press sharply and hold for ten seconds, release, and repeat 3 to 6 times. This is a powerful point for stimulating liver function, detoxifying the liver, and helping to cure hepatic diseases. It's also effective for alleviating headache and eyeache caused by congested liver, and for clearing hangovers.

– *San-yin-jiao* ('Triple Yin Intersection'). This powerful point is located at the junction of three major Yin organ meridians – spleen, liver and kidneys – about four finger-widths up from the top of the ankle, along the inside of the calf, just behind the bone. This point may be used to correct all sorts of sexual dysfunction, boost sexual energy, and balance menstrual cycles. It also helps strengthen bones, tendons and muscles, which are the tissues governed by these organ-energies.

– *Yung-chuan* ('Bubbling Spring'). This point is located in the centre of the ball of the foot, about 2½ inches (6cm) down from the second toe, along the kidney meridien. Pressure on this point balances the entire energy system and specifically stimulates the adrenal cortex. It's also effective for regulating heart function.

– *Ren-chung* ('Human Centre'). Located in the depression in the middle of the upper lip, just below the nose, this is the terminus of the Governing Channel, which runs up the spine, over the head, and ends at this point. Pressure here helps draw energy up the

Governing Channel into the head and links it with the Conception Channel for transport back down the front, thereby opening the Microcosmic Orbit of energy circulation. If someone faints or goes into a state of shock, quick sharp pressure at this point can help revive them.

– *Feng-chih* ('Wind Pond'). These points are located on both sides of the upper cervical vertebrae, where the neck ends and the skull begins, about 1½ inches (4cm) apart. To find them, clasp the hands behind the head and use the thumbs to probe the base of the skull. Pressure on these points, which are located along the bladder meridien, helps to clear blocked nasal passages and balances the flow of air between right and left nostrils.

Working with Sexual Energy

In traditional Chinese medicine, as well as internal alchemy, sexual energy is regarded as the most powerful form of *chi* in the human body. Semen is the basic essence from which men derive vitality. Indeed, one of the most common causes of premature ageing, chronic fatigue and immune deficiency in middle-aged men is the excessive loss of semen due to unrestricted ejaculation. When a man's body is constantly forced to replenish semen, the required nutrients are borrowed from various other parts of the body, particularly the glands and cerebrospinal fluids, weakening these vital bodily fluids and depleting the essential nutrients of which they are composed. In women, however, orgasm is regarded as an effective means of balancing the endocrine system, generating energy and promoting health, because no vital fluids are lost.

The two basic ways of working with sexual energy in chi-gung are 'Dual Cultivation' (*shwang-shiou*) with a partner and 'Solo Cultivation' (*dan-shiou*), which involves sexual self-massage. The latter method, including specific 'sexercises' is covered extensively in the author's previous book *Guarding the Three Treasures*, while the former is presented in detail in *The Tao of Health, Sex, and Longevity*. Readers who wish to integrate their sexual activities with their other chi-gung practices may refer to the appropriate sections of these books for guidance.

A wide range of electronic and magnetic devices are available on the market today, designed to help stimulate and balance the human energy system at the mere push of a button or turn of a dial. Some of these devices are in fact quite useful when utilized within the context of an overall healthcare programme in which traditional chi-gung practice is the prevailing method of working with energy. Others are totally useless, if not downright harmful, and none of them can ever serve as a substitute for correct breathing, physical exercise, and the internal alchemy of still or moving meditation. The only true healing energy is the pervasive free energy of the universe, and only living organisms can channel and utilize this energy, which responds to the focused attention of a calm, balanced mind, not to a button or dial on a machine. Anyone who looks to electronic devices as a short-cut for the time and disciplined effort required for personal practice in energy work will definitely be disappointed. Such devices should be used with the guidance of qualified health professionals with a background in the technology involved and within the overall context of a complete system of holistic healthcare in which chi-gung plays a central role.

The various ways of working with energy discussed above are presented here to give the reader an idea of the broad scope of energy work that may be included in any programme of chi-gung practice. All of them have their own particular benefits for various different purposes, but it's very important to remember that the primary tool for working with energy is, and always will be, the natural technology of breath control performed in conjunction with proper posture under the volitional guidance of a clear, calm, internally focused mind. Breath is the great regulator of energy in the human body, and spirit is its supreme commander. Together spirit and breath guide energy on all paths of chi-gung, and breath control is the core practice in all modes of energy work.

CHAPTER 7

Fundamentals of Form: Posture, Breath and Integration

'Externally, practise the form,' advises an ancient Chinese maxim. 'Internally, practise the meaning.' Correct form is very important in chi-gung, and without it the inner meaning of the practice is easily lost. How the various parts of the body are held in balance in a particular posture, how the limbs and torso move through the forms, and how the movements are integrated with the various phases of breath – all of these factors exert decisive influence on the magnitude, balance, transformation and flow of energies in the channels. Different breathing techniques mobilize and modulate breath and energy in different ways, and every practitioner of chi-gung should have a variety of basic breathing methods in his or her repertoire for appropriate applications in practice. The various forms of posture and breath used in chi-gung are external factors: they establish the fundamental framework for practice. Energy and mind are internal factors: they reflect the main meaning and represent the major goals of practice. In order to understand the inner meanings of the outer forms of practice and accomplish such internal goals as balancing energy, activating internal alchemy, expanding awareness, and harmonizing the mind, one must first establish a stable external foundation in practice by carefully cleaving to the basic rules of form, such as proper posture, correct breathing and the integration of breath with body and energy.

In the following pages we shall review the basic points of attention in the four fundamental body postures used for moving and still styles of chi-gung practice and discuss seven different methods of breathing that may be used in chi-gung, each with its own distinctive effects on respiration, circulation and energy. Then we'll take a look at how breath is synchronized with body in moving forms of chi-gung, and how to breathe in harmony with the movement of energy in still forms.

Four Postures for Chi-Gung Practice

Regarding the importance of proper posture in chi-gung, an old Chinese medical text states, 'When posture is not proper, energy is not smooth; when energy is not smooth, mind is not stable'. Even the smallest point of posture can make a big difference in how smoothly energy circulates through the body during practice, and this in turn determines how energy influences the mind. Conversely, if the mind is not stably balanced prior to practice, energy will not flow smoothly through the system, and this in turn will throw posture off balance. For most people, it's much easier to start by balancing the body rather than the mind, and therefore establishing proper posture in the body is usually the first step in practice. In chi-gung, posture is the fundamental foundation upon which a strong, stable practice is built.

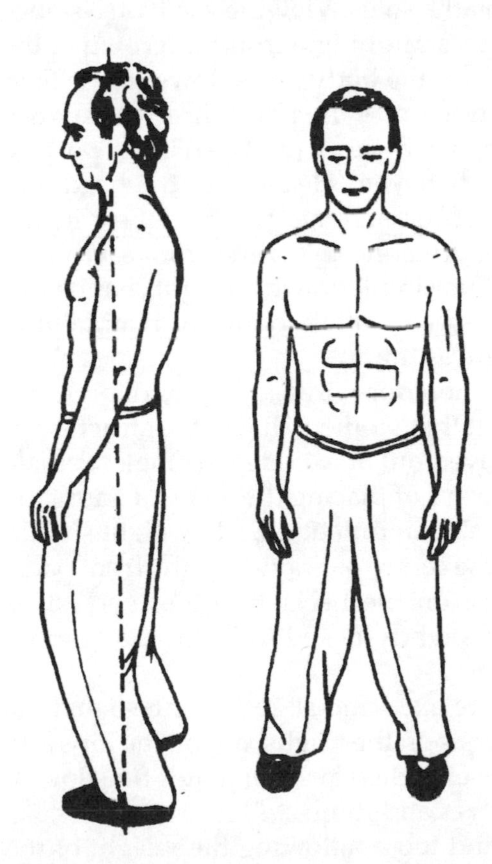

Fig. 11 **The 'Horse' stance, the most important posture for practising chi-gung; note the alignment of the crown, solar plexus and abdomen with the centre of the feet**

Standing (Fig. 11)

Moving forms of chi-gung are usually practised in the traditional 'Horse' stance, which may also be used for still standing meditation. This is a very stable posture for standing practice, with a firm but flexible foundation in the legs, a low centre of balance below the navel that makes it easy to adjust and maintain directional equilibrium, and a 'tower of power' rising through the spine to link the energy of Earth in the sacrum with the energy of Heaven in the head. So important is the Horse stance in Chinese martial arts and chi-gung, that traditional masters often required new students to spend the first year practising nothing but 'Standing Pylon' in the Horse posture, until they could stand stably in that position for up to two or three hours.

The primary guideline for proper posture in the Horse stance is to keep the top of the head in perfect alignment with the lower elixir field in the abdomen, the Yin Confluence at the perineum, and the midpoint between the feet of an imaginary line drawn between the two Bubbling Spring points on the soles. Viewing the Horse stance from the side, there should be a straight line from the crown of the head down through the centre of the body to the lower elixir field and on down through the perineum to the point directly between the two Bubbling Spring points in the feet. The Horse posture facilitates free flow of energy between 'Heaven' in the head and 'Earth' in the sacrum and feet, opens energy circulation in the Governing Channel that runs up along the spine from sacrum to cerebrum, and draws energy into circulation in all eight channels of the Macrocosmic Orbit. Major points of attention for maintaining proper posture in the Horse are as follows:

- **Feet** should be exactly shoulder-width apart and perfectly parallel. Some teachers suggest that women, due to the structure of the pelvis, place their feel splayed out at a 45-degree angle. Female practitioners should try both ways of placing the feet and adopt the one which feels more comfortable in practice. Body weight should rest evenly on both feet, with the centre of gravity on the front pads, of 'balls', of the feet, not back on the heels. The toes should be spread for better balance and slightly flexed to 'grip' the ground, but without tensing the feet.
- **Knees** are kept unlocked, relaxed and slightly bent, so that the main burden of body weight rests on the thighs, not on the hips and lower back. Keeping the knees unlocked also facilitates free flow of blood and energy between calves and thighs.
- **Hips** should be relaxed and loose, allowing the weight of the

upper body to be supported primarily by the thighs. Tuck the pelvis slightly forward to pull in the buttocks and straighten out the curvature in the lower spine. Keeping the buttocks tucked in makes it much easier to keep the spine aligned and maintain proper balance in the Horse. It also encourages energy to rise up the spinal channels from sacrum to cerebrum.

• **Abdomen** should also be relaxed, so that the diaphragm may expand freely down into the abdominal cavity on inhalation. However, an excessively flaccid abdominal wall is a disadvantage, because it expands too far on inhalation thereby negating the therapeutic benefits of compression, and is difficult to draw inward for the abdominal lock and the final phase of exhalation. Strengthening your 'abs' is therefore a good way to enhance your chi-gung practice.

• **Chest** should be neither tense nor jutted out in front during chi-gung practice. If the spine is straight and the shoulders are relaxed, the chest will naturally fall into proper position. By slightly rolling the shoulders forward (without stooping the upper spine), the entire thorax will relax, thereby facilitating deep abdominal breathing.

• **Spine** must be held erect throughout a session of chi-gung practice. Imagine a string attached to the crown of the head, pulling the entire spinal column upward. Proper spinal posture is facilitated by keeping the back of the neck straight and the chin pulled slightly down, but without tilting the head forward, and by keeping the buttocks tucked in. This stretches the spine and keeps the vertebrae well aligned.

• **Shoulders** should be loose and completely relaxed, so that the arms hang naturally down by the sides, the chest remains relaxed, and the muscles of the neck and upper back are free of tension.

• **Elbows** should be kept unlocked to allow the arms to dangle loosely by the sides and the energy to flow freely up and down the arm channels. The hollows of the elbows face inward towards the ribs, so that the palms are facing toward the back.

• **Hands** must remain completely relaxed during practice, with fingers slightly curled and palms hollowed. 'The hands are the flags of energy,' states an old chi-gung adage, which means that they respond to even the slightest 'wind' of *chi*. The *lao-gung* points in the centre of the palms are the most powerful transmitters of energy in the entire body, but any tension in the hands tend to impede their conductivity.

• **Head** is kept straight, as though suspended from a string. Except when required as part of a particular exercise, do not tilt the head forward or backward or from side to side during practice.

• **Neck** remains aligned with the spine and stretched upward by tucking the chin slightly downward, without tilting the head forward. Try to keep the muscles of the neck and throat relaxed. Any tension in the neck tends to block the free flow of energy into the head.

• **Eyes** are usually kept half-open during moving chi-gung exercises to help maintain balance and directional equilibrium. Eyelids and eyeballs should remain completely relaxed, and the eyes should not be focused on any particular object. Just keep the eyes in an unfocused gaze, aimed either straight ahead or at the ground a yard or so (a meter or two) in front. In still meditation, the eyes may be kept closed to turn attention inward and facilitate visualization of internal energy.

• **Mouth** should also be relaxed, without any tension in the jaw or lips. Except when doing mouth exhalation, keep the lips closed, but not so tightly that it causes tension in the face, and keep the upper and lower teeth touching, but without clenching the jaw.

• **Tongue** should be kept relaxed in the mouth, with the tip pressed lightly against the palate behind the upper teeth. This forms a 'bridge' for energy to pass from the Governing Channel into the Conception Channel in the Microcosmic Orbit circulation. Raising the tongue to the palate also helps stimulate secretion of highly beneficial saliva from the salivary ducts below the tongue. This should be swallowed as it pools in the bottom of the mouth. You may also curl the tongue back so that the tip is pressed against the soft palate at the top of the throat; this provides a stronger stimulation to salivary secretions.

Sitting

There are two basic sitting postures for chi-gung: sitting cross-legged on the floor, sofa or platform (Fig. 12); and sitting on the edge of a low stool or chair with the feet flat on the floor (Fig. 13). These postures are used mainly for still meditation practice, although some moving exercises, such as the Eight Pieces of Brocade set, may also be performed in sitting posture.

The cross-legged position is known as the 'Lotus Posture', and it has two variations – half lotus and full lotus. If your legs and knees are limber enough to hold the full lotus, that's the most stable and balanced sitting posture for still meditation, but it's best to learn this position from a qualified yoga or chi-gung teacher. The posture illustrated and described here is the half lotus, which is much easier for most people to hold without experiencing discomfort.

Fig. 12 **Sitting posture: legs crossed in the 'Half Lotus' position**

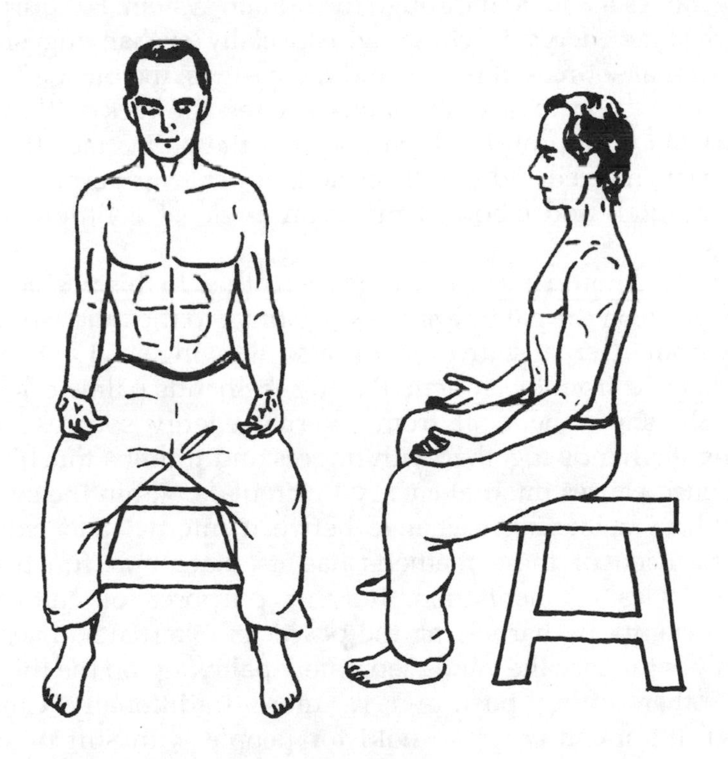

Fig. 13 **Sitting posture: sitting erect on a low stool**

If you're sitting on the floor, it's best to use a mat or carpet. If you use a bed or sofa, be sure that the sitting surface is very firm. Place a small, hard cushion, folded towel or telephone book under the buttocks to elevate and tilt the pelvis. This makes it easier to hold the lotus posture for prolonged periods without straining the lower back, hips and thighs, or getting numb in the legs. Cross one leg so that the foot is tucked comfortably under the opposite thigh. Then cross the other leg and place that foot on top of the opposite thigh, as shown in the illustration. The soles of both beet should be facing upward. Sit with spine held erect, but don't let the chest stick out in front. Shoulders should be completely relaxed and slightly rounded, neck straight, chin drawn slightly inward, head held as though suspended from a string.

There are many different ways of placing the hands during still meditation. Hand postures, known in Sanskrit as *mudra*, are regarded as very important aspects of meditation practice in Hindu and Buddhist tradition, as well as in Taoist practice. As 'flags of energy' that are particularly sensitive to *chi*, the hands, and how they are held during practice, have a decisive influence on how energy moves in, out and through the human system. For purposes of cultivating energy in chi-gung, especially exchanging energy with external sources in nature and the cosmos, the most effective and beneficial way to place the hands is to rest the back of the hands comfortably on top of the thighs, so that the palms face the sky, with fingers relaxed and slightly curled, upper arms perpendicular to the ground, and elbows bent at an angle of a little over 90 degrees.

The hands should not be touching each other. In this position, the energy gates on the palms are most receptive to the inflow of fresh energy from external sources, while also allowing stagnant energy to be expelled from the system. Placing the hands palms-down on the thighs shuts them off from external energy sources, while cupping the hands together with fingers and thumbs touching or intertwined causes internal energy to circulate within the system, rather than facilitating exchange between internal and external energies. Each of these methods has its place and function in various styles of meditation, but for purposes of cultivating internal energy by harnessing the power of external sources, the best way is to place the hands separately palms-up on the thighs.

The other sitting posture is a more traditionally Chinese method. It's much easier to hold for people with stiff or weak knees, poor circulation in the legs, or lower back problems, and it tends to extend energy circulation from the two main channels of the Microcosmic Orbit into all eight channels of the Macrocosmic Orbit.

Use a low stool or chair that allows a 90-degree angle between thigh and calf when sitting. A firm cushion, pad, or folded towel may be placed on the stool for comfort, but the sitting surface should not be too soft. Sit on the edge of the stool so that the buttocks are flush against the surface but the genitals are over the side. Feet should be flat on the ground or floor, parallel and shoulder-width apart. Spine, neck, and head are kept straight and properly aligned, as in the lotus posture, with hands placed apart and palms up on top of the thighs.

Lying (Fig. 14)

The lying posture is generally used only when it's not possible to practise in the standing or sitting positions due to illness, old age or physical handicaps. Since the body is lying parallel to the ground in this position, there is virtually no potential gradient between sacrum and head, which reduces the polarity and flow of energy through the system. It also puts uneven pressure on the spine, which further impedes free flow of energy. Nevertheless, practising chi-gung in this posture still has its benefits: the movement of the diaphragm massages the internal organs; the basic vital functions of circulation, digestion, nerves and endocrine response are stimulated and balanced; the pH of blood and other bodily fluids is normalized; tissues are oxygenated, and so forth. It is only the

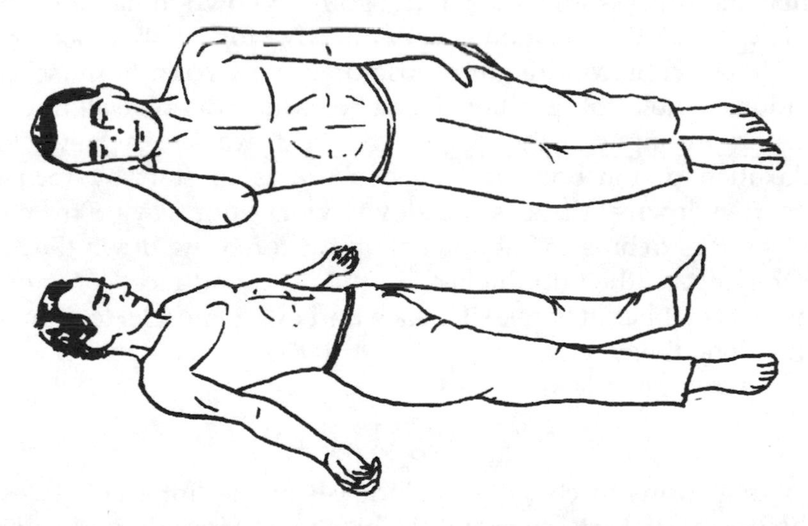

Fig. 14
Reclining posture: lying on the right side; lying on the back in the 'Corpse' posture

higher stages of internal alchemy that are somewhat impeded by practising in the reclining position, but the basic physiological benefits remain much the same.

There are two basic lying positions – side and back. In both positions, it's very important to lie on a firm, flat surface. Most beds are too soft for practising chi-gung in the reclining position. This can usually be corrected by placing a board under the mattress; otherwise, lie on a mat or carpet on the floor. When lying on the side, it's customary to lie on the right side: not only does this take pressure off the heart, it also facilitates inhalation through the left nostril, which, due to its upper position, tends to remain more open when lying on the right side. The left nostril is associated with the right hemisphere of the brain, which houses the intuitive faculties and is therefore more conducive to working with internal energy and spirit. The head should lie on a small, firm pillow, with the right hand placed between head and pillow and the left arm stretched comfortably down along the left side. Legs should be slightly bent, with the knees and ankles more or less together, although the upper leg may be brought forward a bit so that the knee and ankle are resting on the surface just in front of the other leg. The main point of attention here is to keep the spine as straight as possible.

The other lying posture involves reclining flat on the back, legs apart, arms slightly spread out to the sides with palms facing upward. The head should be resting on a small firm cushion, with a rolled towel under the neck for added support to prevent unbalanced pressure on the upper spine. Known in hatha yoga as 'The Corpse', this position is very effective for totally relaxing the whole body. Since it requires absolutely no flexion of muscles or tendons to hold this position, it can be used to dissolve all traces of tension throughout the body. The best way to achieve total relaxation of the body in this position is to start by focusing attention down at the toes and slowly work your way up from feet to legs, legs to hips and abdomen, up the torso and down the arms to the fingers, then up the neck to the head and face, consciously and very deliberately relaxing each and every muscle, tendon and joint along the way.

Walking (Fig. 15)

Walking forms of chi-gung include all of the 'internal' styles of Chinese martial arts, such as Tai Chi Chuan, Hsing Yi and Pa Kua. A distinctive feature of these traditional 'soft-style' Chinese martial

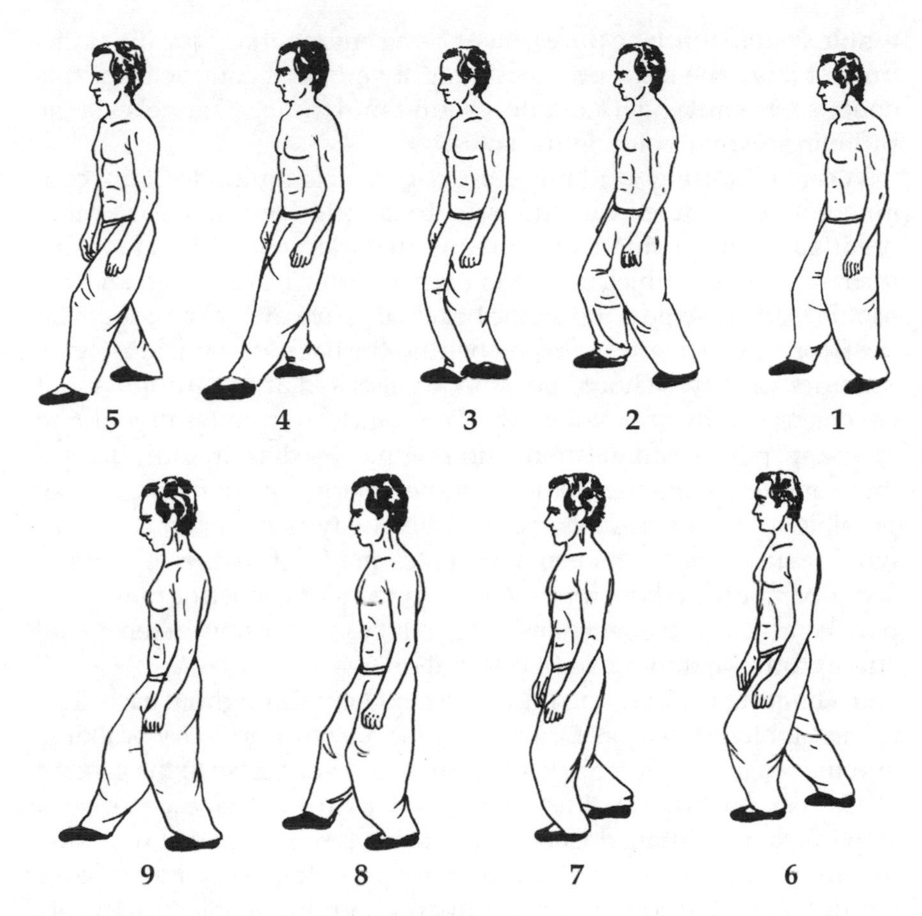

Fig. 15 **Walking posture: the 'Tai Chi Walk'**

arts is that they may be practised purely as chi-gung sets to cultivate energy and awareness, or to cultivate martial power and fighting skill for combat. When practised as chi-gung to cultivate energy, the manoeuvres are performed very slowly and deliberately in a predetermined sequential order; when used as martial arts in combat or competition, the movements are executed with lightning speed, and each step arises in specific response to the opponent's movements.

Walking may also be practised as a form of chi-gung in itself, without the elaborately choreographed steps, arm and leg extensions, and twists and turns of the torso that characterize Tai Chi Chuan, Pa Kua and other internal forms of martial arts. The best time and place to practise walking chi-gung is early in the morning, just after dawn, barefoot on an open lawn, while the grass is still damp with dew. This is an excellent way to energize the whole system with the pure potent Yang energy that prevails at this time of day. The dew serves as a highly efficient conductor of this energy, transmitting it from the ground into the leg channels via the Bubbling Spring point on the soles.

When practising walking chi-gung, you should do it in conjunction with deep diaphragmic breathing and a clear, calm, meditative state of mind. Other than a dew-damp lawn at dawn, this form of practice, which is also known as 'Tai Chi Walking' and the 'Lotus Step', may be done on the beach, in a driveway, or indoors on the floor. Hands may be clasped behind the back, or hang loosely by the sides, and eyes should be aimed unfocused at the ground about two metres in front of your step. Ten to fifteen minutes of walking chi-gung, performed in conjunction with deep diaphragmic breathing completely recharges the whole energy system. If it's not possible to do it barefoot, the next best way is either in cotton or wool socks, or in soft shoes with soles made of leather or cotton. Socks of synthetic fibre and shoes with soles of rubber or plastic are poor conductors of energy and tend to block the upflow of terrestrial energy and the downflow of celestial energy.

In chi-gung walking, the knees are kept bent throughout each step, not straightened out on forward extension as in ordinary walking, and the soles of the feet are kept parallel and very close to the ground at all times, not lifted at different angles. This means that each forward step is taken by lifting the entire rear foot off the ground at once (not the heel first), bringing the foot forward while keeping the sole parallel and close to the ground, then setting the whole foot evenly and flatly down on the ground in front (not the heel down first, then the toes). The body thus moves forward slowly and smoothly, in a straight line, without the head bobbing up and down and the torso swaying from side to side on each step as in ordinary walking. The spine is held erect and aligned with the neck, the head is kept straight, the arms hang down relaxed by the sides, and the pelvis is tilted slightly forward to keep the buttocks tucked in and the lower spine straight. Taoist texts refer to this gait as 'walking like the wind'.

This style of chi-gung draws terrestrial energy from the earth into the system, circulates it in the Macrocosmic Orbit, and stores it in the reservoirs of the Eight Extraordinary Channels. It builds strong ankles, knees and thighs, improves balance and coordination in the body, and cultivates concentration, clarity and focused attention in the mind. While moving chi-gung exercises practised in the standing posture involve movements of the arms, head and torso, with the legs kept stationary, walking forms move the feet and legs, while keeping the upper body still. These two styles of 'moving meditation' therefore complement one another very well and may both be practised in the same session.

Seven Ways of Breathing in Chi-Gung

Deep diaphragmic breathing is the core technique in all styles of chi-gung, moving as well as still. Without breath control, chi-gung is nothing more than 'going through the motions' of moving or holding the body in a particular manner. Breath control is the key to energy control, and breath is the bridge that allows mind to take command of body and regulate all of its vital functions.

Like physical exercise, there are many different ways to exercise the breath, each with its own particular benefits and purposes in practice, so it's a good idea for practitioners of chi-gung to familiarize themselves with a variety of basic breathing exercises. Though each of the seven breathing methods introduced below has its own unique features and applications, all of them utilize the diaphragm to drive the breath, thereby massaging and stimulating the internal organs and glands, and all of them boost circulation of blood and energy, enhance immune response, regulate the nervous and endocrine systems, improve digestion, elimination, and other vital functions, and balance the polarity of energies throughout the system.

Incremental Bellows Breath

This is a version of the classic Bellows Breath used in *pranayama* to clear the lungs, oxygenate the blood and stimulate the brain. It may be used as a preliminary exercise to balance the breath and stimulate the circulation of blood and energy in preparation for chi-gung practice, or by itself for a quick lift any time of day.

Method: Take three sharp, short inhalations in quick succession through the nose, one on top of the other, followed by three sharp, short exhalations, and continue in this manner without pause for one or two minutes only. Exhalation may be done through the nose or by blowing the breath out through pursed lips as though blowing out a candle. Nose exhalation has a stronger clarifying effect on the brain, while mouth exhalation works more on clearing the blood and body.

Benefits: Bellows breathing has manifold benefits, especially as a preparatory exercise for chi-gung. It expels stale air and residual toxins that have accumulated in the deeper recesses of the lungs and opens up the bronchial and nasal passages. It increases the amount of carbon dioxide eliminated from the blood through the lungs, while increasing the amount of oxygen assimilated from the air, thereby purifying the bloodstream and stimulating metabolism. The swift, strong contractions strengthen the diaphragm and tone the abdominal muscles, which in turn improves the body's capacity to perform deep abdominal breathing. They also provide an invigorating vibrational massage to the internal organs and glands.

Bellows breathing is particularly beneficial to the brain. It greatly enhances microcirculation throughout the brain, delivering abundant supplies of oxygen and glucose to the neurons to support vital cerebral functions. The vigorous exhalations give rise to rhythmic waves of enhanced circulatory drive that extend throughout the bloodstream, travelling up the carotid arteries to the brain where, in addition to irrigating the whole brain with oxygen, they also cause a gentle rhythmic expansion and contraction of the brain itself. This cerebral massage stimulates secretions of essential neurotransmitters and balances vital cerebral functions of the brain. The resulting mental clarity is one of the primary benefits of this breathing exercise, particularly in preparation for still meditation practice.

Natural Abdominal Breathing

This is the main breathing method used in all forms of chi-gung practice. It's also the way you should learn to breathe throughout the day. It's the way babies and animals naturally breathe, and the way our respiratory systems were designed to function. Breathing this way during ordinary daily activity is one of the most effective steps you can take to protect your health and prolong your life.

Method: First of all, the entire breathing apparatus should be completely relaxed, especially the diaphragm and ribcage, with shoulders loose and slightly rounded. Inhale slowly and smoothly through the nostrils, letting the air travel in a steady stream down to the bottom of the lungs, and press the diaphragm downward. This is turn will cause the abdominal wall to expand outward. If you wish to apply the abdominal lock, do so at the end of inhalation, but do not draw the abdominal wall in too far: pulling it in about 1 inch (2 to 3cm) is more than enough to achieve beneficial compression in the abdominal cavity. When ready to exhale, relax the abdomen and release the breath in a long, slow, even stream, letting the diaphragm rise up again and the abdominal wall contract inward toward the spine. Before commencing the next inhalation, pause briefly to permit the diaphragm and abdominal wall to relax and fall back into their natural position, then start the next cycle.

Benefits: Abdominal breathing provides a stimulating massage to all of the organs and glands in the abdominal cavity, particularly the all-important adrenal glands, which sit on top of the kidneys directly below the diaphragm. It turns the diaphragm into a 'second heart' to assist in the circulation of blood and greatly enhances respiratory efficiency in the lungs. It also catalyses internal alchemy by gathering energy into the 'cauldron' of the lower elixir field below the navel, opening the Microcosmic Orbit circuit of energy circulation, and facilitating the transformation of hormone essence from the adrenals and other glands into vital energy.

Reverse Abdominal Breathing

This is a more advanced variation of abdominal breathing that significantly amplifies compression in the abdominal cavity and gives an even stronger boost to the circulatory system. It may be used in all chi-gung exercises, but it requires more focused attention to the breathing process, more careful timing, and more deliberate effort. Therefore, it is more appropriate for moving exercises than for still practice, unless the latter is focused primarily on cultivating energy rather than spiritual work. When practising still sitting for spiritual cultivation, the attention and effort required for this breath tends to distract the mind.

Method: Inhale the same way as in natural abdominal breathing, except as the diaphragm descends into the abdominal cavity, rather than letting the abdominal wall expand outward, you should deliberately contract it inward towards the spine, thereby further increasing the compression within the abdomen. The deliberate contraction of the abdomen during inhalation automatically applies the abdominal lock. To further enhance the compression provided by this breath, the anal lock should also be used on completion of inhalation. On exhalation, as the diaphragm rises, simply relax the abdominal wall and let it expand outward again.

Benefits: This breath greatly enhances abdominal compression. It also increases the relative difference in pressures between the abdominal and chest cavities, thereby providing a very strong pumping effect on circulation. It stimulates secretion of gastric juices in the stomach and duodenum, squeezes stale blood from the liver, and enhances peristalsis in the bowels. It's also a good way to cultivate volitional control over the breathing process.

Chi *Compression Breath*

This breath may be used to increase the assimilation of atmospheric *chi* from air, pack it into the lower abdomen for storage, and guide it to particular organs and tissues for healing purposes. It also gives a strong boost to blood circulation and increases the beneficial effects of internal organ massage by enhancing and maintaining abdominal compression.

Method: This breath is basically the same as natural abdominal breathing, except that each of the four stages of breath control is lengthened and the three locks are applied more strongly and held a bit longer to enhance and sustain compression. It helps to visualize energy as radiant light streaming down into the lower elixir field on inhalation, condensing there during compression, then entering the spinal channel through the coccyx and rising up to the head on exhalation. If you wish to send energy to heal an ailing organ or injured tissue, visualize the energy as bright light streaming into the target organ or tissue on inhalation, condensing there on compression, and flowing out as dark fog or smoke on exhalation, thereby clearing away the negative energy responsible for the injury or illness.

Inhalation and exhalation should be a bit longer and slower than in other breathing exercises, and the compression stage may be held for up to 10 seconds, although if you hold it for that long, it's better to use a sitting posture as a precaution against dizziness that may occur as a result of enhanced cerebral circulation. Prior to applying the neck lock, swallow hard, even if you have no saliva to swallow, because this manoeuvre helps pack energy down into the lower elixir field, thereby enhancing abdominal compression and boosting energy into the Microcosmic Orbit circulation.

Benefits: This breath increases the beneficial compression of the abdominal organs and glands, while also enhancing the assimilation and storage of energy from external sources in the lower elixir field and major channels. It stimulates the central nervous system and activates the immune responses of the parasympathetic branch. It may be effectively used to guide healing energy to cure or strengthen specific organs and tissues, or to pack extra energy into the reservoirs of the Eight Extraordinary Channels, especially when practising at special times and places that offer the practitioner a 'bumper crop' of potent energy for harvest and storage.

Alternate Nostril Breathing (Fig. 16)

This exercise is designed to alternate air flow between right and left nostrils, thereby balancing breath, and also to balance energy flow and the cerebral functions of the right and left hemispheres of the

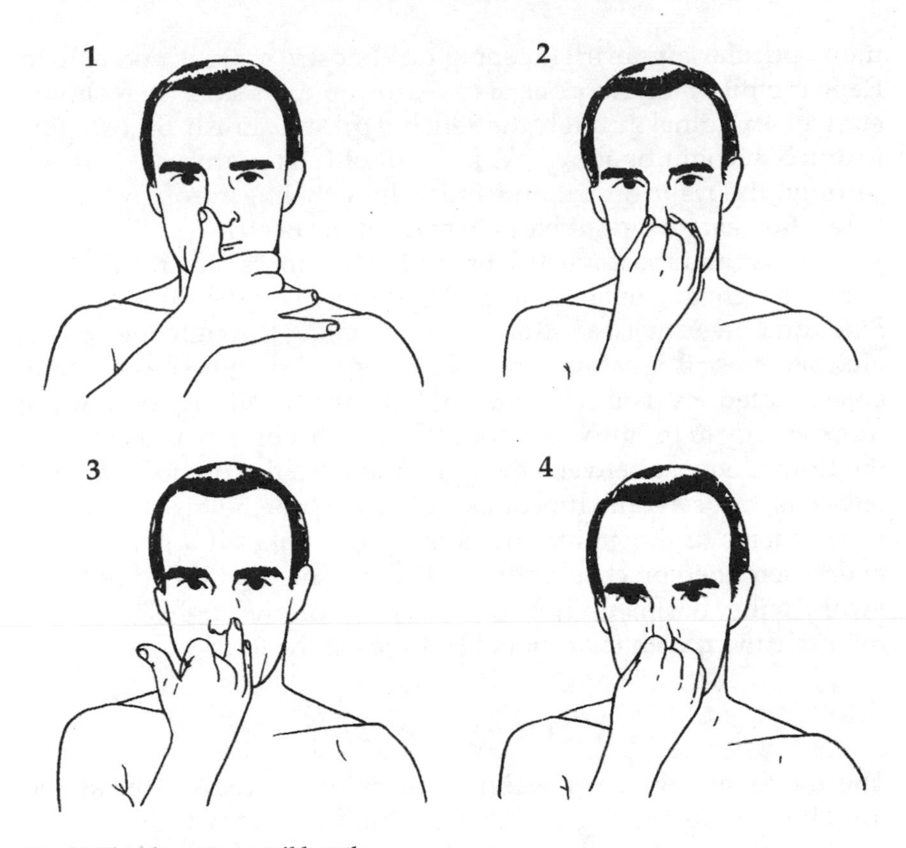

Fig. 16 **The alternate nostril breath:**
1. Right thumb blocks right nostril, inhale through left nostril
2. Both nostrils blocked, brief compression
3. Right thumb opens right nostril, while ring and little fingers block left nostril; exhale through right nostril
4. Both nostrils blocked, brief intermission

brain. It may be practised as a chi-gung exercise in itself, in the standing or sitting postures, or as a preliminary exercise to balance the breath in preparation for moving or still chi-gung.

Method: Inhale deeply through both nostrils, then use the thumb of the right hand to seal shut the right nostril, and exhale slowly and evenly through the left nostril. Keeping the right nostril sealed with the right thumb, take a long, slow inhalation through the left nostril. When lungs are full, fold the index and middle fingers of the right hand against the palm, and use the fourth (ring) finger to seal shut the left nostril. Keep both nostrils sealed briefly while you compress the breath and apply the three locks, then release the thumb from the right nostril (keeping the left nostril sealed), and exhale through it. Keeping left nostril sealed, inhale through the open right nostril, then seal it with the thumb, compress and lock, then open the left nostril (keeping right nostril sealed), and exhale. Repeat until you have done six breaths on each side. Men should start by exhaling through the left nostril and finish by exhaling through the right, as above. Women should start with an exhalation through the right nostril and finish by exhaling through the left side, also using the right hand to control the nostrils.

Benefits: Alternate nostril breathing balances the flow of air between right and left nostrils and helps open up the sinus cavities. Since air flow is twice as strong when inhaling through one nostril, alternate nostril breathing exposes the nasal membranes to more concentrated levels of *chi* than in ordinary breathing, permitting more energy to be absorbed from the air. This breath also balances the flow of energy between the right and left sides of the body, and balances the cerebral functions governed by the right and left hemispheres of the brain. The latter effect makes it a particularly good exercise to practise during still sitting meditation, for it helps awaken the dormant intuitive faculties of the right lobe and integrate them with the rational faculties of the left.

Vibratory Breathing

There are many different healing sounds and sacred syllables used for vibratory breathing in Tibetan Buddhist, Taoist and Hindu traditions, but generally it's best to learn these directly from a qualified master, because many of them must be adapted specifically to the individual's energy system. A few, however, may be practised without special adaptations.

Vibratory breathing involves the sounding of various syllables to create waves of vibration in the throat. These vibrations spread through the tissues up to the brain and down into the deepest recesses of the lungs and heart, stimulating the fluids, massaging the cells, and opening various energy centres. These vibrations are also transformed into beneficial electromagnetic pulses by virtue of the piezoelectric properties of crystalline molecular structures in bones, connective tissue and electrolytes.

Method: Take a deep inhalation through the nose, compress the breath down into the lower abdomen, then open the mouth and throat and sound the syllable loud and clear with a long, even, controlled exhalation, continuing until the lungs are completely empty. Never interrupt the sounding of a healing or sacred syllable, and don't stop until exhalation is complete.

One of the most effective syllables for vibratory breathing is 'ah', which is the sound associated with the throat chakra. Use whatever pitch feels most natural to your voice and keep the throat wide open while you're sounding it. Focus not only on the sound, but also on feeling the vibrations spreading out from your vocal cords, penetrating deeply into the surrounding tissues.

In Tibetan tradition, which emphasizes the importance of sound as a manifestation of energy, *mantra* are used extensively in meditation, both for spiritual as well as healing purposes. There are three sacred 'seed syllables' which Tibetan meditation masters teach that encompass the sounds and effects of all other *mantra*, and indeed of all sound in the universe. These three syllables are 'Om', 'Ah' and 'Hum' (pronounced 'hoom'). The first is associated with the upper elixir field energy centre in the head. When toning it, lips should be well rounded for the initial 'ooh' sound, which should take up about three-quarters of the exhalation, followed by the 'mmm' with lips sealed. 'Ah' governs the throat chakra and all spiritual faculties related to that energy centre. 'Hum' is related to the heart chakra and human consciousness. In the latter tone, the initial 'hu' (pronounced 'hooo') takes about one-quarter of the exhalation, followed by a long vibratory 'mmm'.

When used for energy work in vibratory breathing, the effects of these syllables are universal and therefore independent of any religious connotations they might have in various cultural traditions, so anyone may practise them for health without worrying about creating conflicts with personal religious beliefs.

Benefits: Vibratory breathing stimulates the entire breathing apparatus with a vibratory 'massage', and this effect extends up into the brain as well. It loosens any residual mucus accumulated in the recesses of the lungs and stimulates microcirculation in the brain. The major energy centres along the spine (chakras) respond to vibratory breathing by opening and transmitting energy. The vibrations are also transformed into electromagnetic pulses by crystalline structures in various tissues, and these pulses have therapeutic healing effects on the internal organs and glands.

Energy Gate Breathing

In this mode of breathing, attention is switched over from the flow of air in and out of the lungs to the flow of energy in and out of various energy gates, using intent, visualization and feeling to activate, amplify and sustain the stream of energy through the gates. This is especially beneficial when practising at times and places where the ambient energy of nature and the cosmos is particularly pure and potent (see page 125).

Method: Start by breathing in the natural abdominal mode, focusing attention on the various points of breath control until body, breath and mind are balanced and harmoniously tuned. Then shift your awareness over to one or more of the major energy gates, such as the 'Medicine Palace' on the crown of the head, the 'Yin Confluence' at the perineum, the 'Labour Palace' points on the palms, or the 'Bubbling Spring' gates on the soles of the feet. First visualize the gate itself, then visualize energy streaming in through the gate on inhalation and focus attention on the feeling at the gate as energy flows through it. Use intent and visualization to guide the energy into the lower elixir field for storage, or else to heal a specific organ, tonify tissues, or stimulate vital functions. On exhalation, you may wish to guide energy back out through the same or a different gate, or draw negative energy out of a specific organ or tissue, or simply condense and pack the energy collected on inhalation into the 'Sea of Energy' in the lower elixir field

Benefits: This breathing method collects energy from external sources and guides it into the lower elixir field for storage, or into ailing organs and injured tissues for healing. It may also be used to expel excess Fire energy from the system and to drive stagnant and toxic energy out of specific organs and meridians. Therefore it's a good way to recharge your energy 'batteries' and refill your energy reservoirs. It's also an effective practice for cultivating volitional command over energy, developing the faculties of visualization and intent, and learning how to see and feel energy moving in, out and through the body.

Integration of Body and Breath

Establishing unison between the slow rhythmic movements of the body and the deep cyclic waves of the breath is a central point of attention in moving forms of chi-gung. In all such exercises, the breath always sets the pace, and the body follows. As breath grows deeper and longer, movements of the body become slower and more deliberate, with the mind orchestrating the two aspects of the practice.

In most exercises, unless specifically stipulated otherwise, upward and inward movements of the arms and head are done on the inhalation stage of breath. Downward and outward movements are performed during the exhalation stage. For example, if an exercise calls for the arms to be raised up above the head, that movement is made on inhalation, while the arms return down to the starting position on exhalation. Similarly, arms are drawn inward towards the body on inhalation and extended away from the body on exhalation.

If compression and the three locks are applied upon completion of inhalation, this stage of breath occurs halfway through the body movement, when the arms are fully extended above or drawn in close to the torso. The brief intermission of breath between the end of exhalation and the beginning of the next inhalation happens when the arms and hands have completed one full cycle of movement and returned to the starting position.

In order to use movements of the body to guide energy mobilized by breath, it's essential to maintain rhythmic synchronicity of body and breath throughout the exercise, and this requires focused attention and presence of mind. As soon as the mind drifts off in thought or gets distracted by external phenomena, body and breath lose their synchronicity, and energy scatters.

Integration of Energy and Breath

In still forms of chi-gung practice, in which the body remains motionless, breath must be synchronized in unison with the movement of energy rather than the movement of the body. This is accomplished by utilizing the mental faculties of visualization and intent and by developing a feel for the movement of energy in the body, such as in the 'Energy Gate Breathing' discussed above.

On inhalation, you should visualize and try to feel energy rising upward through various channels in the system, or flowing into the body through the gates. On exhalation, energy moves downward through the system, or outward through the gates. It's important to distinguish between energy moving within the system and energy moving in and out of the system through various gates. For example, energy ascends up the Governing Channel along the spine from sacrum to brain on inhalation, and down the Conception Channel in front, from brain to lower abdomen, on exhalation. However, when drawing energy in through the gate on the crown of the head on inhalation, it travels downward to the lower abdomen, and when driving it back out the same gate on exhalation, it travels upward to the head. In other words, when moving energy *within* the system, inhalation coincides with upward movement, and when moving energy *in* and *out* of the system, inhalation coincides with in-flow and exhalation with outflow, regardless of whether the energy moves upward or downward from the gate once it's inside the system.

If compression and the three locks are applied in breathing, visualize and try to feel energy collect and condense wherever the mind had guided it upon completion of inhalation. During the brief intermission between exhalation and the next inhalation, energy stops moving.

These are only general guidelines for still practice. Whereas in moving exercises the unison of body and breath is crucial to success in mobilizing and guiding energy through the body, in still practice the unison of energy and breath is not as essential, because energy responds primarily to the mind in sitting practice. Therefore, if the practitioner has developed strong faculties of visualization and intent, he or she can easily mobilize and guide energy entirely with the mind, without using the breath for assistance. In this case, breathing remains on 'automatic pilot' in the background, while the mind works directly with energy. For beginners, however, integrating breath and energy so that they move together facilitates energy work in the practice of still meditation.

CHAPTER 8

Precepts of Practice: Principles, Pointers and Precautions

In a word, the guiding principle in chi-gung practice is 'Tao', the 'Way' of nature and the universe. The natural order and universal laws which govern the movements of stars and planets, the cyclic rounds of season and time, the blow of wind and flow of water, the wax and wane of the moon and tides, also prevail within the microcosmic universe of the human body, regulating its 'rivers' of blood and 'winds' of breath, moulding its 'mountains' of flesh and 'minerals' of bone, and turning the wheels of growth and decay, life and death. Chi-gung provides a convenient and effective way through which Humanity may harmonize itself with the powers of Heaven (cosmos) and Earth (nature), thereby restoring the primordial balance which the artifice of civilized life so easily upsets. The more technologically advanced human beings become, the further they fall from grace with nature. While there's nothing an individual can do to reverse the course taken by human civilization as a whole, anyone can easily re-establish his or her own personal primordial link with nature and the cosmos simply by practising chi-gung.

According to traditional Chinese views on health, all disease and degeneration in the body can ultimately be traced to basic imbalances of energy. Therefore, the way to cure, as well as prevent, disease and decay is to restore and maintain natural balance in the human energy system. Chi-gung does that by establishing harmonic resonance between one's personal energy field and the greater energy fields of nature and the cosmos, either through individual practice or by transmission of emitted energy from a master. This brings the natural order and balance of the universe into the disordered, imbalanced human system. It's a basic fact of life that whenever some part of the human system loses synchronicity with its macrocosmic counterparts in nature and no longer follows the patterns ordained by the creative template of the universe, health will suffer, vitality is sapped and the natural order of life is disrupted. The only way to correct this situation is to re-link the imbalanced energy system of the ailing individual to the naturally balanced energies of more powerful fields and to restore the internal landscape of the body according to the universal patterns of nature. This is precisely what chi-gung does.

While the methodology of chi-gung revolves upon the rhythmic coordination of body and breath, balance and posture, inhalation and exhalation, the main agent involved in practice is the mind. It's the mind that brings body and breath together in chi-gung, and it's the mind that brings the universal Tao of nature and the cosmos into the personal realm of the individual human system. In order to do this, the mind must over-rule many objections from the ego and the emotions, which are accustomed to commandeering human energies for their own peculiar purposes – purposes that are almost always counterproductive to health, longevity and spiritual development. To prevent the ego and emotions from plundering energy and distracting attention during practice, it helps to keep in mind some of the most important principles of balance and harmony that define the Tao and use them as guidelines for working with energy in chi-gung.

Guiding Principles of Balance and Harmony

Movement and Stillness

Movement and stillness are the complementary poles of mobility, the Yin and Yang of motion. One of the most basic precepts of chi-gung practice is to find the perfect balance, the ultimate equilibrium between movement and stillness. To do this, one must 'seek movement within stillness' and 'seek stillness within movement'. Integrating movement and stillness is a primary principle in all styles of chi-gung practice, for somewhere between the state of motion and immobility, action and inaction, change and continuity, there is a precise point of perfect balance and harmony in which form and function merge. Indeed, modern physics informs us that actually there is no such state as absolute stillness, for all phenomena and objects ultimately boil down to energy oscillating in polar fields. Thus, what we seek in chi-gung is the ideal degree of oscillation, the perfect pulse that tunes the human rhythms of body, breath and mind in a harmonious chord of unity and balances them with the universal rhythms of nature and the cosmos.

In the internal, or 'soft' style, school of Chinese martial arts, the fusion of internal stillness with external movement is the key to generating power, for stillness and serenity of spirit are prerequisites for mind to exercise complete command over energy as the body moves.

Internal and External

When practising chi-gung, it's important to bear in mind the close links between internal and external. In the ordinary view, our physical bodies form a very clear, concrete boundary between our 'insides' and the outside world, but from the chi-gung point of view, there is no precise border between the human energy system and external energy fields, because all energy fields intersect and interact. Furthermore, the human energy system as a whole constitutes a microcosmic replica of the greater force fields of nature and the cosmos, and the human system therefore responds by harmonic resonance to the vibrant forces of greater systems. In fact, one of the most effective ways to rebalance the human energy system with chi-gung is to establish harmonic resonance between the internal energies of the human system and the external energies of nature and the cosmos.

Another way chi-gung works to link and balance internal and external factors is to mentally 'exercise' the invisible network of energy meridians on the inside by physically exercising the body and breath on the outside. The external physical body thus becomes an avenue of access for working with and balancing the internal energy body, and the balance of internal energies in turn determines the health and functional vitality of external physical parts. The internal alchemy of essence, energy and spirit may be catalysed and controlled externally by balancing body, breath and mind with chi-gung. However, since energy, not matter, is the basic 'active ingredient' in the internal alchemy of chi-gung, internal and external factors are integral elements of practice that intersect and constantly interact, and therefore they cannot be separated.

Finding the Centre

For something to have balance, it must have a centre to serve as the point of balance. In the human system, the central point of balance for the body as well as for energy is the so-called 'lower elixir field' (*dan-tien*) or 'sea of energy' (*chi-hai*), located in the lower abdomen, just below and behind the navel. Anatomically, this point is located precisely in the middle of the triangle formed by drawing a line between the navel and the Gate of Life directly opposite the navel on the spine, with the other two lines drawn from the navel and the Gate of Life down to the Yin Confluence point at the perineum. In terms of energy, however, the entire lower digestive tract, including the large and small intestines, constitutes the centre of balance for the human system, for these tissues have a great capacity to store energy.

The integration of proper posture, rhythmic bodily movement and deep abdominal breathing in chi-gung all depend on focused awareness of directional equilibrium in the body – top and bottom, front and back, left and right. All these axes of balance in chi-gung find their true centre in the lower *dan-tien*, and all postures and motions used in moving exercises revolve upon this point of balance, while in still forms of practice this point constitutes the central foundation of stability in all meditation postures. One reason that it's so important to develop a strong, stable Horse stance (see page 161) for standing practice is to ensure that the bulk of weight in the body is supported by the thighs, thereby allowing the pelvis and sacrum, which house the centre of balance, to swivel and shift freely in all directions during practice to maintain constant directional equilibrium.

Soft, Slow and Smooth

These three words sum up the essential qualities of chi-gung exercise. Softness (*rou*) has always been regarded as a quintessential quality of the Tao. As the *Tao Teh Ching* states:

> Nothing under heaven is more yielding than water;
> But when it attacks things hard and resistant,
> There is not one of them that can prevail.
> That the yielding conquers the resistant
> And the soft conquers the hard
> Is a fact known by all men,
> But utilized by none.

The power of softness is the foundation of the internal or 'soft' styles of Chinese martial arts, which overcome the brute power of hard muscle with the irresistible force of soft, supple energy. Again, the *Tao Teh Ching* clarifies this point:

The ten thousand creatures and all plants and trees
Are supple and soft in life,
But brittle and dry in death.
Truly, to be stiff and hard is the way of death;
To be soft and supple is the way of life.

In physical terms, to be soft in practice means to be completely relaxed (*sung*). Energy channels open and energy flows freely through them only in those parts of the body that are kept completely relaxed. Any sort of tension immediately reduces the flow of energy to that part of the body. Keeping everything very slow (*man*) is one way to help maintain a soft, relaxed state. Another reason for slow-motion movements in chi-gung is to keep the body in tune with the rise and fall of breath, which becomes very deep, long and slow during practice. Slow deliberate movements also foster mental concentration and synchronize the whole system with the deep, low-frequency pulse of the earth, which vibrates at 7.8 hertz (cycles/second), much slower than the human system normally oscillates in ordinary daily activity. When it comes to chi-gung practice, truly it is said, 'Haste makes waste!'

Smooth (*sun*) rhythmic movement is the third parameter of chi-gung exercise. Like the planets orbiting the sun and the moon revolving around the earth, like cats walking and fish swimming, all movements in chi-gung are performed with a seamless smoothness in which one step leads naturally to the next, without apparent effort and no hurry. Abrupt, choppy movements and sudden changes of pace have no place in chi-gung practice, for they impede the free flow and smooth transitions of energy which chi-gung is designed to induce.

Balancing Body, Breath and Mind Together

Body, breath and mind are the temporal manifestations of primordial essence, energy and spirit, and by bringing these three postnatal aspects of human existence into balance, chi-gung induces a similar balance on the primordial level. Balancing the body is the easiest of the three balancing acts, because it's the most concrete. It's done by performing a series of loosening and stretching exercises that completely relaxes the body, stimulates circulation and opens the energy channels. Balancing the breath is a matter of learning how to breathe properly, so that the breath becomes deep, long, slow and even and is driven by the diaphragm rather than the chest. When the breath is balanced, all the other vital functions of the body follow suit.

But balancing the mind is a somewhat more difficult and subtle task, because there is nothing tangible with which to work. So the best way to balance the mind is to focus attention fully on balancing body and breath. First of all, it's important to realize that the mind 'breathes' too. Rather than breathing air, or energy, however, the mind breathes thoughts and feelings, which rise and fall as ceaselessly as waves on the ocean. So the first step in balancing the mind is simply to recognize thoughts and feelings for what they really are – the natural breath of awareness – and to let them pass without trying to hold on to them or becoming distracted by them.

Trying to suppress thoughts, or hold on to them, is just like trying to hold your breath: it throws your whole system off balance and impedes the free flow of energy. If you pay no particular attention to thoughts, they simply appear and disappear naturally, like clouds in the sky or bubbles in soda water. It's your attention that gives thoughts their power to distract your mind and throw your energy system off balance, so the best way to prevent that is to keep your attention occupied by focusing it on the various points of balance in posture, movement and breath, while simply letting thoughts and feelings rise and fall like waves on a distant ocean, far in the background of your mental landscape.

Sacrum and Cerebrum

Throughout our discussion of chi-gung, as well as in all the traditional Chinese literature on the subject, there appears frequent mention of the lower elixir field in the sacrum and the upper elixir field in the brain, but very little mention of the middle elixir field in the solar plexus. All forms of chi-gung, moving as well as still, focus attention on refining energy from the sacrum and then raising it up the spine to the head to nurture spiritual vitality. The middle elixir field rarely comes into the picture.

There is good reason for this. The lower elixir field houses the basic energies and instincts of nature, such as the appetite for food, our survival instincts and sexual drive. In the microcosm of the human system, the sacrum represents the power of Earth. The upper elixir field in the brain is the seat of prenatal spiritual awareness, the postnatal mind and the various cerebral functions, all of which represent the power of Heaven in the human system. The middle elixir field, located just below the heart, houses the unique consciousness of Humanity, including the ego, the emotions and all the complexities of human nature. Inscriptions found on 2000-year-old jade tablets in China state, 'Celestial energy is activated above, the terrestrial energy below'. Sacrum and cerebrum are the seats of terrestrial and celestial energies in the human body, and the microcosmic counterparts of Earth and Heaven within the human system, while the solar plexus is the seat of the energies of Humanity (emotions and ego).

Sexual energy – as well as all of the basic animal energies of the sacrum – are by nature primordially pure, and therefore they do not cause any problems as long as they remain properly balanced and are expressed naturally. Problems arise only when these energies come under the control of our emotions and ego, which use them for all sorts of deviant, often dangerous, purposes that often prove counterproductive to health and longevity. When this happens, our emotions rob us of these powerful energies and cause havoc in our lives, and our minds must then deal with the messy problems our egos create in our lives and in our relationships whenever they're allowed to co-opt these lower energies. Our physical senses ('Five Thieves') and emotions ('Chief Hooligan') steal our power and waste it on activities that ruin our health, shorten our lives and obscure our spiritual awareness, leading us into temptation that can land us in prison, put us in the hospital or bury us in an early grave.

Nevertheless, a tremendous amount of our potential power is stored in the sacral energies, especially sexual energy, and this power, if properly transformed and utilized through internal energy work, can be used to preserve health, prolong life and provide a big boost on the path of spiritual development. Nature deliberately designed sexual energy with so much power in order to ensure the eternal self-propagation of the species, and there is no higher power in the universe than the power to generate life. Taoists have known for a long time that sexual energy, for better or for worse, is the most powerful force in the human energy system, and therefore they developed practices to harness this power for health, longevity and spiritual development, and to prevent it from driving us to act in ways that are counterproductive to these goals.

Sheer suppression of sexuality and other basic drives, as is the custom in so many religious orders, not only produces pent-up emotional frustration that can suddenly erupt like a volcano, it also deprives the individual of his or her greatest source of power. Chi-gung practices were thus designed to draw the energies of the sacrum into circulation in the Governing Channel that runs up the spine, transform them into higher forms of energy, and guide them into the upper elixir field in the head to nurture spiritual vitality. The middle elixir field is usually bypassed in this upward movement of energy from sacrum to cerebrum to avoid inflaming the emotions and diverting this powerful energy to the deviant purposes of the ego.

However, when sacral energy enters general circulation in the channels of the human energy system, sooner or later it is bound to reach the middle elixir field, but not until its Fire has first been cooled and refined into Water in the upper elixir field in the head. This is how it works: sacral energy is first drawn up the spine directly into the head, bypassing the middle elixir field in the solar plexus; in the process of raising and refining this energy, the Fire of sexual and other lower energies is converted into the Water of spiritual energy. Having passed through the upper elixir field to nurture spirit, this Water energy is then brought back down the front of the body via the Conception Channel to the lower elixir field, and en route it passes through the middle elixir field in the solar plexus. Having already been refined into Water, this energy no longer inflames the emotions with raw sexual passion, aggression and other animal instincts, nor does it tempt the ego with lust. Instead, it has a balancing, calming and spiritually uplifting influence on this volatile emotional energy centre.

Human emotions certainly have their role in life, particularly in personal relationships, and the ego is the individual's only identification tag in society. But if they are allowed to take command of the body's arsenal of lower energies, without guidance from the higher wisdom of spirit, they invariably end up causing trouble for ourselves as well as others. Hence one of the major precepts of balance and harmony in chi-gung is to place the powerful energies of the sacrum under the firm command of the cerebrum, so that they may be used for positive purposes such as spiritual development. As spiritual power grows stronger through this practice, the mind's command over the body's lower energies also grows progressively stronger, making it ever easier to control them. We need all the energy we can muster in life, particularly for higher spiritual practices, so no one can really afford to waste these lower energies. That's why it's so important to refine and recycle them with the internal alchemy of energy work, and to keep them from falling prey to the 'Five Thieves' and 'Chief Hooligan'.

Primacy of Energy

All balance and harmony in the universe is achieved on the level of energy. It's the balance of nuclear forces that keeps atoms and molecules bound together to form matter, electromagnetic forces that determine stability and change when polar fields intersect and interact, and the state of balance in the human energy system that governs physical and mental health. Physics tell us that all forms of matter ultimately boil back down to energy oscillating at various frequencies, while metaphysics reveals that energy is also the primary element through which mind manifests its command over matter and expresses its creative power. Energy is therefore the most fundamental element in the universe, the basic building block of all matter, and the functional bridge between body and mind.

The internal school of Chinese martial arts has an old maxim, 'Use four ounces of strength to topple a thousand pounds of weight'. This is the essential principle of balance involved in Tai Chi Chuan, Pa Kua, Judo and Aikido. When energy is properly balanced and correctly applied, only a very small amount is needed to deflect the oncoming force of very large objects. The same principle applies in internal alchemy: when internal energy is properly balanced and circulated, it can overcome any obstacles in the physical body, dissolve hard tumours, restructure damaged tissues, and restore normal vital functions. Energy is an extremely efficient tool for repairing the physical body, and it becomes even more powerful when the light of conscious awareness is focused on it during practice.

Integration

Integration is a key precept of balance and harmony at all levels of chi-gung practice. Rather than separating everything into different branches, chi-gung tries to effect an overall integration of all the factors and forces involved in practice. Thus the Three Treasures of essence, energy and spirit and their temporal manifestations in body, breath and mind are all integrated through chi-gung practice in a unified state of functional balance and harmony, and that state in turn is integrated with the rhythmic pulse of nature and the cyclic transformations of the cosmos. Sexual energy, which in some spiritual traditions is spurned and segregated from practice, is also integrated into the mainstream of internal energy work in Chinese chi-gung, thereby harnessing its formidable power for health, longevity and higher spiritual purposes. Practice extends from meditation, breathing and exercise to diet and sex, work and play, integrating every aspect of daily life with the same basic principles of balance and harmony that prevail in the main practices.

When you harness the power of the universe with chi-gung, you are working with the same fundamental force that animates every living organism and the same elemental energy that produces stars and galaxies, atoms and molecules. The only way to tap into that power is to step beyond the limited confines of what one usually regards as the individual 'self' and fully integrate all aspects of your being with their macrocosmic sources in the universe. To do this, you must breathe not just with your body but also with your mind, then expand your breath to breathe with the entire planet and the whole universe. That's integration.

Important Points of Practice

When practising chi-gung, the following points may serve as general guidelines to derive maximum benefit from your practice and keep body, breath and mind in the state of balance and functional harmony required to amplify and regulate the human energy system with the power of the universe.

General Points

1. Always practise in the three-stage format of warm-up, main practice and cool-down. The warm-up stage balances body, breath and mind in preparation for the main practice of mobilizing and circulating energy, and the cool-down stage collects and stores the energy in the lower elixir field centre in the abdomen. If you practise without adequate preliminary preparation, your system will not be properly balanced to work with energy, and if you fail to take measures to collect and store the energy you've generated, much of the energy will scatter and be lost.
2. Make your practice an integral part of your daily routine, and practise regularly. If you only practise sporadically, your channels will not stay open, and your system will lose its synchronicity with nature and the cosmos. Only with regular practice will you obtain the cumulative benefits which chi-gung confers. Even if you only have time to practise for 15 to 20 minutes, as long as you do it daily you will still realize the benefits, albeit at a slower rate than one who devotes more time to practice.
3. Chi-gung is not a 'magic bullet' that will immediately correct all problems, especially in an unbalanced lifestyle. It works best when practised as an integral part of the overall healthcare system known in Taoist tradition as *yang-sheng dao*, the 'Tao of Cultivating Life'. This includes diet, sexual discipline, judicious use of herbal and nutritional supplements, a positive attitude towards life, emotional

equilibrium, and other factors that support health and nurture life. Trying to use chi-gung to counteract the ill-effects of poor dietary habits, reckless sexual activities, and other negligent behaviour that ruins health and shortens life is like trying to 'make merit' by giving money once a week in a temple or church, then going right back out and doing the very same things you're trying to compensate for with your donation. Practised within the context of a supporting programme that cultivates every aspect of life, chi-gung is the most powerful tool in the entire *yang-sheng* arsenal. Without that context, it's only a device for delaying the inevitable ill-effects of self-destructive habits.

4. Don't bring the problems of your daily life into your practice, but do bring the results of your practice into your daily life. This will gradually solve all of your problems and integrate all aspects of your life with your practice.

Points of Attention for the Body

1. The spine is the most important part of the body for chi-gung practice. Known as the 'Stairway to Heaven', it serves as a conduit for the lower energies of the sacrum (Earth) to rise to the higher energy centres in the brain (Heaven). It's the central pillar of balance for the entire torso and head and the conductor of nerve signals from brain to body. For best results in practice, the spine should always be kept erect and in straight alignment with the neck and head, with the buttocks tucked in a bit to reduce the curvature in the lower spine. Try to keep the spine flexible and responsive to synchronized movement with the rest of the body by relaxing the muscles along the spine and keeping the vertebrae evenly aligned. Limbering and loosening the spine is one of the main purposes of the warm-up stage of practice.

2. The tensest part of the human body is usually the shoulders and neck area. Tension here blocks the free flow of energy up from the spine into the head, which in turn 'short-circuits' the Microcosmic and Macrocosmic Orbit circulations (see pages 212–13). Try to keep the shoulders loose and the neck muscles relaxed throughout a session of chi-gung practice, even if that requires you to take a short break and perform one of the shoulder-loosening warm-up exercises.

3. The tongue is the bridge that links the terminals of the Governing and Conception Channels at their junction in the roof of the mouth. These channels, which conduct the Microcosmic Orbit of energy circulation, meet just below the nose, so by keeping the tongue lightly pressed to the palate behind the upper teeth, it forms a

bridge for internal energy to flow down from the head to the throat and chest and onward down to the lower abdomen.

4. Whatever clothing one wears during chi-gung practice becomes functionally part of one's body. Synthetic fibres such as nylon and polyester tend to serve as insulators, blocking the free flow of energy along the surface of the body and impeding the exchange of energy between the human system and external energy fields. Natural fibres such as cotton, wool and particularly silk are good conductors of energy, and therefore all clothing worn during chi-gung practice should be made of such natural fibres. The other aspect of clothing that influences energy work is colour. Dark, heavy colours such as black, brown and grey tend to hold energy, thereby impairing free flow, whereas light, bright colours such as white, sky blue, pink, light green, purple and yellow allow energy to move freely. White has always been the traditional colour of choice among yogis in India as well as martial artists in China because it reflects and transmits energy. If you want to maximize the movement of energy in your practice, always wear light colours, never black.

5. Remove all metal objects from your body before practice, such as watches, bracelets and necklaces. A small ring or two won't interfere much, although it's better to remove them, too. Metal has a tendency to hold energy, so if you're wearing metal around your neck or wrists, where energy flow is strong, the metal will draw it into its own matrix and reduce the flow available to your system. As for watches, even when you're not practising you should never wear a quartz crystal watch, because the high-frequency oscillations in the crystal mechanism throw the natural oscillations of human energy off balance, particularly along the wrists, where energy pulses are especially sensitive. Traditional mechanical winding watches do not cause such problems.

6. Always practise on an empty stomach and empty bladder, and if your bowels feel full, try to empty them as well before practice, although it's not essential to do so. Practising on a full stomach is counterproductive because much of the body's energy is preoccupied with digestive duty in the stomach, and this could also cause indigestion. If the bladder is full during practice, it will cause uncomfortable pressure, particularly since it is located right in the middle of the lower elixir field. Conversely, it's best not to eat any solid food for about an hour after a practice session, so that the energy you've collected has a chance to get properly settled in the energy centres and channels, rather than be diverted prematurely to digestive duty. Similarly, try not to empty your bladder for at

least 20 minutes after a session (another good reason to do so before), because some of the energy collected during practice will initially settle into the bladder's urinary fluids, due to their high content of electrolyte minerals, so if you urinate immediately after a session, you'll lose a measure of energy. Within half an hour, however, the energy is transformed and drawn into the reservoirs of the major channels and centres.

7. Chi-gung practice tends to stimulate secretion of beneficial saliva from the ducts below the tongue, but it can also cause you to cough up phlegm from the bronchial tubes. It's important to distinguish between the two, and only spit out phlegm and mucus, which are waste products, but swallow the clear watery saliva that collects beneath the tongue. This saliva has very potent healing properties and enhances digestive functions in the stomach. It also contains vital essence in the form of enzymes, which are meant to be kept within the system.

8. When practising moving exercises, always pace the body to the rhythm established by the breath, not the other way around. In the beginning stages of practice, before the breath has grown deep and slow, you'll find yourself moving faster, whereas later, when your breathing has deepened to only four or five breaths per minute, your body should be moving proportionately slower. There is no predetermined proper pace for the physical movements of the body in chi-gung. Instead, they should closely follow the pace established by the breath, which in turn is determined by the mind.

9. Keep the body in balance at all times by using the navel as a point of reference for maintaining directional equilibrium.

Points of Attention for the Breath

1. Make your breath as **silent** as possible. This requires breathing to be done softly and slowly, without excessive effort or haste. As the 4th-century AD alchemist and writer Ko Hung states, 'Everyone should make it their aim that their own ears might not hear the sound of either inhalation or exhalation'.

2. Air should flow in and out of the nostrils in a very **fine** stream, like a silent gentle breeze. It should not come in sudden gusts or rough choppy waves, nor should it be coarse and heavy. As Ko Hung stipulates, 'One should suspend the feather of a wild goose in front of the nose and mouth so that the feather might not stir while the breath is being expelled'.

3. Both inhalation and exhalation should be very **slow**. This requires close attention to the breathing process with a calm, quiet

mind. If you're in a hurry to finish your practice, your breathing will accelerate its pace in accordance with your intention, so try to suspend time during actual practice. The slower your breathing becomes, the slower your body moves in harmony with breath, and the stronger your energy will flow through the channels.

4. Make each breath as **deep** as possible, but without exerting excessive effort on inhalation. Forcing the breath to fill the lungs causes the shoulders to hunch and the neck muscles to tense and also makes the breath rise up to the top of the lungs. As air streams into the bottom of the lungs on inhalation, let it push the diaphragm down into the abdomen to allow maximum expansion of the lungs.

5. Inhalation and exhalation should both be as **long** as possible. You may progressively increase the length of each breath by gradually breathing more slowly and deeply, and by keeping your mind focused on your breathing.

6. Like all aspects of chi-gung practice, the breath should also be **soft**. The way to keep your breathing soft is to keep the diaphragm, ribcage and throat completely relaxed. Any sort of tension in the breathing apparatus tightens the breath.

7. The entire breathing process should be **continuous**. Each stage should flow smoothly into the next, without interruption, like the swinging pendulum of a clock. Compression and intermission should occur as brief natural pauses that do not cause the next inhalation or exhalation to come in a fast gust.

8. The inhalation and exhalation stages should be as **even** as possible. To breathe evenly, the mind must be calm and quiet and the emotions must be completely pacified.

9. Achieve the above eight qualities of breath gradually. It takes time for the diaphragm and ribcage to expand sufficiently to allow deep diaphragmic breathing. As your practice progresses, you should aim for an average breathing rate of four to five breaths per minute.

10. When it comes to chi-gung practice, 'silence is golden'. Try not to speak to anyone during a practice session, because speech disrupts the smooth flow of internal energy, diverting it to the throat and thereby scattering energy. If you absolutely must speak during a session, at least be sure not to interrupt a breath to do so. First complete the entire breath through exhalation and intermission, place both palms over your navel to keep your energy centred in the lower elixir field while you talk, then speak very calmly and slowly, with minimum breath and as few words as possible.

Points of Attention for the Mind

1. Turn mental attention and sensory perception inwards. Rather than listening to external sounds, listen to your breath and heart. Don't let external sights and sounds distract your attention during a practice session. Energy follows the mind, so if you keep your attention focused inwardly, energy will collect internally. If you let external distractions draw your attention outward, energy will pour out with it.

2. Silence the human mind by turning off your 'internal dialogue'. This does not mean the cessation of thoughts and feelings, which continue to appear and dissolve on their own accord. Just stop talking to yourself about particular thoughts, and instead let the stream of consciousness flow naturally in the background of your mind. Intent is the master of the mind: intend your attention to focus on body and breath instead of thoughts, and that's what it will do.

3. Set all problems and worries of daily life aside prior to a practice session. Emotional equilibrium is a basic prerequisite for success in practice.

4. Cultivate the 'Right Mind' for practice. This means having respect and confidence in your practice, but no preconceived notions about it, and no grand expectations regarding results. Practise persistently and diligently without seeking any particular rewards.

5. Do not harbour any doubts about the validity of the teachings or the efficacy of the practices after you have taken up chi-gung. Any doubts you might have should be addressed through reading or teachers prior to accepting chi-gung into your life. Doubt is a tactical weapon the ego uses to undermine confidence in any idea or practice that threatens the ego's dominant command over mind. As your practice progresses and spiritual awareness develops, the ego's importance diminishes, so sometimes the ego tries to defend its position by sowing doubts about ideas and practices that your higher self has already verified and accepted. The most common grounds for such doubt are excessive expectations that have not been met, so by eliminating all expectations from your mind, you leave no grounds for the ego to plant weeds of doubt in your garden of practice.

6. The importance of slowness in body and breath has already been mentioned, but the most important place to move slowly is in the mind. If your mind is racing with thought or in a hurry to do something else during a practice session, body and breath will also

become rushed. By suspending the internal dialogue and turning attention inward, ignoring both external distractions and internal thoughts, you can virtually dissolve time for the duration of a practice session, focusing awareness exclusively on the various facets of balance and harmony in breath and body.

7. Stay calm throughout your practice sessions, and try to bring that calmness into your daily life afterward. Any sudden fright or abrupt interruption during a practice session can severely upset energy balance. Cultivate calmness as a spiritual virtue, and your command over energy will increase as a result.

8. Keep the mind focused on the body and the breath as points of reference throughout a practice session. Inevitably your mind will wander off in thought or external distraction, and whenever that happens, body and breath lose their synchronicity. The moment you catch your mind paying attention to something else, simply apply intent to shift attention immediately back to body and breath. The harmony of body, breath and mind is the key to success in chi-gung practice.

Precautions

All of the chi-gung exercises and breathing methods introduced in this book are perfectly safe to practise without a teacher, as long as they are done according to the accompanying instructions and within the general guidelines provided in this and other chapters. Deviations and other problems arise only as a result of negligence to the basic precepts and carelessness in the actual performance of the practices. In order to prevent problems and avoid unforeseen difficulties from arising as a result of practice, it's a good idea to observe the following precautions:

1. Do not practise advanced forms of chi-gung without the personal supervision of a qualified teacher. This is especially important in the Western world, where poor diet, chronic stress, anxiety and other factors have created some severe imbalances in the human energy system, particularly in young people. Advanced chi-gung practices can severely aggravate such imbalances by bringing them up suddenly. When this happens, it's important to have a teacher available who can make the adjustments required to correct severe imbalances that manifest suddenly.

2. When seeking a teacher for advanced chi-gung, be very careful and very selective. A good teacher can help you progress swiftly, but a bad teacher can cause you to regress and experience deviations. Apparently minor points of posture and breath can

have major impacts on energy in the more advanced forms, so it is very important to have qualified instruction. Furthermore, when studying and practising chi-gung with a teacher, the teacher's energy field has a direct impact on the energy of the student. Therefore, a teacher's character and overall attitude is just as important as his or her professional qualifications when it comes to selecting a chi-gung master. Ask around and find out as much as possible about a particular teacher before committing yourself.

3. Once you've joined a particular school or practice group, focus exclusively on study and practice, and do not get involved in 'chi-gung politics' and ego rivalries between different masters and schools. There is no boundary between mind and energy in chi-gung, so if you allow a teacher's or fellow student's personal biases to enter your mind, it will put a negative imprint on your energy as well.

4. To get maximum benefit from chi-gung practice, regulate your sexual activities by adopting Taoist sexual yoga to govern your sex life. This is especially important for males. Essence, particularly sexual fluids, constitutes the basic fuel of internal alchemy, so if sexual essence is constantly depleted due to excessive ejaculation, chi-gung is practised on an 'empty tank', which is like running a pump without sufficient water to prime it, and this can cause further imbalances in the energy system. Celibacy is not necessary, nor even desirable, in chi-gung, but one should learn to discipline one's sexual energy in accordance with the basic precepts of practice. For men, this means practising ejaculation control, carefully regulating frequency of emission, and learning how to fully satisfy a woman's sexual needs; for women, it means learning how to draw orgasmic energy up the spine to the head and how to 'digest' the sexual energy assimilated from a male partner (see page 293). Don't practise chi-gung immediately after sex, and don't have sex immediately after a chi-gung session.

5. Pay careful attention to your diet. Especially avoid excessive consumption of refined sugar, greasy and fried foods, red meats and all 'junk food'. Such products are highly acidifying, resulting in a condition of chronic excess acidity (acidosis) in the blood and other bodily tissues, and this in turn inhibits the free flow of energy. One of the worst things to ingest when practising chi-gung – or any time – is sweet carbonated 'soft drinks', which are so acidifying that the body is forced to leach calcium from the bones and teeth to maintain viable blood pH. Calcium plays a vital role in energy transmission within the body, especially in the nervous system, so any sort of calcium deficiency impedes chi-gung practice. Diet

provides the basic nutrients for essence-to-energy conversion in chi-gung. Putting the wrong kind of food in your body when practising chi-gung is like putting diesel fuel in a petrol engine, or pouring sugar into a petrol tank. It will cause malfunctions in internal alchemy and greatly reduce the efficiency of the entire energy system.

6. Avoid exposing your body to wind while practising. Chi-gung causes the pores of the skin to open up wide, and exposure to wind can therefore result in catching a chill or some other form of 'wind injury'. Wind, which is a powerful form of environmental *chi*, can also cause energy to scatter during practice, making it far more difficult to collect it internally.

7. Similarly, avoid all extremes of hot and cold, both during and immediately after practice. Dress appropriately to counterbalance excessive heat or cold in the atmosphere. Avoid taking a shower or bath for at least 20 minutes after practice, so that the pores have a chance to close again.

8. Do not practise chi-gung when you are angry, over-excited, grieving, or in any other way emotionally upset, and do not permit yourself to get emotionally upset during a practice session. Remember that 'e-motion' is 'energy-in-motion', and it can have a very harmful effect on your internal energy balance if it erupts during practice, or if you commence practice while it is still running rampant through your system. You can rebalance your emotions with a few minutes of deep diaphragmic breathing whenever you get emotionally upset, but do not commence a full session until you've completely calmed down again.

9. Avoid chi-gung practice during thunderstorms, lightning, hurricanes, typhoons, earthquakes and any other extremes of weather or natural disasters. The human energy system responds directly to changes in weather and ambient environmental energy, so when these changes are extreme or sudden, they can cause abrupt and extreme imbalances in human energy. If you are practising chi-gung at such a time, the aberrant energy patterns prevailing externally can become imprinted on your internal energy system, giving rise to serious imbalances and physiological malfunctions.

10. When feeling ill or fatigued, do not push yourself to practise too much. Practise only to the point that it provides relief, and select simpler, gentler exercises. On the other hand, do not stop practising entirely when you are ill or tired, because that would only prolong the problem. If you are so sick that you are confined to bed, you can practice a few basic breathing exercises in the reclining posture.

You can also work with acupressure, light, sound and other types of energy work at such times.

11. Arrange your practice so that you will not be interrupted during a session. Even if you only set aside 20 minutes for practice, it's very important not to be interrupted during that time, so that you can complete the three stages of warm-up, main practice and cool-down. Take the phone off the hook, or make sure someone else answers it, and be sure that no one is going to rush in and demand your immediate attention during a practice session. Such sudden interruptions can be very harmful to your energy, and if it happens regularly, it will completely negate the benefits of practice.

12. Avoid talking during and immediately after practice. This has been noted above as a point of attention for breath, but it's worth restating here as a general precaution. Some people feel compelled to talk all the time, and this 'motor mouth' syndrome seems particularly prevalent in crowded urban environments and places where mass media play a major role in people's lives. As the Ching dynasty master Liu I-ming notes, 'When the mouth speaks, energy scatters'. If this happens during practice, the scattering of energy may occur just when energy is moving through a major channel or chakra, and this can result in energy deviations, headaches, sudden dizziness and so forth. As a general precaution, keep your lips buttoned during practice, except to exhale when mouth exhalation is required, or to sound a healing syllable or chakra tone. Try also to remain silent for at least a few minutes immediately after practice.

If you keep the above precepts in mind whenever practising chi-gung, not only will it prevent deviations and other problems from arising, it will also greatly enhance the quality of your practice, accelerate your overall progress, and increase the benefits you derive from the time and effort you invest in practice. As with any other skill, 'practice makes perfect' in chi-gung, but unlike ordinary sports and callisthenic exercises, there is a lot less margin for error in chi-gung, and even the smallest mistakes can make a big dent in the results obtained. And since the mind is so intimately involved with energy in chi-gung, anything and everything that is kept in mind during practice has a direct impact on the balance and flow of energy. Therefore, it's very helpful to familiarize your mind with the basic precepts that govern chi-gung and memorize the most important points of practice, so that these principles, rather than extraneous thoughts and unrelated ideas, are what come to mind whenever you engage in practice.

CHAPTER 9

Introduction to Traditional Styles of Chi-Gung

Many different styles of chi-gung evolved through the ages in China, each one focusing on a particular aspect of practice, all of them cultivating personal power by working directly with energy. Some styles aim mainly at acquiring power for martial prowess, some focus more on refining energy for spiritual development, while others are practised primarily for purposes of health and healing. Almost all traditional styles of Chinese chi-gung fall into one of the major 'Three M' categories – medical, martial or meditative – although some of them overlap, and all of them promote health and longevity. Most of them evolved in association with a major school of thought in China, or as a distinctive lineage founded by a particular master and handed down by personal transmission from generation to generation.

It would require an entire book to fully elucidate any one of the major traditional styles of chi-gung, so instead we'll simply scan the field and take a brief look at the main features of a small selection of the most important styles that are still taught and practised today.

Tai Chi Chuan (Supreme Ultimate Fist)

Tai Chi Chuan is probably the single most popular style of chi-gung throughout the world today. It consists of a series of rhythmic movements and postures strung together in a seamless sequence and performed softly, slowly and smoothly, like a slow-motion dance, in close conjunction with deep abdominal breathing. An internal form of martial arts that can generate enormous power as well as a 'moving meditation' that develops concentration, clarity and other spiritual faculties, Tai Chi Chuan is one of the most comprehensive, well balanced styles of physical and spiritual self-cultivation in chi-gung tradition.

Chang San-feng (1279–1368) (Fig. 17), a renowned martial arts master and Taoist adept who resided at the famous Shao Lin Temple where the Buddhist monk Bodhidharma (Ta Mo) taught after his arrival in China from India, is credited as the founder of Tai Chi Chuan. It is said that he was inspired to create this soft, flowing, meditative style of martial arts by a battle he witnessed between a snake and a crane while wandering one day in the mountains. Watching the snake bob and weave in circles in precise response to the crane's tactics, and the crane brushing off the snake's attacks with swift but soft strokes of its wings, Chang realized the superior power of the soft over the hard approach to combat, the tactical wisdom of circular movements, and the importance of moving in response to as well as in anticipation of the opponent's tactics. Subsequently, he retired deep into the mountains to meditate on what he had observed and gradually he developed the basic postures and movements of Tai Chi Chuan.

Fig. 17 **Chang San-feng, the founding father of Tai Chi Chuan, was a master martial artist, accomplished meditator and Taoist sage; he spent many years practising and teaching at the famous Shao Lin Temple**

No one knows exactly how Chang's lineage was transmitted over the next 500 years, other than the fact that it was handed down from master to select disciple in great secrecy and never taught in temples or martial arts schools. It was not until the late eighteenth century that Tai Chi Chuan became known to anyone other than secret initiates. At that time, it was revealed by a martial artist named Yang Lu-chan, who had been a servant in the household of Chen Chang-hsing and learned the secret art by surreptitiously spying on Master Chen's private family classes. The Chen clan, one of whose ancestors had been a close disciple of Chang San-feng, had been maintaining the Tai Chi tradition as a family secret for 500 years, and Yang was the first outsider to learn it. Whoever else Chang San-feng may have taught, it seems that the Chen clan were the only ones who kept the tradition alive, and today 'Chen Style' is recognized as the oldest form of Tai Chi Chuan.

Meanwhile, Yang Lu-chan modified the style he had learned from the Chen family and taught it to his own son Yang Chian-hou, thereby founding his own lineage, known today as 'Yang Style' Tai Chi Chuan. Yang Lu-chan was also the first master to teach Tai Chi Chuan openly, establishing a school in Peking where anyone who passed muster could receive instruction. One of Yang's disciples later founded what is today known as the 'Wu Style', and one of his students created the 'Sun Style'. Today, the Chen, Yang, Wu and Sun styles are the major forms of Tai Chi Chuan taught throughout the world.

Probably the most famous Tai Chi master known in the Western world is Cheng Man-ching, who learned the art from Yang Lu-chan's grandson and brought it to Taiwan in 1949, where many Westerners came to study with him. Cheng simplified the original 108 movements into only thirty-seven, thereby making the form much easier to learn and remember. According to tradition, there were only thirteen positions to begin with, so Cheng's simplification represented a return to the basics, not a departure from the path.

Tai Chi Chuan involves slow rhythmic movements of the whole body, with one posture transforming smoothly into the next in a continuous stream of motion. Body weight shifts alternately between left foot and right, with the centre of balance always kept down in the lower abdomen. Recalling the lesson of the snake and the crane, defensive and offensive manoeuvres always occur in alternate sequence, with every strike developing into a subsequent parry and every parry flowing into a following strike. The combination of deep diaphragmic breathing and slow, continuous, rhythmic movements generates a very powerful energy field around the body and a highly concentrated flow of energy within.

When used for martial purposes, both the external force field and the internal energy are focused to deflect or deliver blows, sometimes without any physical contact. When used to develop physical strength, protect health and prolong life, the energy is continuously circulated throughout the Eight Extraordinary Channels of the Macrocosmic Orbit, while the field is used to draw terrestrial and celestial energies into the system from nature and the cosmos. In both applications, the mind must remain clearly focused, fully concentrated, and completely calm throughout the practice, which makes Tai Chi Chuan a very effective form of moving meditation for spiritual cultivation. An off-shoot of Tai Chi Chuan known as 'Pushing Hands' involves two people standing face-to-face with hands lightly touching. By feeling the other person's energy through the hands and thereby anticipating his or her next move, both partners continuously rotate their arms and shift their weight from one foot to the other, protecting their own space while looking for an opening in one another's defence through which to strike, like the snake and the crane observed by Chang San-feng.

Today, you can find qualified Tai Chi Chuan teachers almost everywhere in the world. A good place to look for a teacher is around dawn in any public park in any city with a sizeable Chinese population. As all chi-gung adepts know, dawn is the best time to harvest chi and public parks are the only places in big cities where the potential gradient, oxygen level and negative ion count in the air are sufficient to generate a strong flow of internal energy and facilitate harmonious exchange between the human system and the powers of Heaven and Earth.

Eight Pieces of Brocade (Pa Tuan Chin)

This set of chi-gung exercises was developed in the twelfth century by Marshal Yueh Fei, the great Chinese military strategist who sacrificed his life trying to protect the Sung dynasty from defeat by the Mongols. Although Yueh Fei was a military man, the chi-gung set he created is not a martial art. It was designed to strengthen the body, particularly the legs, back, shoulders and neck, to balance the vital functions and tonify the internal organs, to build immunity and resistance and enhance vitality, and to drive stagnant energy and toxic residues from the system. Today it remains one of the most widely practised styles of chi-gung in China as well as the rest of the world.

The Eight Pieces of Brocade consists of eight individual exercises, each of which is designed to strengthen a specific part of the body and stimulate a particular organ-energy system, while also bringing the whole system into harmony with the forces of nature and the cosmos. It is one of the most comprehensive, effective and versatile chi-gung sets ever developed. As with Tai Chi Chuan, various versions of the original set have evolved in China over the centuries, under the tutelage of different masters, so the form you learn depends on who you learn it from. It may be practised as a complete set, in which case you should follow the original sequence because when practised together each exercise builds on the results of the previous one and paves the way to the next, or you may select one or more of the exercises for inclusion in your own programme. Two of the exercises in the recommended set for daily practice introduced in the next chapter are taken from the Eight Pieces of Brocade.

This set may be performed in either the standing or the sitting posture, although the latter should be used only when age, illness or physical disability make it difficult or impossible to practice in the standing posture. Specific exercises may also be practised selectively to strengthen weak or disabled parts of the body, or to restore functional balance in ailing organs. To give you a general idea of the scope and style of this excellent set, here are the names of all eight exercises, literally translated from the Chinese and listed in the original sequence:

1. 'Upholding Heaven with Two Hands to Regulate the Triple Burner'
2. 'Seven-fold Spinal Stretch to Expel the Myriad Ailments'
3. 'Upholding Heaven with a Single Arm to Regulate the Spleen and Stomach'
4. 'Turning the Head and Twisting the Tail to Expel Fire from the Heart'
5. 'Drawing the Bow to the Left and the Right as though Shooting at a Hawk'
6. 'Twisting the Fist and Focusing Fierce Eyes to Cultivate Energy and Generate Power'
7. 'Embracing Legs with Two Arms to Make the Kidneys Firm and Strong'
8. 'Turn and Glance Behind to Eliminate the Five Ailments and Seven Dangers'

Hsing Yi ('Form and Intent')

Developed as a form of martial art for combat and competition, Hsing Yi is said to have been created by Marshal Yueh Fei, the progenitor of the Eight Pieces of Brocade set, during the Sung Dynasty. Along with Tai Chi Chuan and Pa Kua Chang, Hsing Yi is one of the three great internal energy styles of martial arts that evolved in China after Ta Mo fused spiritual and physical cultivation at the Shao Lin temple. The name 'Hsing Yi' reflects the primary role which intent (*yi*) plays in forming the various postures and controlling the forms (*hsing*) the body adopts during practice.

As a martial arts form, Hsing Yi is a very powerful fighting technique that consists of a series of consecutive linear attacks that always move forward towards the opponent. As an exercise set, Hsing Yi has developed various forms, each of which contains eight steps that are performed slowly in sequential order and in close conjunction with deep diaphragmic breathing. Each step has a specific tactical application in combat, alternating between offensive strikes and defensive parries. When used in actual martial competition, the moves are executed very fast and not necessarily in the order in which they appear in the exercise sets. Instead, each move suggests itself spontaneously to the combatants as they compete, based on what each one feels the opponent's next step will be.

Besides the eight-step sets of martial manoeuvres, Hsing Yi also includes a series of single-step chi-gung exercises to boost circulation of energy, balance the body, regulate the breath and concentrate the mind. All Hsing Yi exercises are designed to generate great power by fully concentrating energy behind every strike. For example, when a punch is applied, body, breath and mind are coordinated in such a way that the power is drawn up from the ground through the legs, transferred to the torso with a twist of the hips and brought up to the left or right shoulder, which focuses the full force of the gathering power plus the weight of the body into the punch, sending it down through the bones of the arm and out through the knuckles of the hand at precisely the moment of contact. This requires a combination of balance and physical coordination, plus unwavering mental focus, so that intent spontaneously gives rise to form.

Pa Kua Chang (Eight Trigrams Palm)

Pa Kua is the most elegant, mesmerizing form of Chinese martial arts. Tradition attributes the creation of this style to an eccentric, flamboyant martial artist by the name of Tung Hai-chuan, who appeared in Peking during the late eighteenth century and proceeded to challenge and defeat all of the reigning martial arts champions of the time by using this style of combat. Its true origins remain unknown, but like Tai Chi Chuan it was probably developed by Taoist recluses in remote hermitages hidden among the misty peaks of China's sacred mountains.

It is said that the only one who could match Tung's fighting ability was a famous Hsing Yi master whom he challenged to a duel. The match continued non-stop for three days, with neither combatant gaining the upper hand, after which they called it a draw and sat down to drink tea and discuss philosophy instead.

When performed by an accomplished master, such as Lo Te-hsiu of Taiwan, Pa Kua is truly beautiful to behold. Theoretically based on the principles symbolized by the 'Eight Trigrams' in the *I-Ching* ('Book of Change'), Pa Kua is performed by walking continuously in circles using the 'Lotus Step', with sudden and seemingly effortless reversals of direction, deep dips and swift swerves, and exquisitely executed turns. The circular path followed in this form is divided into eight sectors, each one governed by one of the Eight Trigrams. Based on the prevailing situation between the opponents at any given moment, each trigram suggests the most appropriate tactic as the Pa Kua combatant passes through the related sector of the circle. The permutations and combinations of moves in this style are countless, and it requires not only a high level of mastery in the form but also a deep understanding of Taoist philosophy as elucidated in the *I-Ching* to utilize Pa Kua Chang for martial arts competition or combat.

The fighting form of Pa Kua Chang is known as the 'postnatal' style and is extremely intricate and complex. However, there is also a slow-motion set that is used purely to cultivate energy, enhance vitality, boost immunity, protect health and prolong life, and this is known as the 'prenatal' style. The latter consists of eight elegant manoeuvres, each of which commences with a smooth 180-degree reversal in direction as one 'walks the circle' with the Lotus Step. Each manoeuvre in the prenatal style is designed to strengthen particular parts of the body, tonify specific organs and balance energy flow throughout the entire system, while also harmonizing the whole system with the macrocosmic energy fields of Heaven and Earth.

Like Hsing Yi and Tai Chi Chuan, Pa Kua Chang should be learned from a qualified teacher, not from a book, because it involves carefully choreographed sequences of steps and movements, like a dance, rather than just a series of individual exercises, such as the Eight Pieces of Brocade.

Play of the Five Beasts (Wu Chin Hsi)

This is one of the most ancient styles of chi-gung practice in China, dating back to prehistoric times, when the movements of various animals in nature were copied as models for fighting tactics in martial arts as well as for therapeutic exercises, such as the 'Great Dance', which was developed to cure rheumatism and other symptoms of excess dampness in the flooded basin of the Yellow River. Some of ancient China's most famous physicians, such as Hua To and Sun Ssu-miao, adapted various versions of this style as physical therapy for the prevention and cure of disease. The five animals that served as original models for these forms were the bear, tiger, deer, crane and monkey.

This was the style of martial arts which the eccentric Buddhist monk Ta Mo found being practised in China when he arrived there from India around 500 AD. He combined these animal movements with various breathing exercises and yoga postures from India, and the resulting hybrid became the foundation for all subsequent development in the Chinese martial arts. The Shao Lin Temple, which Ta Mo made famous by teaching there, became the creative centre for the Chinese martial arts, and many of the fighting forms which subsequently evolved there and later spread to Korea and Japan can be traced back to the Play of the Five Beasts, such as Shao Lin White Crane, Shao Lin Tiger and so forth.

Chi-gung forms based on the Play of the Five Beasts are primarily styles of martial arts, some of them relatively 'hard' and 'external', which means that they rely as much on martialling sheer physical strength as they do on guiding internal energy. This makes them particularly effective for building a strong body and developing physical coordination. However, when practised slowly in conjunction with deep diaphragmic breathing, these forms are also good for cultivating and circulating internal energy, balancing vital functions and boosting immunity.

Shao Lin Temple Style (Shao Lin Chuan)

The style of chi-gung practiced at the Shao Lin Temple ultimately became associated more with martial arts than meditation. Ta Mo's original intention was to fuse meditation and martial arts into a single system of practice based on internal energy work, but in subsequent centuries, the Shao Lin Temple became renowned as the headquarters for China's greatest martial artists, and students flocked there to learn how to fight. Chang San-feng, the progenitor of Tai Chi Chuan, spent many years of his life living and teaching martial arts at the Shao Lin Temple, as did many other great masters, and consequently a broad range of styles evolved there.

When the Manchus toppled the Ming dynasty in 1644, and took control of China by establishing the foreign Ching dynasty, the Shao Lin Temple became a hot-bed of patriotic Chinese resistance to Manchu rule. Consequently, the Manchus sent troops to burn it down several times, and to hunt down and kill the most renowned Chinese masters, who had become rallying points for those who wished to restore the Ming dynasty. Therefore, for several centuries Shao Lin martial arts went underground and had to be taught in great secrecy in remote mountain monasteries. Fortunately, most of the forms survived this way, and today they are still widely taught and practised throughout Asia.

Some of the rough-and-tumble Shao Lin forms gave birth to the martial arts traditions of neighbouring countries, such as Korea's Tai Kwan Do, Japan's Karate, and some of the fighting forms of Southeast Asia. These styles are generally regarded as appropriate only for younger practitioners, due to the stress and strain they put on the body. However, like all forms of chi-gung, even the most strenuous Shao Lin fighting style can be slowed down, softened up and practised in conjunction with deep breathing, thereby transforming it from a martial art into a preventive healthcare and longevity programme. A good example of this versatility is Shao Lin White Crane style, which is one of the most powerful, aggressive fighting forms in the Shao Lin repertoire. When the fighting forms are dissected and broken down into individual manoeuvres, they become excellent chi-gung exercises that may be practised as 'moving meditations' for health, longevity and spiritual development.

The Six Syllable Secret (Liu Yin Chueh)

This has already been discussed in Chapter 6 and is mentioned here only to point out that it is regarded as a complete 'set' of chi-gung practice in itself. It first became popular as a self-contained set during the Tang dynasty, when it was commonly prescribed along with herbs as a cure for disease. Some of the six basic postures and movements, each of which detoxifies and guides healing energy to one of the six major organ-energy systems, are quite similar to the manoeuvres used in the Eight Pieces of Brocade set. In fact, these exercises may be practised as a general chi-gung set without using the healing syllables, and the healing syllables may be used alone, in conjunction with deep breathing, to help cure disease, even while lying still in bed. The complete set is described and illustrated in detail in the author's previous work *Guarding the Three Treasures*.

Standing Pylon (Chan Chuang)

This is a very old style of chi-gung practice that is performed standing in the Horse stance, sometimes with the arms hanging loosely by the sides, sometimes raised up in front as in the 'Embracing the Tree' posture introduced in the following chapter. Basically, this is a style of still standing meditation designed to open the energy gates, stimulate complete circulation of energy through all eight channels of the Macrocosmic Orbit, cultivate mental concentration, and develop patience, stamina and strength. Virtually all Chinese martial arts and chi-gung masters teach this form to their students as a basic foundation for other styles of practice. It is a well-balanced style of practice that simultaneously builds physical strength, generates a powerful flow of internal energy, and develops mental clarity and focused attention. Some adepts train themselves to the point that they can maintain this posture for up to an hour or more at a time, and even though there is no physical movement, such sustained periods of practice usually leave the whole body bathed in sweat due to the internal heat produced by the energy which this exercise generates.

Microcosmic Orbit (Hsiao Chou Tien)

This is by far the most popular style of Taoist still meditation and is somewhat related to the *kundalini* yoga of India. It may be practised in either of the two basic sitting postures or standing still in the Horse stance; the preferred posture is sitting cross-legged on a cushion on the floor

It is referred to as the 'Microcosmic Orbit' because it draws energy up from the sacrum (seat of the *kundalini* energy in Indian yoga) through the Governing Channel along the spine into the head, then down the front of the body through the Conception Channel back to the sacrum, thereby inscribing an 'orbit' through the microcosmic 'universe' within the human energy system. As energy ascends through the various 'passes' along the spine, it becomes increasingly refined and awakens various dormant spiritual faculties associated with the major energy centres, or chakras. When it reaches the upper elixir field centre in the centre of the head, it nurtures spiritual vitality and contributes cumulatively to the gradual awakening of primordial awareness. The upper elixir field also transforms the Earth-generated Fire energy of sexuality from the sacrum into the Water energy associated with the spiritual virtues of Heaven. Thus the energy rises up the spine as Fire and flows back down the front as Water, cooling the chakras, calming the emotions and balancing the excessive Fire generated by temporal life.

As the most basic still form of chi-gung practice, the Microcosmic Orbit is an excellent adjunct to any style of moving chi-gung exercise, such as the Eight Pieces of Brocade set. Generally, it's best to practise the moving set first, to mobilize energy and balance the body, then conclude with a period of Microcosmic Orbit practice in still sitting meditation to refine, circulate and store energy.

CHAPTER 10

Basic Chi-Gung Set for Daily Practice

The best way to learn chi-gung is under the close supervision of a qualified teacher, especially in the more advanced stages of practice, where incorrect form and wrong ideas can completely undermine one's practice and even lead to deviations. On the other hand, it's better to learn from a book, or not at all, than from a bad teacher.

The basic chi-gung set introduced below may be learned and practised from the instructions and illustrations provided in this book, without personal supervision from a teacher and without risk of experiencing harmful results or developing poor practice habits, as long as you observe the principles and precautions presented in earlier chapters and carefully follow the instructions given with each exercise. In chi-gung, it's not the degree of complexity that counts for results, but rather one's persistence and diligence in daily practice. Even the most elementary exercises can bestow profound benefits if practised daily and with presence of mind. Indeed, just one simple set can bring deeper, swifter results than the most complicated advanced forms, if that set is practised regularly and sincerely, for the benefits of chi-gung practice are cumulative, and they compound with the time and effort invested.

The set given below includes both moving and still forms. These may be practised together or separately. For example, you might start a session with the moving exercises, and finish with a period of still meditation, or practise the moving set in the morning and the still form in the afternoon or evening. Both moving and still forms are important in chi-gung, and it's always best to combine some of each in any chi-gung programme, for while they both work with the same basic energy, each has its own particular virtues. Moving meditation, which is performed in a standing posture, opens up and replenishes all of the circuits

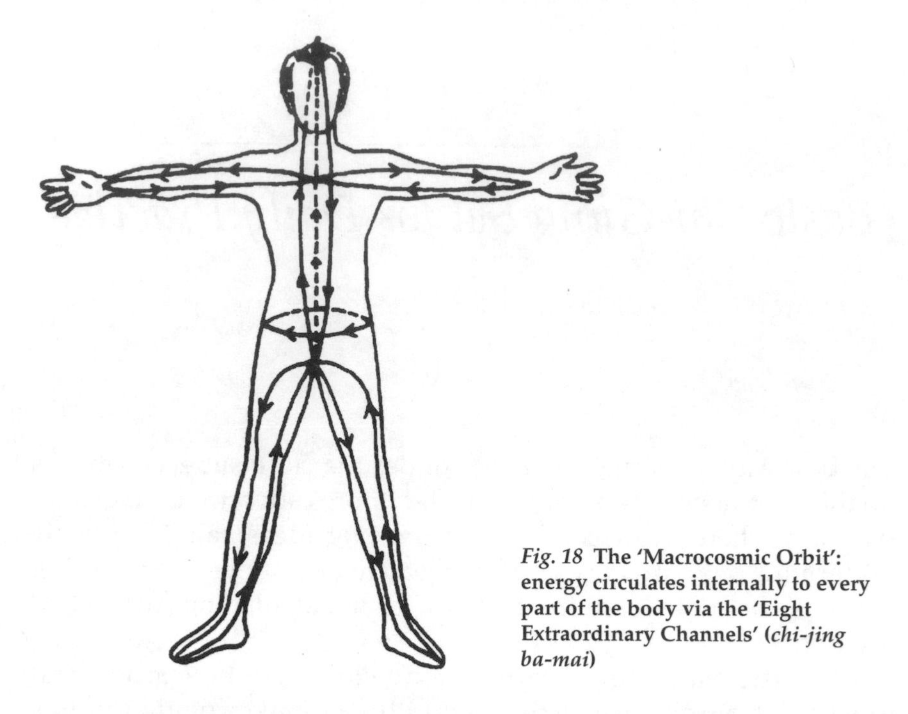

Fig. 18 **The 'Macrocosmic Orbit': energy circulates internally to every part of the body via the 'Eight Extraordinary Channels' (*chi-jing ba-mai*)**

of the Eight Extraordinary Channels. Known as the Macrocosmic Orbit (Fig. 18), these channels serve as general reservoirs of energy for the entire system, feeding *chi* as needed into the twelve organ meridians and all the subsidiary capillaries and providing power to the arms and legs. In terms of internal alchemy, the moving forms work mainly with essence and energy.

Still forms work more with the higher energy centres and focus mainly on energy and spirit. The main circuit in still practice is the Microcosmic Orbit (Fig. 19), which channels lower energies from the sacrum up the spine into the head for refinement and transformation into spiritual vitality, then guides it back down the front of the body to the lower abdomen for storage. Thus the two styles of practice complement one another. If practised back to back, it's best to start with the moving set and conclude with the still.

The best time of day to practise chi-gung is early in the morning, before breakfast. This is the period when Yang energy peaks in the atmosphere, and therefore practising during these hours brings in a much richer harvest of *chi* than at any other time. Practising in the morning is also a good way to tune up your whole system – body, energy and mind – for the entire day. The next best time is late evening, around midnight, when Yin

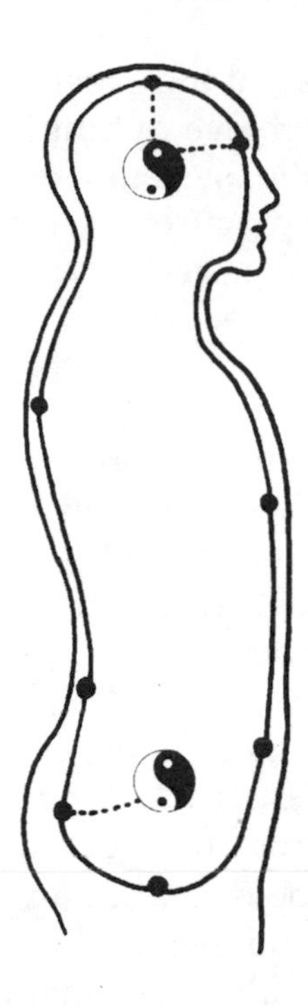

Fig. 19 The 'Microcosmic Orbit': energy circulates internally between the Upper Elixir Field in the head and the Lower Elixir Field in the abdomen, via the Conception (front) and Governing (back) Channels, transforming at various 'power points' along these two channels

switches over to Yang, and the third time is late afternoon, before dinner. Note that while practising in the morning perks you up and stimulates your energy, the same set of exercises practised late at night will calm you down and prepare your system for sleep. That's because chi-gung always works in accordance with the overall prevailing energy conditions, internally as well as externally. At night, the body's biorhythms are ready for sleep, so chi-gung works within that context. In the morning, energy is on the rise in the body as well as in the atmosphere, so chi-gung catches that wave. If you decide to separate your moving and still practices, then it's best to do the moving set in the morning and the still work at night.

Moving Meditation Set

The exercises introduced below have been carefully selected to provide balanced benefits for body, breath and mind and to bring all three into harmony with each other and with external energy fields. If you have the time and inclination to practise the full set every day, that will of course provide the best results but it is not necessary to do the entire series each and every time you practise. If you're pressed for time or feeling fatigued, simply select a few exercises from each of the three stages and just do those. However, do not practise only one stage, such as the main set, at the expense of the warm-up and collection sets. In order to achieve optimum results, maintain proper balance throughout the system, and prevent deviations, it's very important always to practise moving chi-gung exercises in the three-stage format suggested here – preliminary warm-up, main mobilization practice, and final collection and storage stage. Even if you only do one exercise from each stage, do them in the prescribed order.

When practising this set, it's best to follow the sequential order in which the exercises are presented, even if you only select a few of them. They are arranged in such a way that each exercise builds on the results of the previous one and leads naturally into the next. Try this set as it is for about six months of daily practice, after which you may wish to rearrange your chi-gung programme according to your own requirements and interests. There are many different chi-gung exercises introduced in *The Tao of Health, Sex, and Longevity* and *Guarding the Three Treasures*, and any of them may be added to or substituted for the exercises in the set given below. Chi-gung changes your body and transforms your energy and eventually it transforms your mind as well, so you should always remain flexible with your practice. From time to time, you should experiment with different exercises and forms, and amend your daily set every six months to a year, but always be sure to follow the basic principles, and practise in the three-stage format given here.

If weather and other circumstances permit, practise barefoot in a garden. If a garden is not available, then practise out on a terrace, on top of a building or, if necessary, by an open window. It's not a good idea to practise chi-gung in a closed room with air-conditioning or central heating.

Warm-Up: Balancing Body, Breath and Mind for Practice

The first stage of preparation for the main practice is to balance the body by stretching muscles and tendons, loosening joints and vertebrae, and releasing all physical tension. These exercises also stimulate circulation, activate the endocrine system, and open up the energy channels, thereby establishing a strong foundation for the main practice.

Spinal Twist (Fig. 20)

Method: Stand in the Horse, with shoulders completely relaxed and arms hanging loosely at the sides, knees unlocked. Start turning slowly from left to right, using only the thighs for power, and letting the waist, torso and arms follow naturally, turning with the torque produced by the legs. Keep the elbows loose and unlocked, so that the arms flail freely out to the sides on each turn, and let the hands slap against chest and back as each turn is completed. Keep the spine and neck erect, and turn the head around on each turn so that you can see over the back of each shoulder. Gradually increase the extent of each twist until you've reached your limit of flex and keep the entire exercise slow, gentle and rhythmic. Do 3 to 4 dozen turns, or 3 to 5 minutes of practice.

Benefits: This manoeuvre realigns and balances all of the spinal vertebrae from neck to sacrum, stretches and tones all of the muscles along the spine, and stimulates all of the nerves and peripheral branches of the spinal cord. The spine is the central pillar of chi-gung practice and the 'Stairway to Heaven' for energy to ascend from sacrum to head, so any tension, blockage or misalignment in the bones, muscles or nerves of the spine is a serious impediment to practice. This exercise is probably the most important in the entire warm-up set, and may be practised any time of day or night for a quick spinal realignment and recharge.

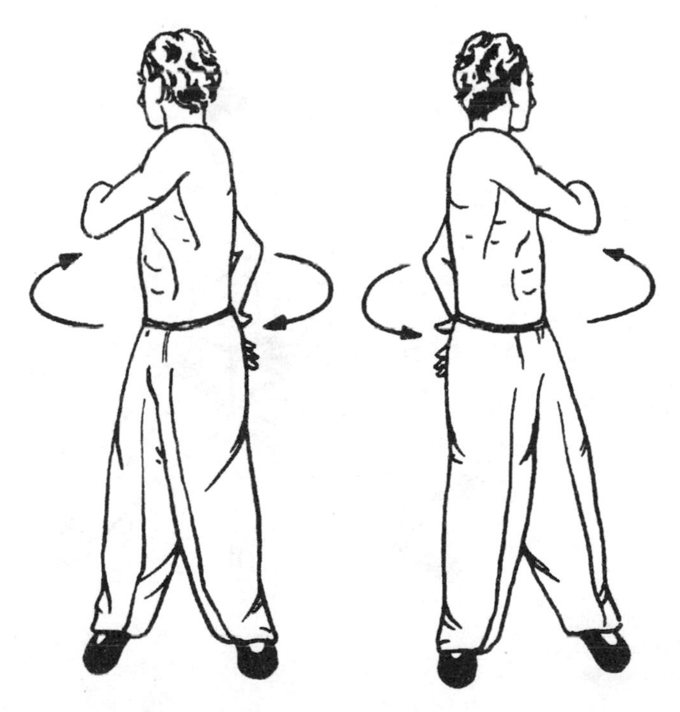

Fig. 20 **The Spinal Twist: the most important warm-up exercise for chi-gung**

This exercise also opens the ribcage and stretches the diaphragm in preparation for deep abdominal breathing, massages the organs, glands and other tissues in the abdominal and sacral cavities, and helps loosen the shoulders and neck.

Wide Hip and Thigh Squats (Fig. 21)

Method: Adopt an extra-wide stance, with feet splayed out at 45 degrees and hands firmly planted at the waist, as shown in the illustration. Keeping the back as straight as possible and head up, squat down slowly as far as you can without losing your balance or causing excessive strain, then rise back up again, slowly, until the knees are straight. Try not to bend forward as you squat down, for that negates the stretch to the thighs. Repeat 6 to 10 times.

Benefits: Wide squats give a deep stretch to the tough tendons, large muscles and major arteries on the inside of the thighs, which tend to tighten up and block circulation. These squats also open up the leg channels of the Macrocosmic Orbit and tone the urogenital diaphragm. Practising the anal sphincter lock as you squat down is an excellent way to strengthen the entire pelvic floor, prevent and cure haemorrhoids, and stimulate sacral gland secretions. This exercise also builds strong legs, which are the supporting columns of all practices done in the Horse stance.

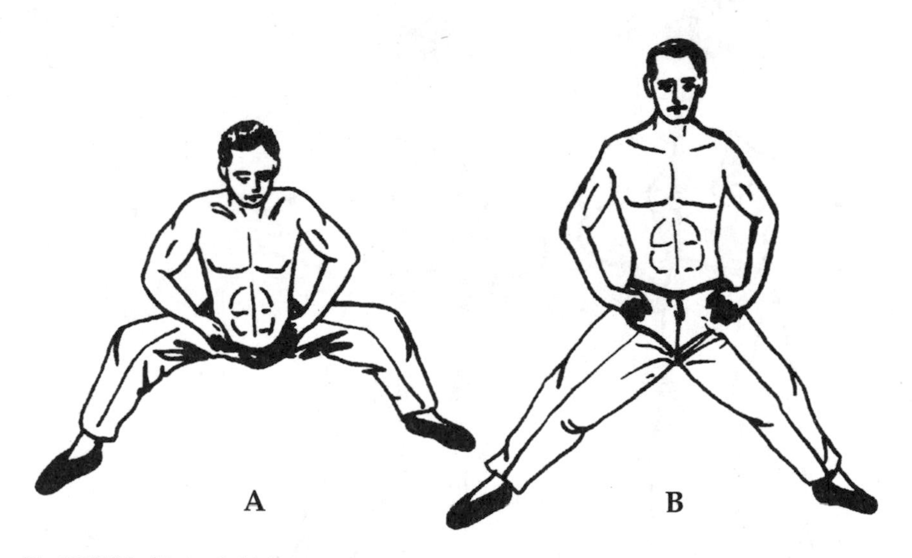

Fig. 21 **Wide hip and thigh squats:**
A. Squat down in wide stance
B. Rise up and straighten knees

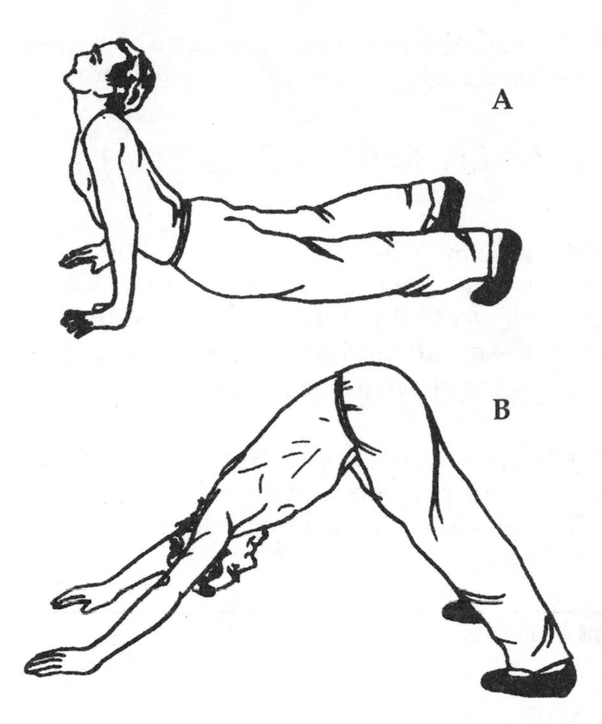

Fig. 22 **Back bows:**
A. Lean forward on arms and bow the back
B. Push upward on hands and arch the back

Back Bows (Fig. 22)

Method: Spread feet a bit more than shoulder-width apart and place hands out on the ground in front, so that the body forms an upside-down 'V' shape, with legs and arms fully extended and spine arched up. Lean forward on the hands and let the hips drop down toward the ground as you also bow the spine and raise the head up and back. Then push up the body again and arch the spine, letting the head drop down and hang loosely between the arms. Repeat 12 to 15 times.

Benefits: This exercise stretches the entire spinal cord lengthwise, rather than from side to side, and further realigns the vertebrae. It also tones the spinal muscles and stimulates the nerves of the spinal cord. The alternate expansion and contraction of the front and back of the body opens the channels of the Microcosmic Orbit and stretches the ribs and diaphragm in preparation for deep breathing. The bobbing up and down of the head promotes circulation to the brain. This exercise also builds strength in the shoulders, arms and legs.

Note: If you find that your upper body strength is insufficient for this exercise, or if you have a back problem that precludes doing it, you may either delete this exercise from your set, or else substitute the 'Spinal Stretch' exercise suggested as a warm-up for still meditation in the next section (see Fig. 45, page 246).

Pelvic Thrust and Pelvic Rotation (Figs 23 a, b)

Method:

- **Pelvic Thrust.** Stand in Horse, with knees unlocked and hands planted firmly on hips. As you inhale through the nose, tilt the pelvis back as far as possible, so that the buttocks stick out at the back, then exhale through the mouth and tilt the pelvis forward as far as possible, straightening the curve in the lower spine. Repeat 6 to12 times, slowly.
- **Pelvic Rotation.** Keeping hands on hips, rotate the entire pelvis in wide circles, letting the upper torso bend in the opposite direction for balance. Inscribe as wide an arc as possible as you

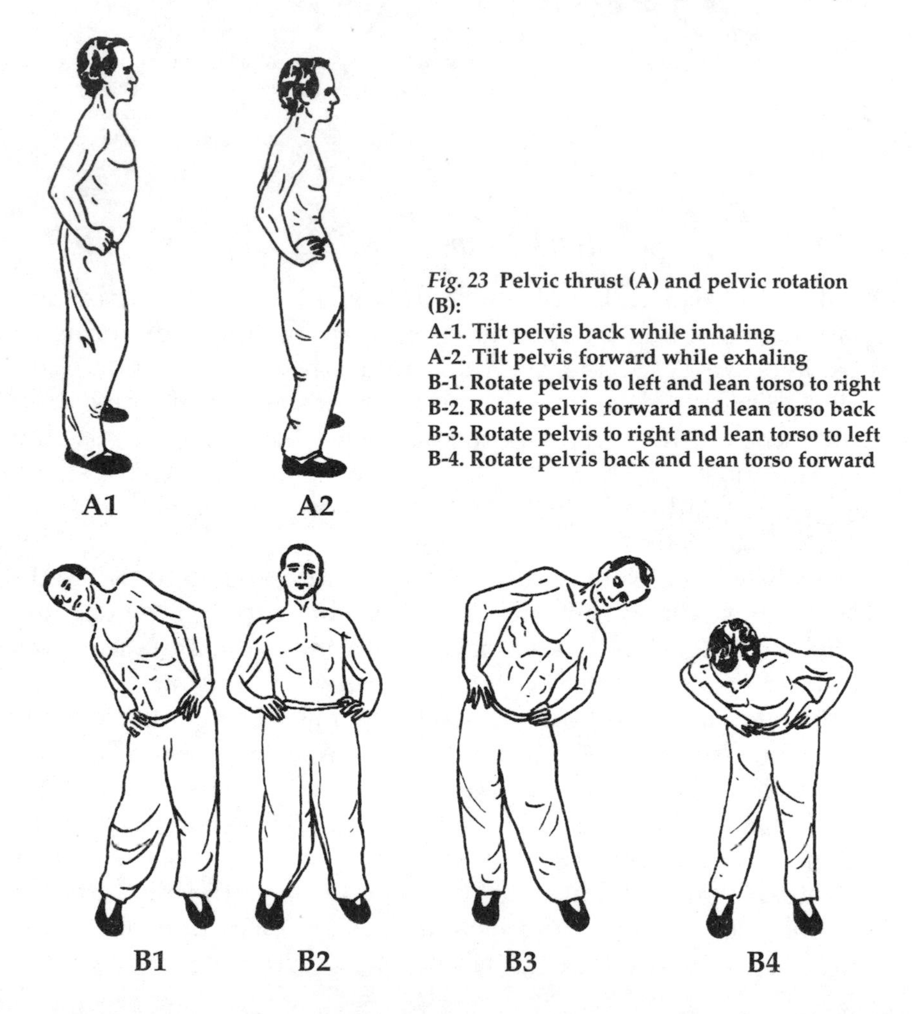

Fig. 23 **Pelvic thrust (A) and pelvic rotation (B):**
A-1. Tilt pelvis back while inhaling
A-2. Tilt pelvis forward while exhaling
B-1. Rotate pelvis to left and lean torso to right
B-2. Rotate pelvis forward and lean torso back
B-3. Rotate pelvis to right and lean torso to left
B-4. Rotate pelvis back and lean torso forward

rotate. Do 6 to12 rotations in one direction, then in the opposite direction, and finally back in the original direction.

Benefits: These two exercises stimulate all of the nerve endings and glands in the sacral region, balancing endocrine secretions and activating the pneumogastric nerves of the parasympathetic branch of the autonomous nervous system. This is excellent therapy for menstrual disorders in women and deficiency of sexual secretions and sexual energy in both men and women. It limbers the lumbar vertebrae and opens up the energy centres along the lower spine and abdomen. The rotations also provide a stimulating massage to the lower bowels, thereby helping prevent constipation and enhancing peristalsis.

Abdominal Lift (Fig. 24)

Method: Stand somewhat pigeon-toed, knees bent and lean forward so that you can place the palms of your hands on the inside of the thighs, just above the knees, and fully support the weight of your upper body by leaning onto your arms. Forcefully expel your breath so lungs are completely empty, then apply the neck lock to prevent any air from re-entering the lungs. With a strong, deliberate contraction, pull the entire abdominal wall in toward the spine, pushing the internal organs and the diaphragm up into the chest cavity. Hold for about 5 seconds, then relax the abdominal

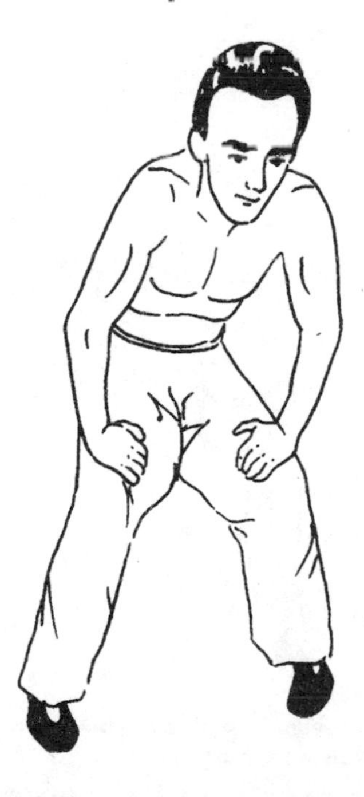

Fig. 24 **The Abdominal Lift: exhale completely, then draw abdominal wall inward and upward as far as possible**

wall, let the organs and diaphragm descend again, release the neck lock, and inhale deeply. Repeat 3 times.

Benefits: This is an excellent way to prepare your breathing apparatus for deep diaphragmic breathing, especially in the beginning stages of practice, when the diaphragm is still stiff. It loosens and relaxes the diaphragm, improving its flex and developing voluntary control over its movement. The deep contraction of the abdomen squeezes stale blood from the internal organs and glands, and the relaxation phase then allows freshly oxygenated blood to flood in and replenish these tissues. It gives a strong boost to circulation by exerting pressure on the vena cava, prevents constipation, relieves gastritis and clears any sort of congestion in the digestive organs.

Side Stretch (Fig. 25)

Method. Stand in the Horse and raise both hands straight up above the head, then clasp fingers together and turn the palms up to face the sky. Stretch up as far as possible by pushing the palms towards the sky, then slowly tilt the entire upper body to one side as you exhale, so that the other side is stretched open. Keep tilting to the side until you've reached your limit of flex and the lungs are empty, then slowly straighten up again while inhaling. Next, tilt as far as

Fig. 25 **Side Stretch: clasp hands and stretch arms to the sky; exhale while stretching to right; inhale while returning to upright posture; exhale while stretching to left**

possible in the opposite direction as you exhale. Repeat 3 times on each side.

Benefits: Opens up the entire chest cavity in preparation for deep abdominal breathing. Tilting to the side alternately expands and contracts both sides of the lungs and opens up energy circulation in the meridians that run along the sides of the torso and into the arms. Also helps realign the spinal vertebrae and tone the spinal muscles.

Wing Tip Flex (Fig. 26)

Method: Stand in Horse and raise arms out to the sides, with hollows of the elbows facing up towards the sky and palms towards the ground. Extend the index and middle fingers, while holding the other two fingers against the palm with the thumb. Stretch hands upward from the wrists, so that index and middle

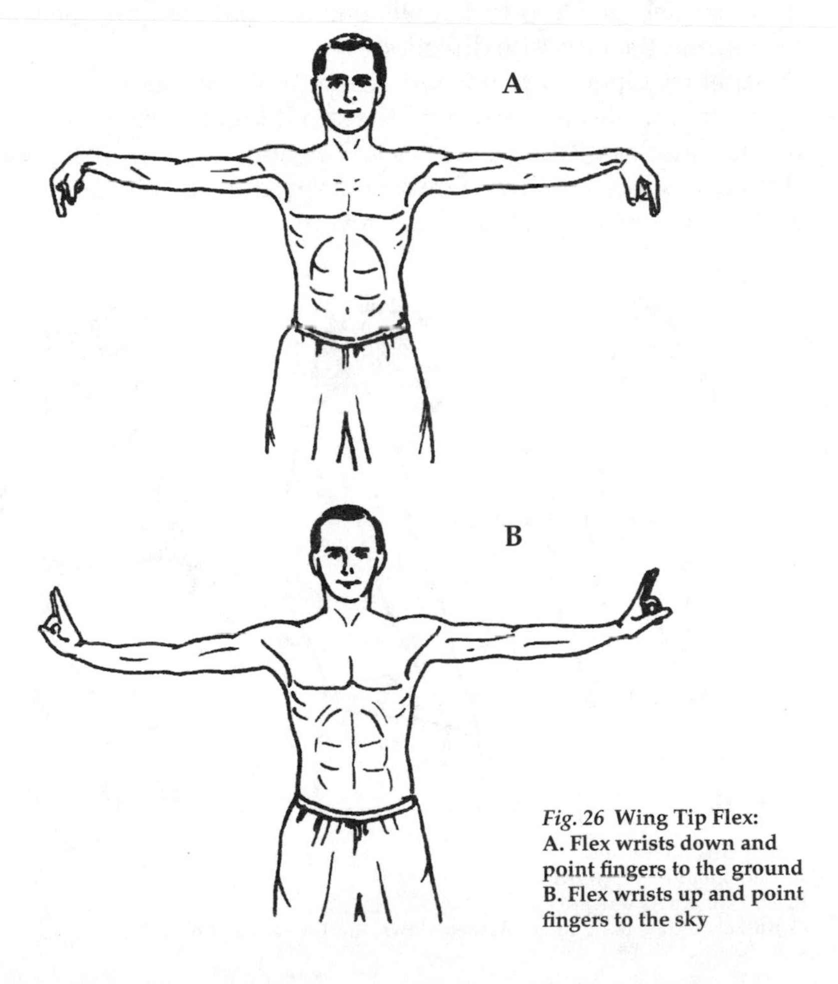

Fig. 26 **Wing Tip Flex:**
A. Flex wrists down and point fingers to the ground
B. Flex wrists up and point fingers to the sky

fingers are pointing to sky, then stretch them downward so that fingers point to the ground. Continue flexing up and down about two dozen times, bending hands from the wrists as far as possible in both directions.

Benefits: This exercise opens up the energy channels that run through the arms from shoulders to hands, stimulating and balancing the flow of energy through them, and drawing energy into the hands. It also stretches and tones the tendons and nerves that run from the hands to the elbows and shoulders.

Shoulder Rolls (Fig. 27)

Method: Roll the shoulders forward, then raise them up towards the ears, then back as far as possible, down and around to the front again, inscribing as wide an arc as possible. Try to keep the shoulder and arm muscles loose as you roll the shoulders around in their sockets. Do 6 to 12 rolls backwards, then another 6 to 12 forward in the opposite direction.

Benefits: Opens up the whole chest in preparation for deep breathing, while also loosening the shoulders and releasing tension in the muscles of the upper back. Tension in the upper back and shoulders blocks the free flow of energy during chi-gung practice, and this exercise is designed to prevent that.

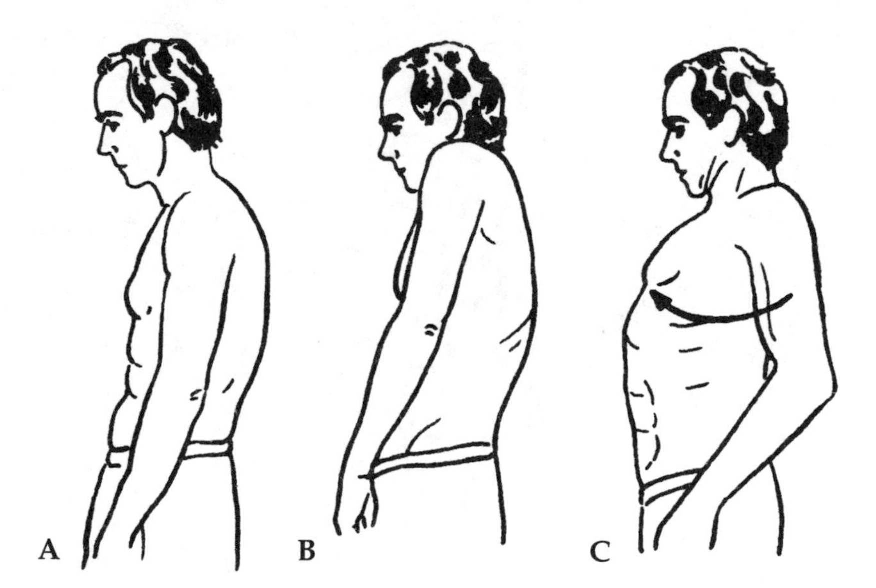

Fig. 27 **Shoulder Rolls:**
A. Roll shoulders forward
B. Roll shoulders upward
C. Roll shoulders back, then roll them down and forward again

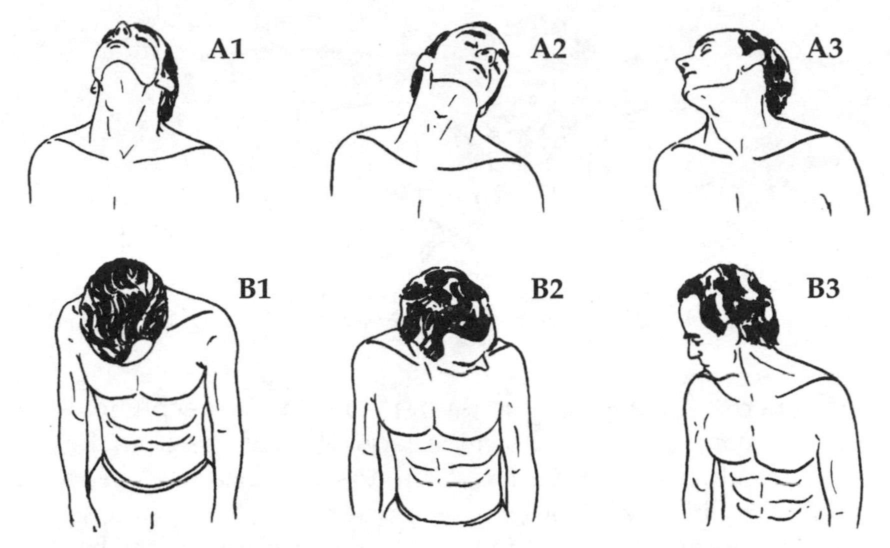

Fig. 28 **Neck and Throat Stretch:**
A-1. Tilt head up and back
A-2. Turn head to left
A-3. Turn head to right
B-1. Tilt head forward and down
B-2. Turn head to left
B-3. Turn head to right

Neck and Throat Stretch (Figs 28 a, b)

Method: Raise the head up and tilt it back as far as possible, thereby compressing the back of the neck. Slowly and gently tilt the head from side to side, going only as far as your flexibility permits without causing pain. After turning 5 to 6 times to each side, return head to centre, raise head slowly back to normal position, and continue tilting forward until head is hanging down in front, chin to chest. Slowly turn from side to side, until you can see over each shoulder, 5 to 6 times to each side, then return to centre position and slowly raise head back to normal position.

Benefits: This exercise stretches and compresses both the back and front of the neck, opens up the throat, loosens the cervical vertebrae, and releases tension from the muscles and tendons of the neck. If the neck is tense, as is so common these days due to chronic tension, it becomes a 'bottleneck' during chi-gung practice, obstructing the flow of energy into and out of the head. A lot of toxins and stagnant energy also get trapped in the neck, and this exercise loosens and clears them away prior to the main practice.

Neck Knead (Fig. 29)

Method: Clasp the hands behind the head, so that the thumbs are free to knead the muscles and tendons along the back of the neck

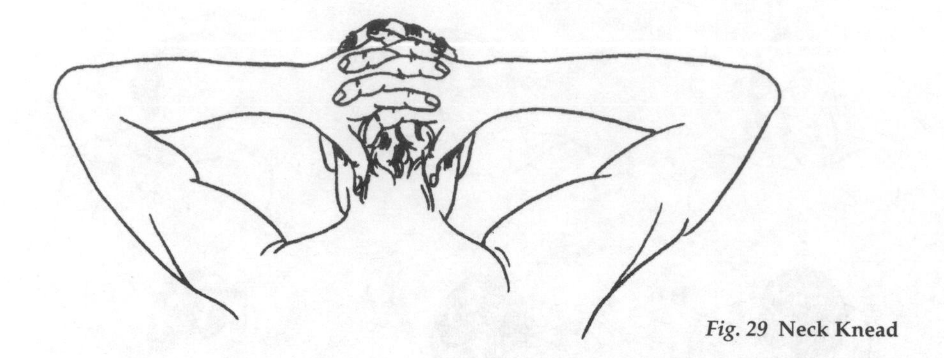

Fig. 29 **Neck Knead**

and upper shoulders. Use the thumbs to massage deeply into the muscular cords on both sides of the cervical vertebrae, from the top of the shoulders up to the base of the skull. Knead as deeply as possible, rubbing in circles as you press into the tissues. Use the thumbs to locate the two 'Wind Pond' points located at the base of the skull, where the neck enters the head, and press deeply on them several times.

Benefits: This is another effective way to release tension from the muscles and tendons of the neck and shoulders, loosening and clearing stagnant energy and toxic fluids from the neck, opening up the energy channels that run from the spine into the head, and stimulating energy to ascend up the spine. Also stimulates and balances the nerves in the neck and helps align the cervical vertebrae.

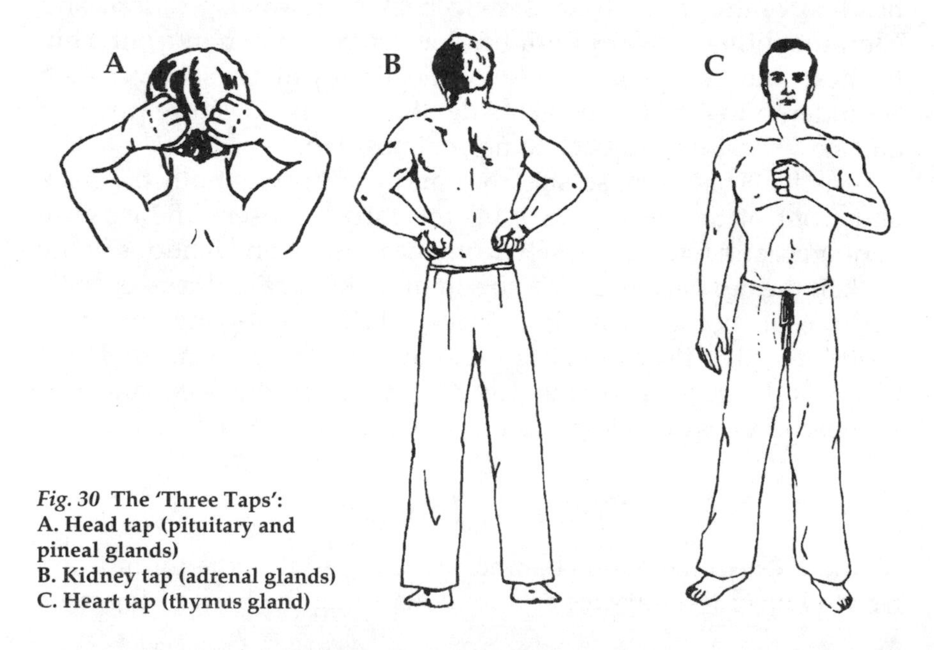

Fig. 30 **The 'Three Taps':**
A. Head tap (pituitary and pineal glands)
B. Kidney tap (adrenal glands)
C. Heart tap (thymus gland)

The Three Taps (Figs 30 a, b, c)

The three taps and their benefits have already been discussed on page 154. When performed in preparation for chi-gung practice, the head tap (pituitary and pineal), heart tap (thymus), and kidney tap (adrenal) stimulate secretions from these vital glands, thereby balancing the entire endocrine system and providing abundant supplies of potent hormone essence for conversion into energy during the main practice. This exercise enhances overall immune response, energizes the entire system with vibratory stimulation, and helps loosen impacted toxic wastes in the neck, brain, lungs and kidneys.

Tongue Stretch and Roll

Method: Open the mouth and stretch the tongue out as far as possible, then roll it back into the mouth and curl the tip up to the top of the throat. Repeat 3 to 5 times. Next, swirl the tongue around in circles between the external side of the gums and the inside of the lips and cheeks, running the tongue along the entire upper and lower ridges of the teeth. Continue for about one minute, or until saliva is secreted from the ducts beneath the tongue. This should be swallowed.

Benefits: The tongue is connected to the heart muscle, so stretching and rolling the tongue tonifies the heart muscle. It also stretches and tones the tongue and trachea in preparation for deep breathing, and stimulates secretion of beneficial saliva from the ducts beneath the tongue. Saliva from beneath the tongue is rich in highly beneficial enzymes, which assist digestion, soothe the stomach, and eliminate bad breath by breaking down the bacteria which cause it.

The second phase of the warm-up stage is to balance the breath, establish rhythmic harmony between body and breath, and attune the mind with the synchronized movements of body and breath. Here's a simple three-step way to do this:

1. Stand in the Horse (see page 161), with arms hanging loosely at the sides, and do about 2 minutes of incremental bellows breathing. This clears stagnant air from the lungs, loosens the diaphragm, stimulates the nasal and bronchial passages, and gives a strong boost to circulation of blood. It also opens up the channels of the internal energy circuits.

2. Next, do some alternate nostril breathing (see page 174), 6 on

each side, to balance the flow of air through both nostrils, balance internal energy flow, and balance the functions of the right and left hemispheres of the brain.

3. Third, synchronize your breathing with the movement of your body by performing the breathing exercise known as 'Opening the Energy Gates', or 'Body Breathing' (Fig. 31). Inhale slowly through the nostrils and raise the arms slowly out to the sides, but only to about a 30- to 45-degree angle with the torso, then exhale and lower the arms slowly back down to the sides. Focus attention on the hands and on the lower abdomen, and try to make inhalation and exhalation even and long. In addition to synchronizing the movements of body and breath, this exercise also opens up the energy gates in the palms and at the lower elixir field just below the navel, inducing energy to flow through these gates along with the inflow and outflow of air in the lungs. While doing this exercise, focus your attention fully on the attunement of body and breath to bring your mind into balance with them. Body and breath move like partners in a slow dance, with breath leading and body following, and the mind serving as chaperone to keep them both in step.

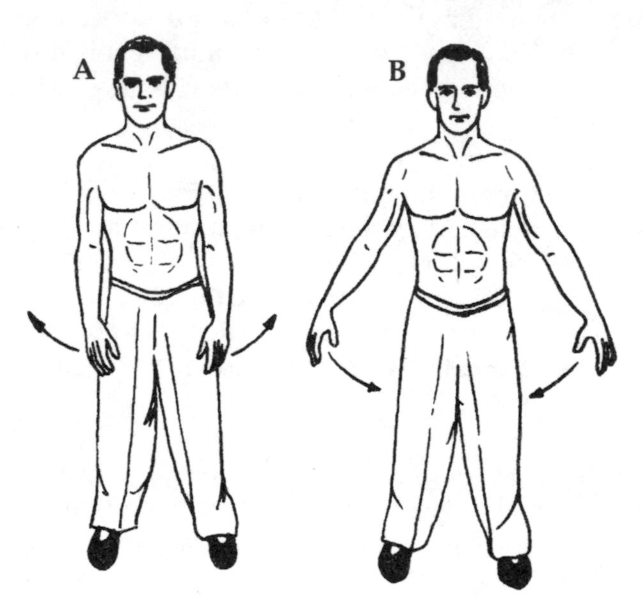

Fig. 31 **'Opening the Energy Gates':**
A. Inhale deeply and raise arms slowly up and out to the sides
B. Exhale smoothly and lower arms back down to the thighs

Main Practice: Mobilizing, Circulating and Balancing Energy

With body, breath and mind balanced and moving in harmony, you're now ready to do the main practice, which involves a series of slow-motion body movements performed in conjunction with deep diaphragmic breathing. In between each exercise, you should perform three slow 'Opening the Energy Gate' breaths to draw energy collected in the previous exercise down into the lower elixir field in the abdomen and to prepare your energy system for the next exercise. During all of these exercises, keep your background attention focused on maintenance of proper posture and correct breathing, and focus the foreground of your awareness on the movement of energy through your system. You may wish to visualize energy as luminous light streaming in and out of various gates and flowing through your channels, or try to feel the energy moving through various parts of the body like currents of warm water. The more clearly you bring energy into conscious awareness, the more strongly it flows through your system. Whenever your mind wanders away from the practice, your energy follows it and dissipates, rather than concentrating in the channels and collecting in the energy centres. When properly practised with stable presence of mind, these exercises drive stagnant energy out of the system, draw fresh energy in through the energy gates, circulate and store energy in the reservoirs of the Eight Extraordinary Channels, distribute energy throughout the entire system, and balance energy in the elixir field centres (chakras).

Iron Bridge (Fig. 32)

This is a version adapted by the author from the classic Iron Bridge chi-gung exercise. It stimulates and balances energy flow between the front and back and the upper and lower parts of the body.

Method: Standing in the Horse, take a full inhalation, then start exhaling slowly through pursed lips in a long steady stream and bend forward slowly, starting from the coccyx and working along the spine, vertebrae by vertebrae, to the mid-back, shoulder area, and finally the neck, until you are bent over with arms dangling down loosely. Do this very *slowly*, even if it requires two breaths to complete the forward bend. Keep the knees unlocked and slightly bent throughout this phase of the exercise. While bent over forward with empty lungs, take a deep inhalation through the nose as you raise your head up as far as possible. Then exhale through the mouth while slowly lowering the head again. On the next inhalation, start rising up slowly, beginning at the lower back and working progressively up the spine to the neck and head.

Your body should return to its original erect posture just as inhalation is complete, but do not stop moving. Bring your hands

Fig. 32 **The Iron Bridge:**
1. Starting posture. 2. Exhale, lean forward, and bend down. 3. Inhale while bent forward and raise head up. 4. Exhale and slowly lower head down. 5. Inhale and rise up slowly. 6. When inhalation is complete, place palms firmly on kidneys and lean back slowly while exhaling. 7. Lean back as far as possible on completion of exhalation. 8. Inhale while rising slowly up and raise arms upward over head. 9. Stretch arms up towards sky as far as possible on completion of inhalation. 10. Exhale smoothly, relax shoulders completely and bring arms slowly down to the sides with palms down

around to the back and place the palms firmly on kidneys, then lean over backwards as you exhale slowly through pursed lips, using your arms as a brace to support your weight. Lean back as far as possible without causing discomfort, until exhalation is complete. Holding this position, take a long slow nasal inhalation, followed by a long slow mouth exhalation. As you commence the next inhalation, slowly straighten up your spine and raise your head up, then bring both hands up from the kidneys and raise them straight up over your head, with the palms facing each other. On completion of inhalation, stretch your arms up as high as possible, extending the stretch down through the shoulders and ribcage, apply the neck lock and briefly compress the breath down into the abdomen. Then relax the neck, release the breath and exhale in a long steady stream through the lips, while turning the palms outward and bringing the arms slowly down to the sides, timing the movement of arms so that exhalation is completed as the hands return to their original starting position. Repeat this cycle 6 times.

Benefits: This exercise stretches and tones the entire spinal column, stimulates the flow and balances the distribution of cerebrospinal fluids, and draws energy into the channels of the Microcosmic Orbit. It also massages the kidneys and adrenal glands, tonifies kidney energy, and stimulates the thymus gland. It engages the entire chest cavity in breathing and flexes the diaphragm from the front and back, enhancing correct breathing technique. It also draws energy into circulation in the arm and leg channels and opens up the entire Macrocosmic Orbit. Raising and lowering the head in front and back while breathing deeply promotes abundant circulation of freshly oxygenated blood to the brain, and the long mouth exhalations purge the bloodstream of carbon dioxide and other wastes.

Palms Raised to Heaven to Regulate the Triple Burners (Fig. 33)

This exercise comes from the Eight Pieces of Brocade set (see page 203) developed by Marshal Yueh Fei during the Sung dynasty. It is designed to open up the valves and gates of the 'Triple Burner.' The Upper Burner governs movement of energy and blood from the top of the throat to the entrance of the stomach, including lungs and heart; the Middle Burner regulates vital functions and energy flow in the major digestive organs from the stomach, spleen and pancreas, to the liver, gallbladder, kidneys and small intestine; the Lower Burner controls excretory orifices and their functions and distributes energy to the bowels and bladder. This exercise balances these three energy systems and regulates the various vital functions of the related organs.

Method: Stand in the Horse, empty the lungs and relax. Bring the hands together in front, palms up, fingers about an inch (2.5cm) apart. As you commence a long slow inhalation, slowly raise the hands up along the front of the body. When palms reach neck level, turn them around 360 degrees so that they face the sky again and continue raising them upward as you complete inhalation. Lungs should be full by the time hands reach forehead level. Compress the breath and apply the locks and continue raising the palms until

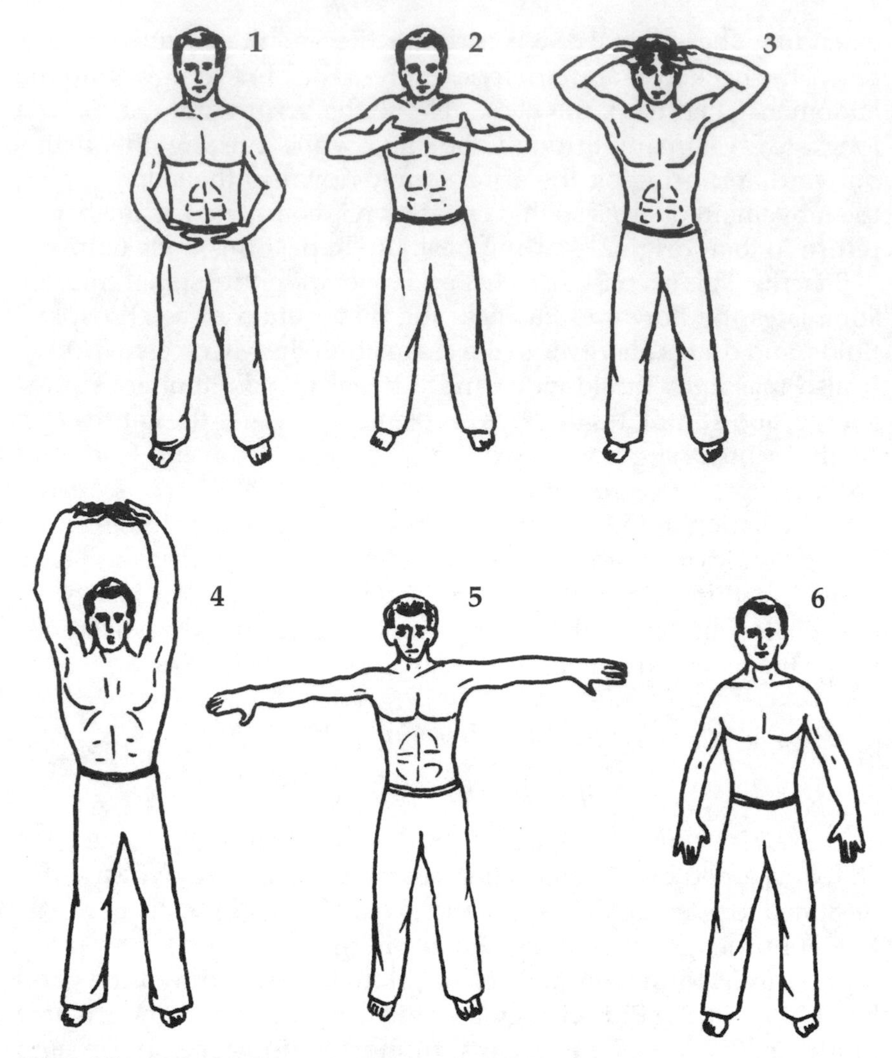

Fig. 33 **Palms Raised to Heaven to Regulate the Triple Burners:**
1. Starting posture. 2. Inhale and raise palms slowly up the front of the body. 3. Turn palms around to face upwards and continue raising them towards the sky while continuing inhalation. 4. Palms raised to heaven upon completion of inhalation. 5. Exhale smoothly and evenly while bringing arms slowly down to the sides. 6. Hands return to thighs upon completion of exhalation.

your arms are fully extended above the head. Then relax the locks, release the breath and exhale slowly through the nostrils, while turning the palms out to the sides and bringing the arms slowly back down to the starting position. Turn palms upward and commence the next cycle. Repeat 12 times.

Benefits: This exercise balances energy in all of the internal organs and harmonizes their vital functions. The lungs and heart are brought into balance for optimum respiration and circulation, the kidneys and liver are stimulated to purify the bloodstream, all digestive functions are regulated, the excretory functions of the bladder and bowels are improved, and the endocrine system is balanced. Energy flow in the arm channels is activated, and the protective aura of Guardian Energy that envelopes the body is strengthened.

Shake the Head and Wag the Tail to Expel Fire from the Heart (Fig. 34)

This is another exercise from the Eight Pieces of Brocade set, simplified for easier practice. It drives excess Fire energy out of the system, clearing the channels for cooling Water energy converted

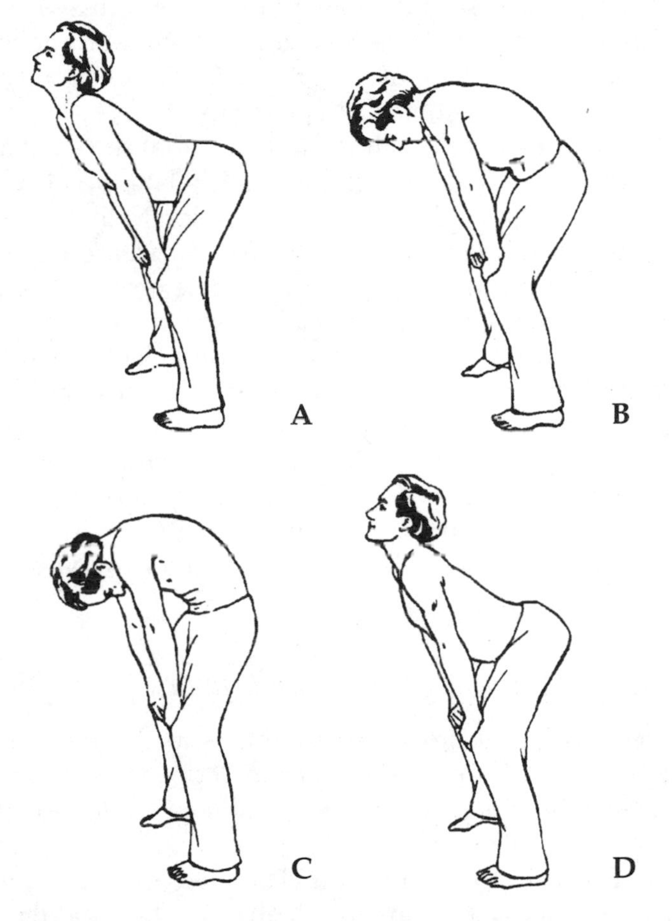

Fig. 34 **Shake the Head and Wag the Tail to Expel Fire from the Heart:**
A. Inhale slowly while bowing the spine and raising the head
B. Exhale through mouth while arching the spine, lowering the head and tucking the bottom inwards
C. Fully arch the spine and bend head down upon completion of exhalation
D. Inhale slowly while bowing the spine and raising the head

internally from vital essence and drawn into the system from external sources.

Method: Plant the feet wider than shoulder-width apart and splay the toes inward at about 45 degrees. Place the palms firmly on the thighs just above the knees, with fingers and thumbs pointing inward, and lean forward so that your weight is resting fully on your arms. As you inhale slowly and deeply, raise the head up and bend the neck back, while bowing the entire spine and sticking out the buttocks at the back, until you reach full extension. The abdominal and neck locks do not come into play in this exercise, but you may apply the anal lock as inhalation reaches completion.

Next, open the mouth and start exhaling slowly from the top of the throat, making a 'haw' sound. This sound draws excess Fire from the heart. While exhaling, bring the head down, tuck the buttocks in and arch the spine upward, until you reach full extension, with chin against chest and rounded back. Repeat 6 to 12 times.

Benefits: The alternate arching and bowing of the back align the vertebrae, tone the spinal muscles and stimulate the nerves of the spinal cord. It also provides strong stimulation to the adrenals and thymus gland. One of the major causes of chronic degenerative conditions today is what's known in TCM as 'excess Fire energy'. This is caused by poor diet, especially excessive consumption of acid-forming foods, incomplete digestion, alcohol and drugs, pollution and chronic stress. This exercise is designed to expel excess Fire from the system by drawing it out through the lungs and energy gates. At the same time, it stimulates the adrenal cortex to release hormone essence for conversion into cooling, restorative Water energy, thereby balancing Fire with Water and increasing immunity and resistance. This exercise also tones the diaphragm and deepens the breath.

Open the Chest and Stretch the Upper Spine (Fig. 35)

This exercise is based on one of the steps in the Eight Pieces of Brocade, but is much simpler to practise. It opens the heart chakra, stimulates the thymus gland and gives a deep stretch to the upper spine.

Method: Stand in the Horse and clasp your hands behind your back by intertwining the fingers. While slowly inhaling, rise up slowly on your toes and raise your clasped hands upward behind the back, but without bending the torso forward. The idea is to stretch the shoulders back as far as possible by raising the arms up in back, which also stretches open the entire front of the chest.

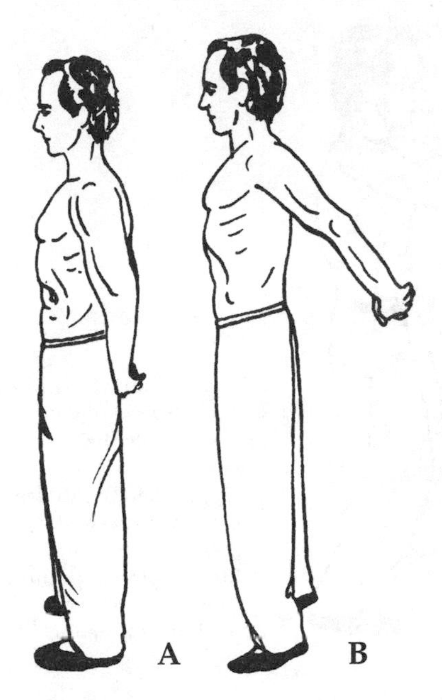

Fig. 35
Open the Chest and Stretch the Upper Spine:
A. Starting posture: Horse stance with hands clasped behind back
B. Inhale while slowly raising clasped hands upwards behind back and standing up on toes, then exhale and return to 'A' posture

When your lungs are full, release the breath and exhale through the nose, while slowly bringing the heels back down to the ground and lowering the arms down at the back. Since there is not much distance involved in these movements, they should be done very slowly to keep them in tune with the breath.

Benefits: Stretches all the vertebrae of the upper spine and opens the whole chest cavity, while also toning the muscles of the calves. Opens the heart chakra and allows energy to flow freely through it. Standing up on the toes stimulates energy along the bladder meridians on the back of the legs, and the upper spine stretch extends that stimulation to the upper branches of the bladder meridian in the upper spine, neck and back of the head. This exercise also draws terrestrial energy up from the earth through the 'Bubbling Spring' points on the soles, and brings it up the back of the legs to the spine and into the head on inhalation, then draws it back down the front of the body on exhalation. In addition, it helps develop physical coordination and balance.

Embracing the Tree (Fig. 36)

This is a still standing exercise designed to activate the internal flow of energy through the channels of the Macrocosmic Orbit. It also condenses energy in the channels and develops conscious awareness of energy moving in the body.

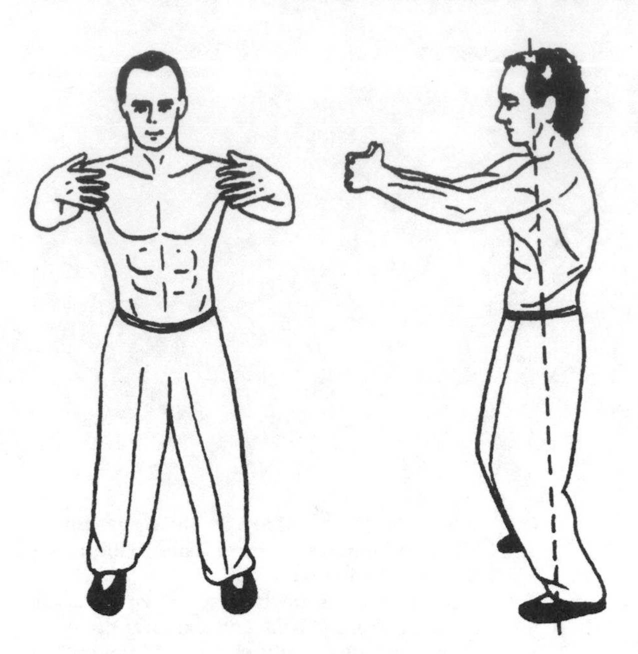

Fig. 36 **Embracing the Tree: front and side views; note the alignment of the Upper (head), Middle (solar plexus) and Lower (abdomen) Elixir Fields with the centre line between the balls of the feet**

Method: Stand in the Horse, with the feet perfectly parallel. Rub the palms briskly together to charge them with *chi*. Inhale and slowly raise your arms up in front of your body. When arms are extended in front of the solar plexus, turn the palms so that they face the heart and hold the arms as if they were embracing a large round tree. Maintaining correct posture is very important here: straight spine aligned with neck and head, buttocks tucked in, shoulders relaxed, and weight resting on the balls of the feet, not on the heels. Breathe consciously in the four stages and use the three locks, while focusing attention on the feelings in your hands, arms and anywhere else that you detect energy moving. Try to maintain balanced posture and stable stance with minimal muscular tension. Continue 'embracing the tree' and breathing deeply from the diaphragm for 5 to 10 minutes, or however long you can. Some adepts practise this exercise for up to an hour at a time.

Benefits: This exercise generates a strong flow of internal energy that runs through all of the Eight Extraordinary Channels of the Macrocosmic Orbit and stores reserve energy in these reservoirs. It beams energy through the *lao-gung* points of the palms into the heart chakra, and draws energy up from the earth through the *yung-chuan* points on the soles into the leg channels. It activates circulation in the Microcosmic Orbit, drawing sacral Fire energy up through the spinal passes to the head, cooling and refining it into Water, then sends it back down the front as Water energy. This exercise also develops a strong Horse stance, which is useful for all chi-gung practice, and cultivates proper posture in the spine.

Merging Heaven and Earth (Fig. 37)

Method: Stand in Horse, with arms hanging loosely by your sides. As you commence a long, slow inhalation, raise both arms slowly up in front, palms facing down, wrists and fingers completely relaxed, until arms are extended out in front, parallel to the ground, and inhalation is complete. Draw the hands in towards the chest, keeping palms facing downward, by bending the elbows, then commence a long, slow exhalation through the nose, while simultaneously pushing the hands down the front of the body toward the ground and gradually bending the knees. At the end of exhalation, hands are down in front of thighs, palms facing the ground and legs bent in a semi-squat. As you commence the next inhalation, extend the hands forward and then upward in a circular movement and straighten the knees, until arms are up in front parallel to ground on completion of inhalation, then draw the hands back in toward the body and push down again on exhalation. The idea of the exercise is to inscribe a large circle in front of the body with the hands, and to rise up and down on the knees, in synchrony with breath.

Benefits: This exercise balances Yin and Yang, merges Heaven and Earth, and fuses Fire and Water, establishing polar equilibrium within the energy system. Terrestrial energy is drawn up through

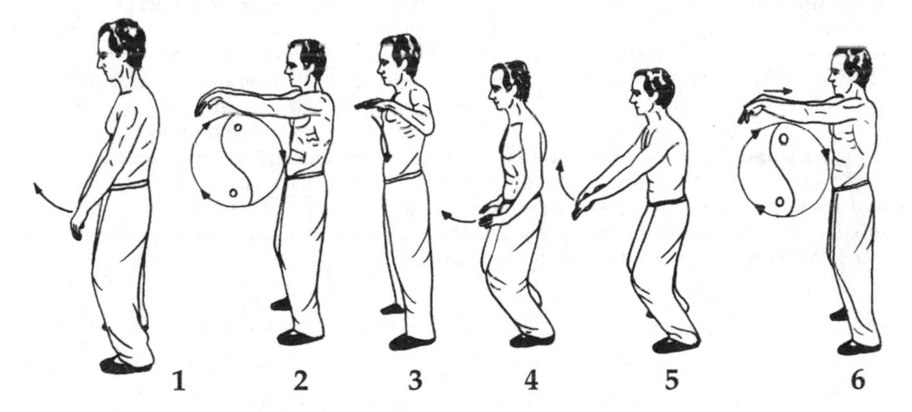

Fig. 37 **Merging Heaven and Earth:**
1. Starting posture: Horse stance, knees bent. 2. Inhale and raise arms up in front, with palms down, and straighten knees. 3. Draw arms back towards chest upon completion of inhalation. 4. Exhale while lowering palms down in front and bending knees. 5. Inhale, raise arms up in front and straighten knees. 6. Continue breathing while inscribing 'Tai-Chi' circle in front of body

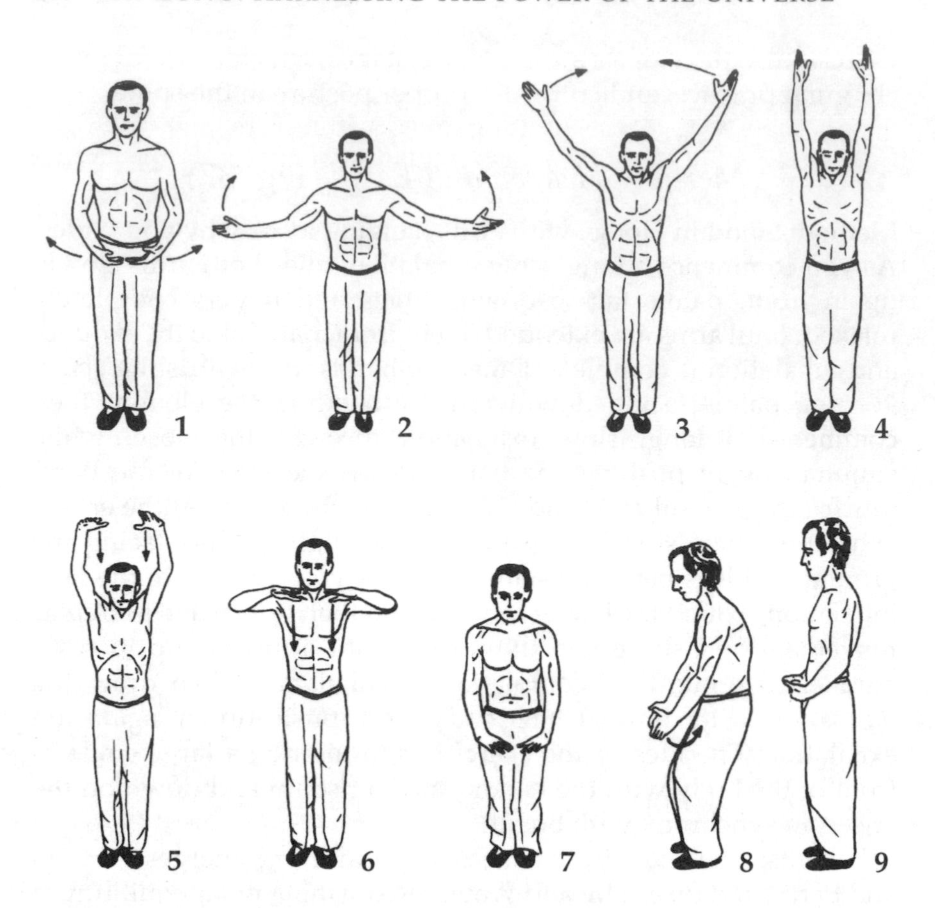

Fig. 38 **Great Tai-Chi Circle:**
1. Starting posture: heels together, toes splayed out at 30 to 45 degrees, palms facing upwards. 2. Inhale slowly while raising arms slowly out and up to the sides. 3. Continue inhalation while raising arms upward, keeping shoulders relaxed. 4. Stretch arms to the sky with palms facing each other and swallow upon completion of inhalation. 5. Turn palms to face the ground, relax shoulders completely, and slowly bring palms down along the front of body while slowly exhaling. 6. Continue exhalation smoothly while bringing palms down the front and slightly bending the knees. 7. Palms fully extended downwards in front and knees bent upon completion of exhalation. 8. Turn palms in and around towards the body while straightening the knees and taking a short inhalation. 9. Exhale after returning to starting posture, with brief intermission to check important points of posture before the next inhalation.

the energy gates in the soles and palms, while celestial energy is drawn down from the crown. The two merge and fuse at the chest on completion of inhalation and are packed down into the 'Sea of Energy' in the lower elixir field on exhalation. It's a very good exercise for developing synchronized movement of body and breath, cultivating balance and physical coordination, and building strong thighs, knees and ankles. This exercise also helps establish and maintain emotional equilibrium and mental clarity.

Great Tai-Chi Circle (Fig. 38)

If you practise only one chi-gung exercise, this is the one to select. It completely opens and balances circulation of energy in the circuits of the Macrocosmic Orbit, while also stretching and toning the body and deepening the breath. Sometimes referred to as 'Imperial Chi-Gung', this exercise is said to have been taught to Chinese emperors to protect health, prolong life and enhance vitality.

Method: Stand straight with the heels together and the toes splayed out at a 45-degree angle. Bring the hands together below the navel, palms up, tips of the middle fingers barely touching. Be sure that your posture is correct before starting – spine and neck aligned and straight, buttocks tucked in, shoulders relaxed, weight resting on the balls of the feet. In this exercise, the tongue should be curled all the way back in the mouth, so that the tip touches the soft palate at the top of the throat.

As you commence a long, slow, deep inhalation, draw the hands slowly out to the sides, keeping palms facing the sky. During the inhalation phase, the big toes should be slightly curled to 'grip' the ground, and the anal lock should be gradually applied. Continue inhaling and raising the palms out and up, until breath is full and hands are stretched straight up above the head, with the palms facing each other. Swallow hard to sink your *chi* (even if you have no saliva to swallow, go through the motions of swallowing anyway), then apply the neck lock and make a final effort to stretch the arms up as high as possible, extending the stretch down through the shoulders to the ribs and waist. In this upstretched posture, the abdominal lock applies itself, so you need not think about that.

When ready to exhale, relax the big toes, release the anal and neck locks, turn the palms down so that they are facing the ground, and start a long slow even exhalation through the nostrils, while bringing your hands slowly down the front of the body and gradually bending the knees, so that by the time your hands have reached the bottom and breath is empty, you are standing in a semi-squat.

Now take an interim inhalation and draw the hands in toward the body, turning the palms around and up to face the sky, while also straightening the legs and locking the knees. This returns you to the original starting position. Exhale, pause briefly with empty lungs to make sure that your posture is correct for the next cycle, then grip the ground with the big toes and commence the next inhalation while raising palms out and up to the sides. This entire exercise should be done very slowly and deliberately for best results. Do 8 to 12 cycles. If this is the only exercise in your session, you might wish to do 20 to 30 repetitions.

Benefits: Completely opens the Macrocosmic Orbit and stimulates energy flow through those channels. Balances Yin/Yang polarity and facilitates energy flow between left and right, top and bottom, front and back parts of the body. Gripping the ground with the big toes activates the liver meridian, drawing energy into the liver on inhalation. Provides a thorough stretch to the shoulders, ribcage, chest and abdomen, thereby enhancing deep diaphragmic breathing. Stimulates circulation of blood throughout the system. While opening the Macrocosmic Orbit of energy circulation, this exercise also amplifies circulation in the Microcosmic Orbit, drawing energy up the spine into the head on inhalation, then down the front into the lower abdomen on exhalation. It's also an excellent exercise for developing focused attention and mental concentration in chi-gung, and for cultivating conscious awareness of *chi* moving through the body.

Cool-Down: Collecting and Storing Energy

It's very important to conclude every chi-gung session with a few manoeuvres designed to collect and store energy, otherwise the energy harvested during the main practice can easily dissipate. Leaving too much energy lingering in the head and upper body after practice can also lead to problems, such as dizziness, headaches, irritability and insomnia. It only takes a few minutes to collect and store your energy in the lower elixir field centre below the navel, and down in the channels and bone marrow of the legs, so be sure not to overlook this important stage of practice.

Harmonizing Internal and External Energies (Fig. 39)

This exercise is designed to 'wrap up' energy lingering in the upper part of the body, both internally and externally, and to 'pack' it into the lower elixir field centre below the navel for storage. Regardless of which combination of chi-gung exercises you select for your main practice, you should always finish a session with this exercise, which is the first step in the collection and storage stage.

Method: Stand in Horse and bring the hands forward a bit, so that the palms are facing each other in front, with the *lao-gung* points perfectly aligned. As you commence inhalation, draw the hands apart and out to the sides, then slowly upward, always keeping the palm points aligned. When inhalation is complete and hands are

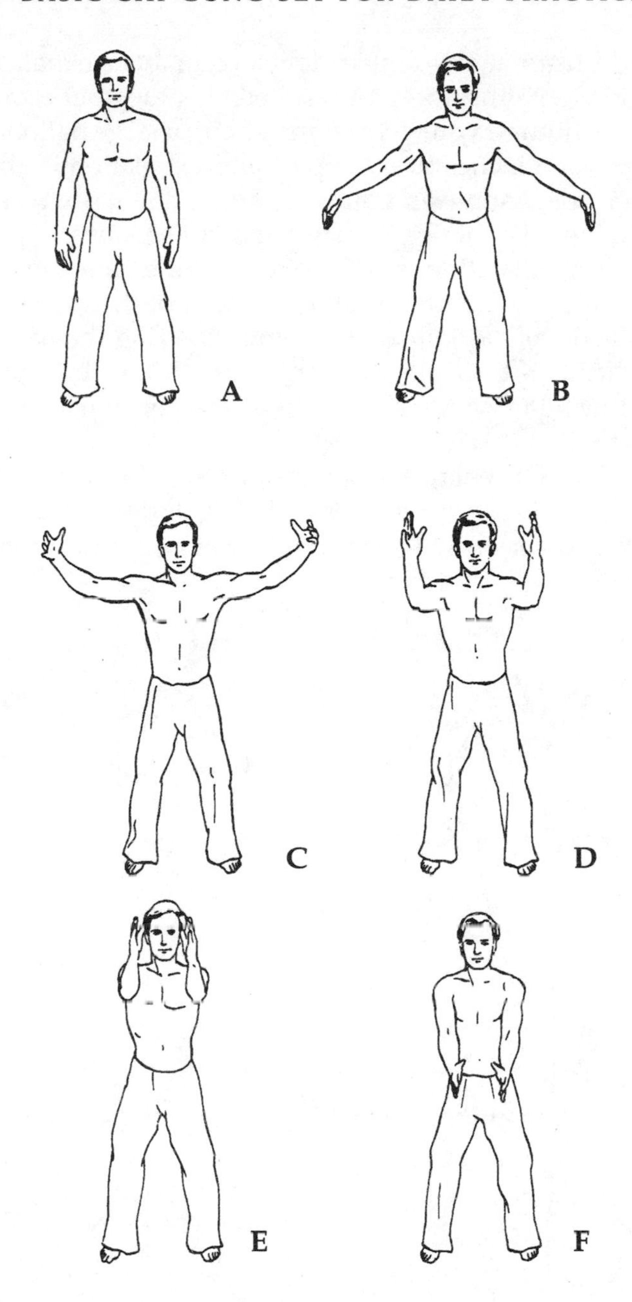

Fig. 39 **Harmonizing Internal and External Energies:**
A. Starting posture: Horse stance, hands extended in front with palms facing each other
B. Inhale slowly while drawing hands out to the sides in front, keeping the palms aligned
C. Arms raised and extended in front with palms facing upon completion of inhalation
D. Bring palms and forearms towards each other while exhaling slowly
E. When palms are head-width apart, bring them down slowly in front of body while continuing exhalation
F. Palms return to starting position upon completion of exhalation

spread out in front at about heart level, commence exhalation and slowly bring the palms, forearms and elbows together in a smooth movement, as though you were compressing a large balloon. When palms are about 8 inches (20cm) apart and exhalation is about half done, lower the hands and arms slowly down in front, until returning to the original position. Repeat 6 to 12 times.

After the last exhalation, continue to hold the hands out in front with palms aligned, about shoulder-width apart, close your eyes and continue deep abdominal breathing, drawing the hands a few inches further apart on the exhalation phase and bringing them closer together again on inhalation, like an accordion. Continue for 3 to 5 minutes.

Benefits: Collects energy from the upper parts of the body, internally as well as externally, condenses it, and draws it down the front into the lower elixir field centre for storage. Harmonizes the

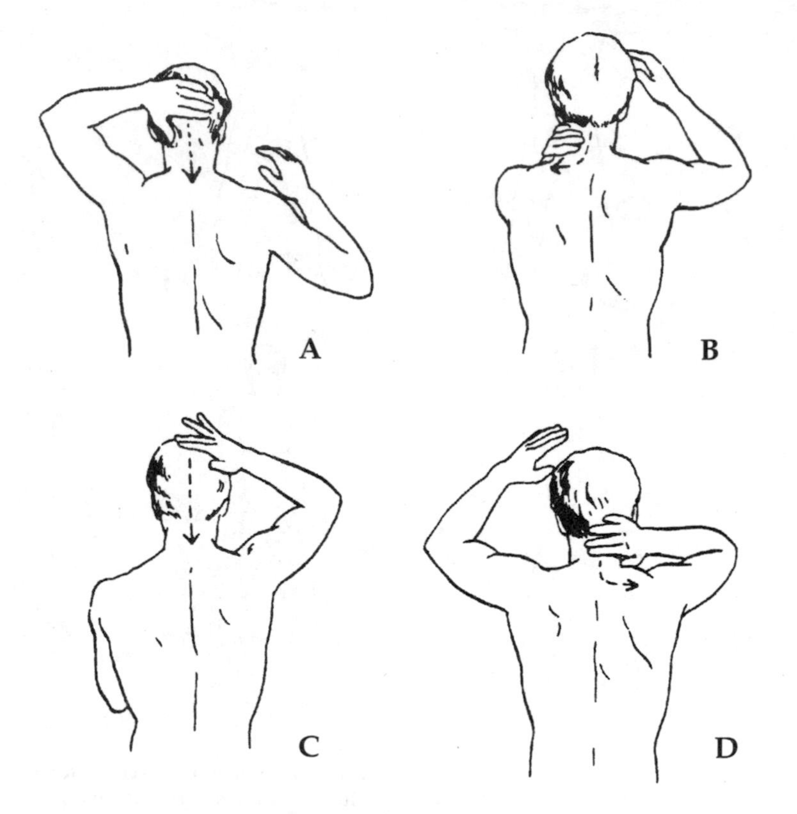

Fig. 40 **Head and Neck Rubdown:**
A. Rub head down from the crown to back of the neck
B. Continue sweeping down along side of neck, while starting to rub down from crown with the other hand
C. Continue sweeping down with second hand
D. Bring first hand back to crown for next rubdown

human energy field with external fields and balances polarity throughout the system. Moves energy through the *lao-gung* points in the palms, and helps cultivate conscious awareness of energy flow. Allows energy to settle naturally into the lower parts of the body.

Note: The latter part of this exercise (standing still with palms extended in front) is a form of still standing meditation and may be practised by itself any time of day or night. When practised at the end of a round of moving meditation, it helps settle energy and transforms some of it into spiritual vitality.

Head and Neck Rubdown (Fig. 40)

Method: Rub palms briskly together till warm, then place one palm on crown of head and rub down the back of the head, down the neck, and down along the side of the neck to the collarbone and chest in front. Follow the first palm immediately with the other one, alternately rubbing down the head and neck and sweeping around the sides to the front and down the chest.

Benefits: Sweeps excess energy from the head and neck and draws it into circulation down the front of the body, settling it into the lower elixir field below the navel. Activates lymph in the neck and stimulates blood circulation in the scalp.

Tapping the Celestial Drum (Fig. 41)

Method: Rub palms together till warm, then place palms firmly over the ears, creating an air-tight seal, with fingers against back of skull. Hook index fingers over middle fingers and snap them against the back of the skull, at the 'Wind Pond' points where the neck ends and the skull begins (see page 158). Snap repeatedly, creating a drumming sound within the skull, 36 times.

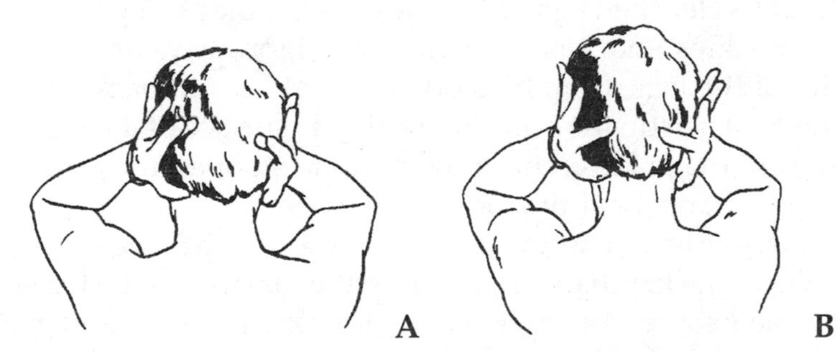

Fig. 41 **Tapping the Celestial Drum:**
A. Hook index fingers over middle fingers
B. Snap index fingers against back of skull

Benefits: Helps clear excess energy from the skull. Vibrations stimulate the pineal and pituitary glands and help balance right and left hemisphere functions. Clears mental static from the brain, preparing the mind for still meditation after a round of moving exercises.

Body Sweep

Method: Rub palms together till warm. Use left palm to sweep down the right arm, from the shoulder down the outside of the arm to the fingers, then from shoulder down the inside of the arm to the fingers. Do the same on the other arm using the other hand. Rub palms together again, and use them to rub down the chest from the throat to the navel, then down the ribcage from the armpits to the hips.

Benefits: Draws excess energy down from the top of the body, sweeping it out to the hands and down into the lower abdomen. Stimulates microcirculation in the skin. Enhances the protective shield of Guardian Energy.

Kidney Rubdown

Method: Rub palms together till warm. Place palms on kidneys and rub gently.

Benefits: Draws energy down into the kidneys and adrenal glands and condenses energy there. Stimulates adrenal secretions and boosts immunity.

Leg Channel Tap (Fig. 42)

Method: Rub palms together till warm, then roll fingers into fists, with thumbs clenched against the outsides of index fingers. Use the curled knuckles and base of palms to vigorously tap down the outsides of the legs, from hips down to ankles and back up again, three times. Then do the same on the inside surface of the legs, from the groin to the ankles. This may be done stooped forward in the standing position, or sitting on a stool.

Benefits: Drives energy accumulated in the legs into the reservoirs of the leg channels, and into the marrow of the leg bones. Leg channels serve as storage centres for sexual energy and general physical vitality, while marrow produces white and red blood cells. When fresh energy is tapped into the marrow, it purifies the marrow and stimulates production of new blood cells.

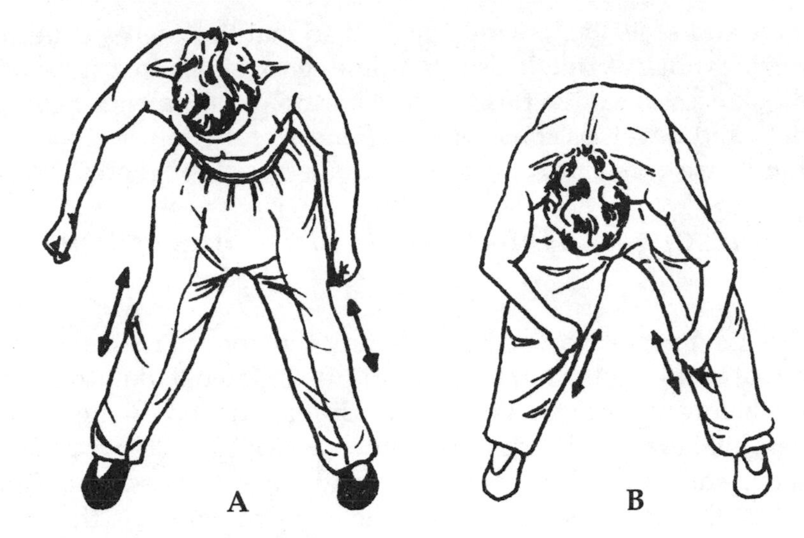

Fig. 42 **Leg Channel Tap:**
A. Tap up and down the outside of the legs from hips to ankles
B. Tap up and down the inside of the legs from crotch to ankles

Navel Rub: Closing the Energy Gates (Fig. 43)

Method: Rub palms together till warm. Place one palm on the navel, with the *lao-gung* point directly over the navel. Place the other palm over the first, then gently rub in small circles, 2 to 3 dozen times.

Benefits: This manoeuvre, which closes the energy gates, draws energy from the entire system down into the navel region for

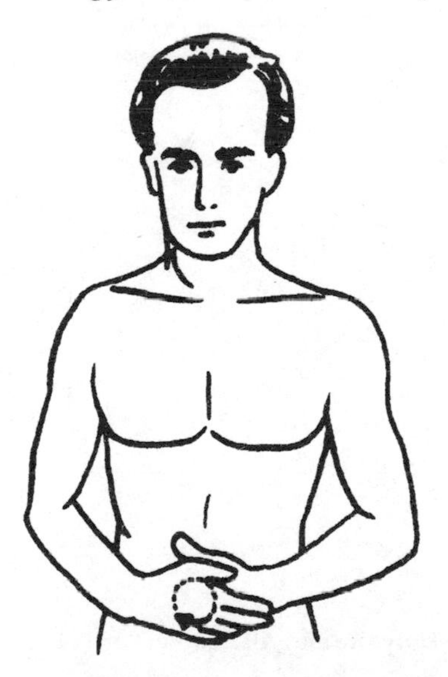

Fig. 43 **Navel Rub: Closing the Energy Gates**

storage and seals the lower elixir field so that the energy collected there does not leak out. It also stimulates gastrointestinal secretions and balances digestive functions. It harmonizes the entire energy system and develops conscious awareness of the lower elixir field as the centre of balance and major storage depot for energy.

Thanking the Universe and All Teachers of Truth (Fig. 44)

This is the proper way to conclude any type of internal energy or spiritual work in Asian traditions and is somewhat akin to saying grace before a meal in Western tradition. Indeed, some practitioners make a similar gesture before as well as after a practice session, and in some schools it is customary to bow to all four points of the compass as a symbolic acknowledgement to the entire universe. Its purpose is to acknowledge the greater wisdom and power of the universe, and of those who have mastered that wisdom and power and teach others how to discover it, and to express personal gratitude for whatever was gained during the preceding practice session. In addition to thanking the universe itself, this is also a gesture of respect to all true teachers who have

Fig. 44 **Thanking the Universe and All Teachers of Truth**

helped transmit the wisdom and power of the universe to humanity. This includes whoever teaches you, as well as your teacher's teacher, and all the teachers in that lineage, plus all teachers who ever taught anyone anywhere, who you regard as sacred, such as Jesus, Buddha or Lao Tze.

Method: After completing the final step in your practice, place your palms together before your heart, bow your head slightly, and silently thank your teachers, their teachers and all teachers of truth, as well as the whole universe, for sharing their wisdom and power with you, and resolve to share what you have gained with others.

Benefits: While this may seem like a mere formality, it can in fact have a profound influence on your practice. After a session of chi-gung, your entire system is very closely interlinked with the energy and awareness of the universe, with the spirits of your teachers, and with any other spiritual entities you personally hold as sacred. Consciously acknowledging their presence and expressing gratitude for the benefits of their wisdom, compassion and power forges a strong connection between your spirit and theirs, and this creates a channel of direct mind-to-mind transmission in your practice. This gesture also helps prevent the hubris that sometimes arises as a result of successful practice, by acknowledging the universe as the ultimate source of all virtue, not your own ego, and seeing yourself as a vessel into which the wisdom and power of the universe pours, like lustral water into a vase.

Still Meditation

Still forms of chi-gung may be practised in one of the sitting postures (see Figs. 12 and 13, page 165), or else standing in the Horse stance (see page 161) with the palms held shoulder-width apart in front facing each other (Fig. 49a) or extended out to the sides facing forward (Fig. 49b). Still and moving meditations are the Yin and Yang of chi-gung forms, and when practised together the effects are highly synergistic and complementary. Both styles of practice mobilize internal energy and balance the human energy system. However, moving forms focus more on the interaction of energy and essence and the synchronicity of body and breath, while still forms engage energy and spirit and work more with the union of mind and breath. Moving exercises are therefore the most beneficial form of practice for cultivating physical health and longevity, while still forms are best for cultivating mental clarity, spiritual awareness and a tranquil state of mind.

When practised together, still meditation is usually done after the moving set, in which case there is no need to prepare body and breath with preliminary warm-up exercises, because both will already be in balance as a result of the moving exercises. When still meditation is practised separately, such as late at night, it's best to first prepare your system for it by balancing body, breath and mind with the following preliminary steps.

Balancing Body and Breath for Still Meditation

• **Body.** First do 2 to 3 minutes of the 'spinal twist' warm-up introduced in the previous section (see page 215), then do 2 to 3 minutes of the following 'serpentine' spinal stretch exercise

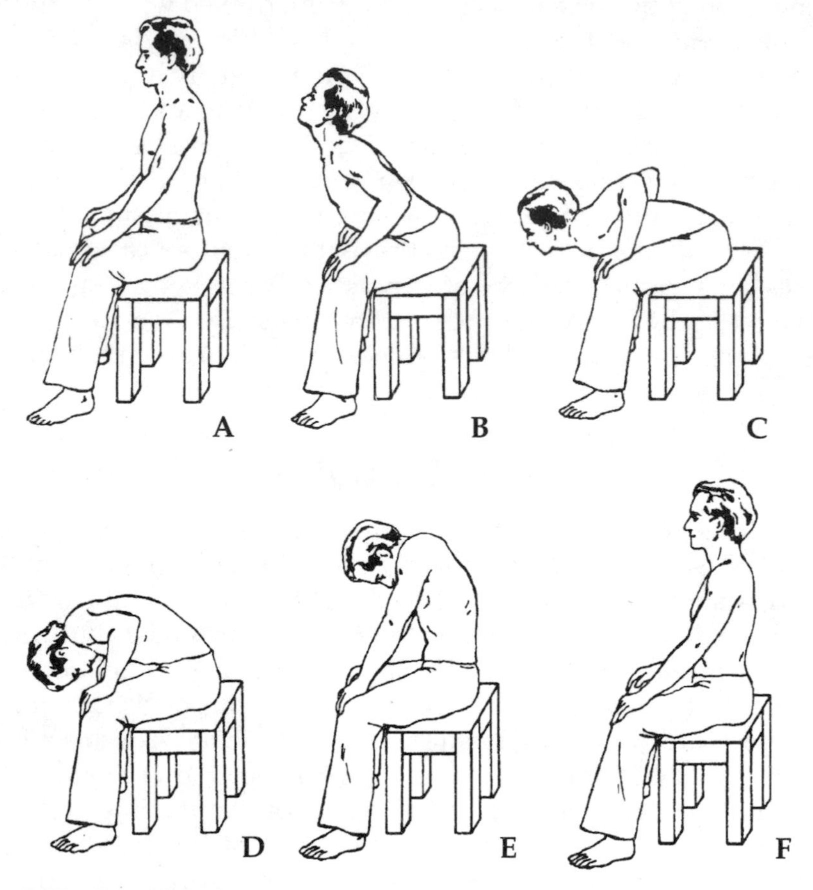

Fig. 45 **The Spinal Stretch:**
A. Starting posture: hands on knees, spine erect
B. Lean forward, leading with the chin and bowing the spine
C. Extend fully forwards and stretch the spine
D. Tuck the head down and arch the spine up, pushing up on hands
E. Push body back up to erect posture and raise up the neck while straightening the spine
F. Return to starting posture

(Fig. 45). Sit cross-legged on the floor or on the edge of a chair with hands palm-down on the knees. Jut the chin out in front and lean forward, leading the body with the head and stretching the spine. When fully extended forward, tuck the chin down, arch the spine and raise the torso back up to the erect sitting position by pushing the hands against the knees and straightening up the spine from the coccyx to the neck. Repeat at a fairly brisk pace for 2 to 3 minutes. This exercise stretches the spine, aligns the vertebrae and stimulates the nerves of the spinal cord. It opens the two major channels of the Microcosmic Orbit circuit in front and back, as well as the central Thrusting Channel that links the energy gates on the crown of the head with the lower elixir field in the abdomen. These are the three most important channels for internal energy circulation in still meditation. It also tones the muscles of the spine to help maintain correct posture during practice.

• **Breath.** While sitting or standing in proper posture, do a minute or two of incremental bellows breathing to clear the lungs, loosen the diaphragm, oxygenate the bloodstream, and eliminate carbon dioxide and other wastes. Then do 6 to 8 rounds of 'Clear Head Cool Heart' breathing (Fig. 46), as follows: Inhale deeply and slowly through the nostrils, while slowly raising the head up and tilting it back and arching the neck and upper spine, until fully extended. Then open the mouth and commence a long slow exhalation, making a 'haw' sound at the top of the throat, while bringing the head forward and down and tucking the chin against the chest as exhalation is completed. Inhale and raise the head up

Fig. 46 **'Clear the Head, Cool the Heart' Breath:**
A. Inhale and raise head up and back as far as possible
B. Exhale and lower head forward and down as far as possible

and back again, repeating 6 to 8 times. This exercise purges excess Fire energy from the lungs and heart, thereby cooling and calming the respiratory and circulatory systems for still meditation. It also clears the brain, releases tension in the neck and shoulders, and activates energy circulation along the spinal channels into the head.

• **Mind.** After completing the manoeuvres outlined above, do a few minutes of alternate nostril breathing. Not only does this further balance the breath, it also balances the right and left hemispheres of the brain, induces a state of mental equilibrium, and allows the intuition and insight of the right hemisphere to function in conjunction with the rational thought and linear logic of the left.

Finally, take a deep inhalation, then open the mouth and throat wide and sound the tone 'ahh' in a long steady stream until the lungs are completely empty. Repeat 3 times. This tone opens the throat chakra, which governs breathing and houses the spiritual faculties involved with perceiving and expressing truth. Sounding this tone before still meditation helps prepare the mind to receive any messages or insights that the universe ('Heaven') may bestow during a session.

Sitting Meditation

There are many different styles of meditation in the spiritual traditions of Asia, each of which has its own tutelary deities, patron saints, sacred scriptures and divine revelations for disciples to work with in their contemplative practices. Since this book focuses on chi-gung as a means of working with energy, and since meditation is a form of chi-gung in which energy is used to nurture spirit and spirit is focused to regulate energy, we will limit our discussion here to ways of working with energy for spiritual purposes and working with spirit to cultivate energy. This is the Taoist approach to meditation – a non-sectarian and non-theistic path of practice that may be applied to any spiritual tradition in the world, without conflicting with any theoretical doctrines and religious beliefs.

One of the primary goals of Taoist meditation is simply to clear the mind of discursive thought and mundane distractions and restore it to a pristine state of open clarity and silent calm, so that we may recover our inherent link with the infinite awareness of the universe. As the Tang dynasty grand master of the Complete Reality School of Taoism, Lu Tung-pin, puts it: 'The mind is primordially pure and calm, completely free and infinitely vast . . . Therefore, managing the mind simply means maintaining it in its original state of purity, clear as mountain water, fresh and uncontaminated, silent as a huge valley, without distraction, immeasurably vast, wide open as the sky, without boundaries.' The point of this practice is not just to sit still for a while each day, then return to our normal state of mental distraction, but rather to cultivate stillness of mind throughout the day. 'True sitting,' writes the Sung dynasty master Wang Che, 'means that the mind is as still as a mountain at all times, regardless of what you are doing, in activity as well as repose . . .'

What people who don't meditate don't realize is that meditation has very practical benefits for health and longevity as well as for spiritual cultivation, and this is particularly true of Taoist meditation, which cultivates the fundamental energy of life. The Taoist classic, *Huai-nan-tze*, states:

> Whatever can be achieved internally may also be attained externally. When one masters the internal, the vital organs are in perfect harmony and the mind is calm . . . When one reposes in blissful serenity and remains undisturbed by habitual attachments, then the vital organs will rest in harmony, suffused with energy that does not leak. Thus, the spirit protects the body internally without roaming abroad.

Mental and emotional stress squanders energy faster than even the most gruelling manual labour. Not only does stress damage the organs and impair immune response by causing secretions of hormones that put the entire system on perpetual 'fight or flight' alert, it also causes a constant leakage of energy due to the worry and emotional turmoil it triggers. Meditation is the most effective antidote against stress, and with prolonged practice, meditation trains the mind not to re-act to stressful situations with the 'fight or flight' response, by cultivating the virtues of detachment and emotional equanimity.

What distinguishes Taoist meditation from all other traditions is the internal alchemy of the Three Treasures, which integrates body and mind with energy. As Chang San-feng, the founding father of Tai Chi Chuan, notes, internal alchemy 'enables the spirit to guide energy, and energy to sustain the body. At this stage, one no longer requires complicated exercises and other techniques in order to achieve longevity.' In other words, when you reach the stage of practice where you can manage your energy directly with your mind through internal alchemy, then meditation becomes the only practice you need to achieve health and longevity, and even physical exercise is no longer necessary, since you will be able to 'exercise' your body with your mind via its complete command over energy. But please don't think that you can abandon exercise, diet, supplements, sexual discipline and other techniques after only a few days of meditation practice. It takes many years of disciplined practice to reach that stage of self-mastery, and until then, all of the various exercises and other physical techniques involved in the 'Tao of Cultivating Life' remain important stepping stones on the path of practice.

A variety of traditional Taoist meditation techniques are described in the author's previous books, so here we will simply run through a typical meditation session together, working with the central Thrusting Channel, the Microcosmic Orbit (Governing and Conception Channels), the energy gate on the crown of the head, and some of the major 'passes' that relay energy along the Microcosmic Orbit. Fig. 47 outlines the major paths of energy flow in this meditation.

Adopt a comfortable sitting posture, either cross-legged on the floor with a cushion to elevate the pelvis and support the spine, or else on the edge of a low stool or chair. If you have not practised a moving meditation set prior to sitting, then prepare yourself first with the preliminary steps introduced above (see page 246).

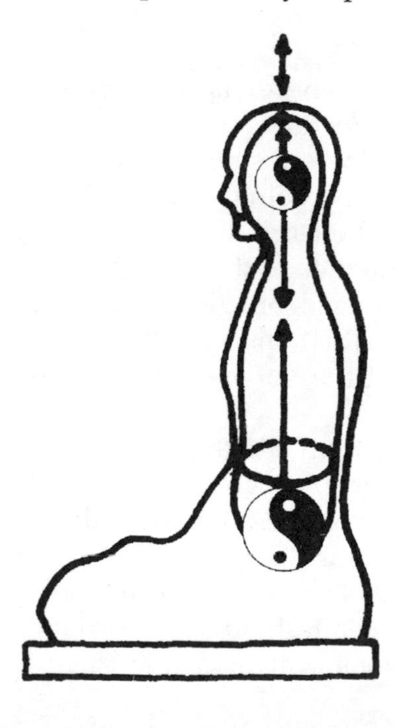

Fig. 47 **Major Energy Paths in Taoist Meditation: Governing, Conception, Thrusting and Belt Channels; Upper and Lower Elixir Fields**

Rest your hands separately on top of the thighs, palms up, close your eyes, and spend the first few minutes of practice working exclusively with your breath. Follow the flow of air in and out of the nostrils, focus attention on the four stages of breathing, and gently apply the three locks to stimulate circulation of blood and energy and harmonize the internal organs. When breath is flowing smoothly and the body feels balanced and stable, shift your attention away from the four stages and three locks of breath control and simply let your breathing function naturally, with the abdomen expanding and contracting with the rise and fall of breath.

Now shift attention to the top of the head and visualize a column of clear white light streaming in on inhalation and travelling down the central Thrusting Channel to the lower elixir field centre just below the navel, where it collects and forms a radiant globe of bright light. Or you might prefer to visualize the energy forming a pool of liquid light below the navel. On exhalation, let the energy in the globe or pool condense and grow brighter. Inhale and draw more luminous energy down through the crown, feeling the throbbing sensation at the gate as it enters and following it down the central channel into the lower elixir field. Try not to lose sight of this light in your mind's eye: enhance the visualization with every breath by focusing attention on its colour and luminosity and any other distinctive qualities it may manifest. For you, it may look white or golden, blue or pink, peach or purple; it might feel warm or cool, wet or dry, smooth or vibrant. Don't try to dictate its appearance: just see and feel it as it comes to you and let your mind's eye witness its activity.

After a week or so of daily practice, the 'Sea of Energy' in the lower elixir field will grow full, and the energy collected there will be ready to flow down to the base of the spine and enter circulation in the Microcosmic Orbit via the coccyx, the first pass of the Governing Channel, which draws energy up the spine into the upper elixir field in the head. Focus on the feeling of energy moving in the sacrum for about a week, until the lower pass opens, then let the energy rise naturally up to the next pass, which is the Gate of Life, located along the spine directly behind the navel. Every time you sit down to practise this meditation, start from the beginning at the crown of the head, follow the energy down into the lower elixir field, watch it grow and glow there, then let it brim over and flow down into the coccyx, until it reaches the point to which it progressed last time, and spend the rest of the session working up from that point.

Master Han Yu-mo, who teaches Taoist internal energy

meditation in Taiwan, has developed an eight-week programme of practice that focuses entirely on opening up and expanding the Microcosmic Orbit circuit of energy circulation (Fig. 48). So let's follow his method by quoting some excerpts from his booklet, *Directions for Meditational Techniques*, translated by Daniel Reid and Ronald Brown and published in 1994, in Taipei. This booklet may be ordered directly from Master Han's meditation centre (see page 312). Here's how it works:

• **First week.** Working with the 'Medicine Palace Gate'
This is the gate through which primal spirit passes in and out of the body, and the major entry point for psychic energy. It is located midway between the crown of the head and the hairline. Visualize yourself as a gourd-shaped vase with its mouth located on top of your head, and slowly draw psychic energy into your body through this opening. After practising this for 3 to 5 days, you will begin to feel a sort of pressure on this spot, or an itchy sensation as though ants were crawling around the roots of your hair at this point. This feeling indicates that this energy gate has begun to open.

• **Second Week.** Working with the 'Great Sea of the Elixir Field'
This point is located 2 inches (5cm) below the navel, midway between the abdominal wall and the spine. It is the foundation of all

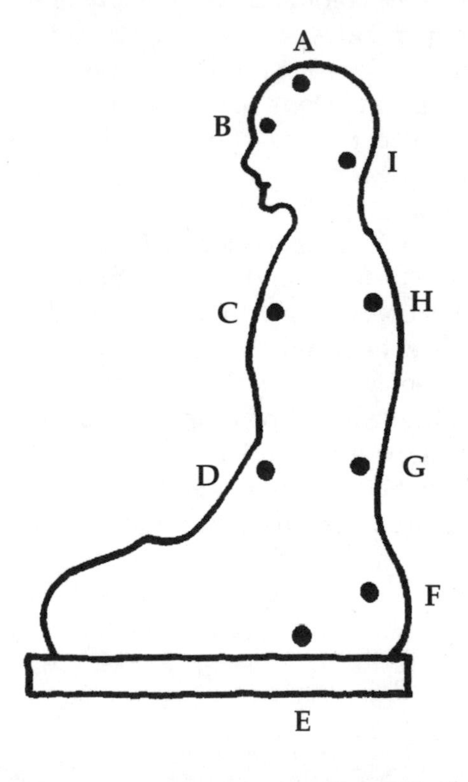

Fig. 48 Major Power Points in the Microcosmic Orbit Internal Energy Meditation:
A. 'Medicine Palace' point on the crown
B. 'Celestial Eye' at the Upper Elixir Field
C. 'Central Terrace' at the heart
D. 'Sea of Energy' at the Lower Elixir Field
E. 'Confluence of Yin' at the perineum
F. 'Tail End' at the coccyx
G. 'Gate of Life' between the kidneys
H. 'Great Hammer' between the shoulders
I. 'Jade Pillow' at junction of neck and skull

internal energy practices. Visualize yourself as a gourd-shaped vase, with the base located at the Elixir Field, and imagine the interior of the vase embracing a Great Sea of energy . . . Slowly draw energy down into this area as you breathe . . . There will be a feeling of warmth there that continues unabated as you sit. This indicates that the Elixir Field is gradually taking shape and filling with energy.

• **Third Week.** Working with the 'Hole at the Bottom of the Sea'
Located at the tip of the coccyx at the bottom of the spine, this point is where energy drains down from the Great Sea of the Elixir Field when it is full of energy. It is also the gate into the Governing Channel, which runs from the coccyx up to the head. After packing energy into the Elixir Field for 2 or 3 weeks, the Great Sea will brim over with energy, which will then automatically drain down into the Hole at the Bottom of the Sea and thereby enter the gate of the Governing Channel. It will cause a feeling of warmth, pressure and tingling there, as well as a sensation of upward thrusting.

• **Fourth Week.** Working with the 'Gate of Life'
The Gate of Life is located directly behind the navel along the spine. It is the first major power point along the Governing Channel. After sitting in meditation for a while and moving energy from the Elixir Field down into the Hole at the Bottom of the Sea, the energy will automatically rise up to the Gate of Life point, without any conscious effort. When energy reaches this point, it feels as if a patch of pure energy were stuck on to the skin at this point. There will also be very concrete sensations of heat, cold and tingling here.

• **Fifth week**. Working with the 'Great Hammer'
The Great Hammer is the point where the horizontal and vertical axes of the skeleton intersect, like the central point on a cross. It is the second major power point along the Governing Channel. After sitting in meditation for a while, energy will naturally flow upward from the Gate of Life to this point. There will be a hot, swollen tingling sensation of pressure here, as if a square patch of cloth were firmly adhered to this area. There will also be feelings of energy rising and falling. After several weeks of practice, energy will enter and exit this point according to the body's needs.

• **Sixth Week.** Working with the 'Mysterious Gate'
The Mysterious Gate is the point from which a person's primordial Yin spirit ('spiritual embryo') enters and exits the body in highly advanced meditation. It is located midway between and slightly above the eyes. When the three major power points along the Governing Channel are filled with energy, energy will automatically rise up over the head and gather at the Mysterious Gate. The Mysterious Gate is the other point through which psychic

energy may be drawn into the body. When one's meditation practice has reached this stage, one may switch over to this point for absorbing psychic energy from Heaven and Earth.

- **Seventh Week.** Working with the 'Yellow Court'

Located in the centre of the chest, the Yellow Court is the central circuit intersection for the body's autonomous breathing process and the first major power point along the Conception Channel, which runs from the head down the front of the body to the perineum. One may now draw psychic energy into the system through either the Medicine Palace Gate or the Mysterious Gate. Energy will be felt descending to this point from the forehead, Mysterious Gate, nose, mouth and palate. It will feel as if ants were crawling up and down just below the skin at this point.

- **Eighth Week.** Working with the 'Belt Channel'

The Belt Channel revolves completely around the waist at the level of the navel. When energy moves here, it is the first clear sign that the Microcosmic Orbit formed by the Governing and Conception Channels has been completely opened and filled with energy. When energy circulates here, the skin will feel as if ants were crawling around just beneath the surface.

The best times to practise still sitting meditation are during the hours around dawn and midnight, and any time in between midnight and dawn, when Yang energy rises, ascends and peaks. Some people get up in the middle of the night especially to practise this meditation, then go back to sleep afterward. Each meditation session should last from 20 to 45 minutes. Longer sessions tend to be counterproductive, because blood circulation often gets obstructed in the legs and lower back, which in turn blocks energy, while shorter sessions do not provide enough time for body, breath and mind to settle into the state of balance and harmony required for the human energy system to assimilate subtle energies from the universe and circulate them through the Microcosmic Orbit. It's also important to practise daily, so that the gates and channels remain open and active.

The term 'psychic energy' refers to highly refined forms of universal free energy which can awaken primordial awareness when assimilated into the human system during meditation practice. This energy is ever-present in the environment, but for most people, it's like 'water off a duck's back', because this energy can only enter the human system if the gates and channels that transmit it are open and functioning, and this can only be achieved through meditation practice.

This energy not only awakens spiritual awareness, but it may also be transformed in the chakras for other uses, such as healing, creativity, physical vitality and so forth. As the highest energy in the universe, its potency includes all the functions of the lower energies, and it may therefore be utilized to support all the basic functions of life. Furthermore, since this is the omnipotent energy associated with spirit, and since 'spirit commands energy and energy commands essence', this energy may be transformed by the spiritual faculties of visualization and intent to produce any type of essence required by the body. In other words, if your practice is sufficiently developed, you may literally 'feed' yourself simply by assimilating and storing abundant supplies of this energy and converting it as needed to repair cells, produce blood, generate heat and so forth.

This is the method that sustains yogis through 200-day fasts in the Himalayas, the principle in the *bi-gu* regime of periodic abstention from food practised by Taoists, and the way that so-called 'breatharians,' who give up all food permanently, continue to live long and healthy lives without eating. It may be difficult for people whose stomachs start growling with hunger the moment they wake up in the morning to imagine going even two days, much less two hundred, without food, but a hundred years ago it was equally difficult for people to imagine sitting in a machine that flies them through the air at 600 mph. The point is that like aerodynamics, the dynamics of internal energy work involved in sustaining physiological life solely by breath are based on scientific principles of universal validity, and they may be learned and mastered by anyone who is willing to put them into practice.

Before ending a meditation session, it's a good idea to dissolve whatever visualizations you're working with, close your mind's eye, and simply rest for a few minutes in the primordial state of emptiness, luminosity and energy, thereby cultivating awareness of the 'shining pearl' of immortal spirit which 'is not born and does not die'. According to Hindu, Buddhist and Taoist views, the fundamental state of the entire universe, as well as that of every being in every dimension of existence, has three essential natural qualities:

- **'Empty'.** This means that everything in the universe is essentially immaterial, empty of permanent concrete form, and that all material things are therefore impermanent and illusory, and ultimately 'unreal'. Thus, the physical body is essentially nothing more than a swirling vortex of organized energy temporarily bound in space and time, and therefore, like all forms of composite matter, the body of flesh, blood and bone will ultimately dissolve and disappear. Only spirit, which is immaterial, is real and permanent, transcending the temporal limits of space and time, and therefore only spirit can survive death and realize the immortal state of existence.

• **'Luminous'**. The essential emptiness of the universe and the spirit is not like a dark void or 'black hole' in space. It shimmers with self-existent luminosity, a shining radiance that does not depend on light reflected from the stars. That brilliant luminosity is the natural glow of awareness. It is the inherently radiant nature of the creative intelligence at work behind the constant interplay of form and emptiness and the ceaseless transmutations of energy and matter that give rise to the manifest universe and 'make the world go round'. In the microcosm of the human system, the same luminosity radiates from the eternal flame of consciousness that glitters within the spirit of each and every being in the universe.

• **'Energy'.** This essentially empty, naturally radiant ground of primordial spirit is suffused with unlimited energy of infinite potential. This energy is the basic 'stuff' of the universe, the immaterial material from which all form and matter arise and into which all composite matter again dissolves. This self-existent energy is governed by the luminous light of awareness and responds immediately to the beck and call of the creative spirit that permeates the entire universe.

In a nutshell, our world and everything and everyone in it, as well as all worlds everywhere, ultimately boil down to luminous empty space suffused with infinite energy, and these three essential qualities – immaterial emptiness, luminous awareness, and infinite energy – are the common denominators in all equations of life and throughout all existence in the universe. The only prerequisites for spiritual immortality are conscious awareness of these three basic facts of life, and conscious application of these facts as a basis for one's daily behaviour and point of view. When the reality of these three facts is truly understood, enlightened awareness dawns spontaneously, and spiritual immortality is attained. This is the ultimate goal of all spiritual practice, and reaching that goal is the only truly valid reason for preserving the health and prolonging the life of the physical body. Therefore, it's a good idea to conclude each meditation session with a brief plunge into the universal ocean of emptiness, awareness and energy, the primordial state of immortal existence that precedes birth and survives death and never ceases for a single instant, just to remind yourself that where you're going is precisely where you came from.

Standing Meditation

Still meditation may also be practised in standing postures. This is also a convenient way to do a bit of still meditation immediately after finishing a set of moving exercises, particularly after completing a round of the energy-collection exercise called 'Harmonizing Internal and External Energies' (see page 239), which puts you in the correct posture for standing meditation.

Still standing meditation moves energy somewhat differently from sitting meditation. In addition to opening the Microcosmic Orbit, it also extends energy circulation through the main channels of the legs and arms, thereby opening all eight channels of the Macrocosmic Orbit. In the sitting posture, external energy enters the system primarily through the Medicine Palace Gate on top of the head, but in standing, it also flows in through the Labour Palace Gate on the palms and the Bubbling Spring Gate on the soles. Standing practice therefore works with a wider range of terrestrial and celestial energy frequencies than sitting, which works primarily with the highest forms of energy associated with spiritual awareness.

In the standing postures, there is a greater distance and therefore a greater potential gradient factor between the Yang pole on top of the head and the Yin pole on the bottom of the feet, compared with the sitting position, in which the base of the spine forms the ground terminal. Energy therefore moves with more dynamic force in the standing position, which is a good way to boost vitality and energize the body but which can also distract attention from the more subtle aspects of spiritual work. Sitting postures draw awareness more deeply into the internal alchemy of energy and spirit in the chakras and major passes of the Microcosmic Orbit, whereas standing meditation focuses more attention on circulation of energy through the entire Macrocosmic circuit and thereby enhancing physical power. Standing meditation also pumps up the external shield of Guardian Energy which protects the body from invasion by negative environmental energies, deviant forces and malevolent entities and increases resistance to the external causes of disease.

It's a good idea to practise both styles of still meditation – standing and sitting – to familiarize yourself with the relative benefits of each. Standing is probably more beneficial to physical health and longevity, but sitting is definitely the best way to cultivate internal energy for spiritual work and develop primordial spiritual powers, such as clairvoyance and clairaudience.

The two main standing positions for still meditation are illustrated in Figs 49 a and b. In the first one, feet should be exactly shoulder-width apart and parallel, as in the classic Horse stance (see page 161) used for moving meditation. After rubbing palms together till warm, hold hands slightly raised in front, elbows bent, with the *lao-gung* points on the palms precisely aligned facing each other. Eyes may either be kept closed, or else half-open, gazing unfocused into the space between the palms. Preliminary preparation of body and breath is the same as in sitting practice, but this may be skipped if you're practising immediately after a set of moving exercises. In addition to working with the energy gates on the head, this position also opens the gates on the palms and soles. For example, you may bring energy in through the crown, draw it down to the lower elixir field, and channel it out through the palms, thereby creating an increasingly powerful force field between the hands. You can also try drawing earth energy up through the

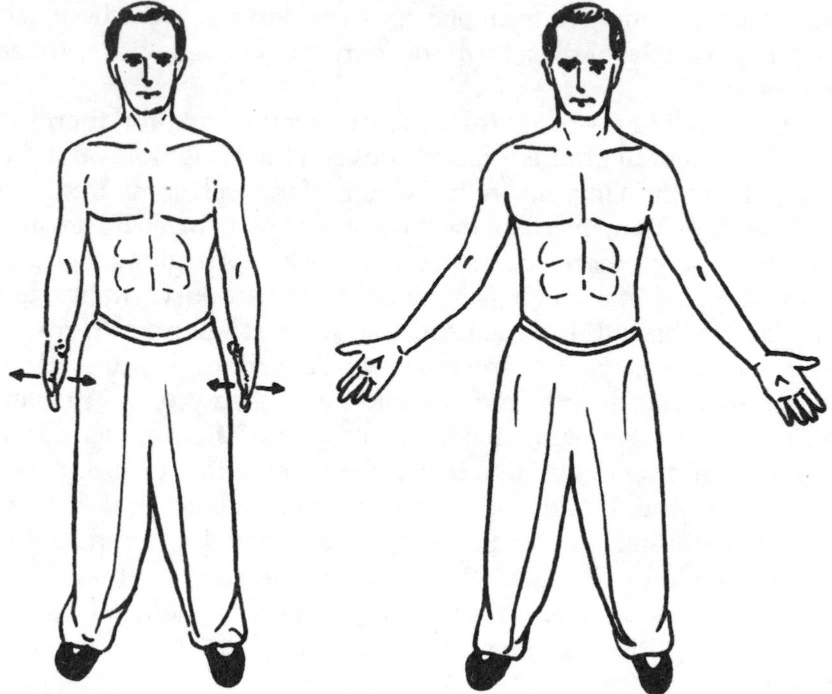

Fig. 49 **Postures for Standing Meditation:**
A. Horse stance, with hands extended slightly in front, palms facing
B. Wider Horse stance, with hands extended slightly out to the sides, palms facing forwards

Bubbling Spring gates on the feet and moving it into general circulation through the Microcosmic Orbit, or out through the palms. Or you might try working exclusively with the palm points by 'breathing' through them, drawing them closer together on inhalation and farther apart on exhalation, and focusing attention on the sensations produced by energy moving through the hands and arms. Another method is to feel the whole energy field around your body expanding and contracting on inhalation and exhalation, which is a good way to fortify your shield of Guardian Energy. Energy is always present in and around the human system, but where it goes and how it acts in the system depends entirely on how your mind chooses to work with it.

The other standing position requires a slightly wider stance, with the feet splayed outward at a 45-degree angle and the hands, which should first be charged by briskly rubbing the palms together, raised slightly up and out to the sides, with palms facing forward and fingers relaxed. Avoid locking the elbows and knees so that energy may flow freely through them. While the first standing posture, in which the palms face each other, recirculates energy drawn from external sources, this posture focuses more on the exchange of energy between the human system and the external environment. Therefore, when using this posture, be sure that the external source with which you are exchanging energy generates pure, potent positive energy, not polluted negative energy. For example, meditating in this posture is a very good way to exchange energy with an ocean, a mountain, a valley, a forest, a sacred temple, a pristine waterfall, a huge old tree and other natural founts of pure energy. Simply stand there facing the external energy source, with the *lao-gung* points aimed directly at it, and breathe through the palms. After a while, you may also try to open the Mysterious Gate point between the brows and draw energy in through that gate as well.

Collection and Storage

As in moving meditation, it's important to collect and store energy in the lower elixir field after still practice (see page 238), although in still chi-gung, you don't need to invest as much time and effort in this phase of practice, because still meditation naturally collects and stores energy in the lower elixir field.

After finishing a session of sitting or standing meditation, simply rub the palms together and sweep down the back of the head and neck, then place them on the kidneys and rub gently for a minute, and finally wrap it all up and close the gates with the navel rub. Conclude with a bow of gratitude to the universe and a vow to share whatever power and wisdom you may have gained with others.

All of this may seem easier said than done but, in fact, when it comes to the internal alchemy of working with energy and spirit in still forms of chi-gung, it's a lot easier done than said. That's because in still practice we're dealing with very subtle energies and faculties of awareness that lie beyond the realm of words and beyond the boundaries of temporal space and time. The only way to engage in this work is to discard words and concepts and operate entirely through intuition, intent and insight. Intent is a Yang faculty of spirit which mobilizes, transforms and guides energy through the system, while intuition is a Yin faculty of spirit through which subtle energies and higher levels of awareness may be felt and spontaneously understood. Even if you are not consciously aware of what's happening while you practise, as long as you set the process in motion with clear intent and careful application of the basic principles, the practice will work for you and deliver positive results. As in any kind of work, persistence pays in energy work and spiritual practice, and before long, your mind's eye will learn to see the radiance of universal energy in the luminous light of primordial awareness, and your heart will feel your ancient links with the eternal wisdom, boundless compassion and infinite power of the universe reawaken and blossom.

CHAPTER 11

Signs and Sensations, Deviations and Corrections

When people start practising chi-gung, they almost invariably experience some unusual reactions and sensations. In most cases, these are normal signs of progress and no cause for alarm. Chi-gung completely reorganizes the entire human energy system and gradually restructures the body as well. Basic vital functions such as respiration and circulation, nervous and immune responses, digestion and metabolism, all become far more efficient, energy levels are greatly elevated, and higher spiritual faculties that have lain dormant since birth are spontaneously awakened. The human system grows more sensitive to even the subtlest changes in the ambient energies of the environment, including weather, seasonal shifts, pollution, unusual cosmic phenomena, and so forth. All of these factors combine to produce a variety of reactions in body and mind as the system starts adjusting to the new currents of power that pulsate through it as a result of chi-gung practice.

People who are particularly sensitive to energy usually notice these reactions soon after taking up chi-gung practice, while others don't begin to experience them until after a few months of regular practice. Still others notice very little or no reactions to these changes. Regardless of your individual degree of sensitivity to these external signs of internal transformations, chi-gung always prompts fundamental changes in the human system, whether you become consciously aware of them or not, but learning to recognize these symptomatic signs can be very useful as guidelines for adjusting your practice and monitoring your progress over time.

Some of the most commonly encountered reactions to chi-gung are regarded as universal signs of progress, clearly indicating that positive long-term changes have occurred in the practitioner's system. Some sensations, however, are simply natural physiological responses of the body and brain to the enhancement in respiration, circulation and other vital functions that are experienced during practice as a direct result of deep abdominal breathing. Reactions that reflect fundamental changes in the system usually disappear after a period of time, as body and mind adjust to these transformations, whereas natural physiological responses to improved respiration and circulation usually recur whenever chi-gung is properly practised, although one soon grows so accustomed to them that they no longer seem unusual.

Most signs and sensations manifest themselves physically, such as feelings of heat or cold, soreness or pressure, perspiration or itching. Others manifest psychically, and sometimes these reactions confuse or alarm the practitioner, even though they are quite harmless. Indeed, some psychic signs should be seen as cause for celebration, since they indicate major 'spiritual breakthroughs' (*shen-tung*).

Psychic responses to chi-gung arise from two major sources. One is the awakening of dormant cerebral functions of the temporal human mind, such as prodigious improvement in memory and learning, activation of latent creative talents, and so forth, due to the stimulation chi-gung provides to large sections of the brain that have never before been utilized. As these formerly unused parts of the brain are brought 'on-line' for the first time, all sorts of creative talents and cerebral powers which one never realized were there suddenly begin to manifest.

The other source of psychic sensations in chi-gung practice is purely spiritual, not the result of improvements in brain function. As the practitioner progresses through the higher stages of internal alchemy and begins to cultivate the universal awareness of primordial spirit, signals may appear that indicate the awakening of formerly hidden spiritual powers, such as telepathy, extrasensory perception, clairvoyance and so forth. Sometimes described in Western psychology as 'paranormal' or 'supernatural', these powers are in fact perfectly natural and par-for-the course for adepts who practise the higher yogas in all mystical traditions. However, since adepts who achieve such powers rarely display them to outsiders, they are often regarded with suspicion by ordinary people as forms of magic.

While most of the reactions one experiences as a result of chi-gung practice are either positive signs of progress or natural physiological responses of the body and brain to improvements in vital functions, some sensations indicate deviations in energy, and these should always be met with prompt corrective measures to prevent them from causing deeper problems to develop. Deviations can occur when energy gets stuck in certain parts of the body, such as the head, or becomes blocked in the meridians due to tension or other obstructions. Deviations can also occur when energy enters the wrong channel or is not properly transformed and balanced during practice. Factors that can give rise to deviations include poor posture, wrong breathing methods, failure to complete the warm-up and/or cool-down stages of practice, and negligence in observing the basic precautions, such as practising when emotionally upset or during inclement weather and aberrant cosmic conditions. When deviations occur, corrective measures should be applied immediately, before they have repercussions in the circulatory, nervous and endocrine systems, or damage other parts of the body.

First we'll take a look at some of the common signs of progress in practice and some of the natural physical sensations produced in response to energy work; then we'll deal with the most frequently encountered deviations and the measures that may be taken to correct them.

Signs of Progress and Sensations in Practice

Numbness and Tingling

Numbness and tingling are quite normal reactions in the beginning stages of chi-gung practice. When sitting in meditation for periods of 20 to 30 minutes or more, the supply of blood to the legs can become constricted, especially in the lotus postures, resulting in numbness. This can also happen when standing in the Horse stance for a long time, before the muscles and tendons grow accustomed to holding this position. With prolonged practice, this reaction disappears, as the joints of the legs get looser, the muscles grow stronger, and the circulatory system adjusts to delivering blood to tissues under pressure. Meanwhile, you can easily relieve such numbness by pausing in your practice to stretch, rub and/or tap your legs to stimulate circulation.

Tingling usually occurs in the extremities, particularly the hands and feet. This has two causes. One is the enhancement of micro-circulation to the extremities, which draws extra supplies of blood and energy all the way out to the fingers and toes. The other cause is improvement in transmission of nerve impulses throughout the nervous system, which is somewhat akin to stepping up the current in an electrical system. Once the nervous system adjusts to this change, the tingling sensations will gradually disappear.

Trembling

Trembling often occurs in the early stages of practice as a natural reaction of the muscles to enhanced circulation of blood and improved nerve transmission. Another common cause of trembling is chronic muscular tension in various parts of the body, such as the shoulders or back. As energy circulates through the channels, any muscular tension it encounters along the way tends to block the free flow of energy, causing the muscles to tremble as energy tries to push its way through those tissues. Trembling can also occur as a result of over-exertion, such as standing for too long in the Horse or exerting too much muscular effort in performing the exercises.

Sometimes trembling occurs spontaneously during chi-gung practice, even without any muscular tension or over-exertion and not as a result of enhanced circulation and nerve function. This may occur in the arms or legs, the abdomen, or even the entire body. Spontaneous trembling is a clear sign of progress, for it means that the major channels of the energy system are opening up and that energy is flowing freely through them. One should neither encourage nor discourage such trembling, but simply take note of it and let it take its natural course. It usually stops as abruptly as it starts, and after the body, particularly the muscles and nerves, becomes accustomed to the higher level of power in the system, such trembling gradually ceases altogether.

Heat

Sensations of heat in various parts of the body during practice can occur as a direct result of improvements in the circulation of blood and energy to parts of the body previously deprived of sufficient circulation. In this case, the sensation will gradually subside as the nerves in those tissues grow accustomed to this stimulating effect. Heat can also rise in certain parts of the body as the result of uneven circulation of energy during practice, due to incorrect posture, incomplete breathing technique, muscular tension, emotional imbalance or other factors. In this case, one should pay closer attention to the basic precepts and precautions of practice and make appropriate adjustments.

Another type of heat often experienced in chi-gung is what's sometimes referred to as 'psychic heat'. This type of heat is generated purely by energy, particularly when it activates latent powers in the chakras, and it indicates concrete progress in practice. For example, as sacral energy begins to rise strongly up the spinal channels, it awakens dormant powers in the various chakras located along the spine, and as these faculties begin to stir, heat is generated. *Kundalini* yoga in Hindu tradition and the *tummo* yoga of Tibet, whereby heat is generated in the abdomen through deep breathing and visualization techniques, are other examples of internal energy practices that produce sensations of psychic heat.

Heat may also be experienced when chi-gung activates healing responses in the body. If bacteria, toxins or other factors that can cause disease are present, the immune system will often 'turn up the heat' to literally 'burn them off'. This is a natural healing response and indicates that the practice is successfully eliminating factors which can cause disease and degeneration in the body. In this case, when those factors are eliminated from the system, the heat produced to deal with them will naturally subside.

Cold

Sensations of cold experienced during chi-gung practice may be due to several factors. In still sitting meditation, especially during the winter, it may simply be due to a net loss of warmth as the body radiates heat out to the surrounding air, which is colder than the body. In this case, one should be sure to wear sufficiently warm clothing, or drape a blanket over the shoulders, during still practice. When practising moving exercises, even in cold weather, this is usually not a problem because the body will generate more than enough internal heat to compensate for external cold.

If you practise chi-gung when emotionally upset, particularly when the emotion involved is chronic fear or acute fright, sensations of cold are a common side-effect and can occur even in the hottest weather. Nervous tension can also trigger cold spells during practice. Practising under such conditions runs counter to the basic precepts of practice and blocks circulation of energy, which in turn inhibits blood circulation, especially to the extremities, resulting in sensations of cold.

Cold sensations can also be a sign of detoxification. If the body is highly toxic, chi-gung will stimulate the immune system to expel the toxic elements from the body, resulting in occasional chills and shivers. This is a natural reaction to the detoxification process and a positive sign that your practice is working to cleanse your body and purify your energy.

Another type of cold sensation sometimes felt during practice is the so-called '*chi* chill'. This has nothing to do with cold *per se*, but is rather a manifestation of *chi* moving through the channels, especially along the surface of the body. You may suddenly feel a chill shivering up and down your spine, or raising goose flesh on your arms or legs. This is a physiological reaction to energy surging through channels that have long been blocked, and it usually disappears after the nerves in those parts of the body become accustomed to the new stimulation.

Sweating

Warm sweating is a natural reaction to chi-gung practice, indicating that energy is circulating through the channels. As energy moves through the system, it causes the pores to open, thereby allowing excess Fire energy to be released through the skin as warm sweat. This is an external sign of internal energy on the move and indicates that one's practice is progressing well.

Sweating is more common in moving forms of chi-gung, but it may also occur in still practice. In still meditation, even though the body is kept immobile externally, energy is moving internally, which opens the pores and pushes excess heat to the surface for elimination. If there is a lot of excess Fire energy inside the system, sweating will occur even when practising in cold weather. When this happens, one should dry off the body with a towel immediately after practice and change into dry clothes. Avoid taking a shower for at least 20 to 30 minutes after practice, to allow the pores to close again.

Soreness and Pain

In the early stages of practice, certain parts of the body may feel sore due to insufficient strength in the muscles and tendons. It takes about six months of regular practice for the muscles and tendons in the legs to develop enough strength to support the body in the Horse stance for prolonged periods. In still sitting practice, soreness may occur in the lower back and waist, as the muscles and tendons in those parts stretch and strengthen to support that position.

Another cause of soreness and pain is incorrect posture. If one stands or sits without attention to the basic points of posture, circulation may become obstructed in the knees, ankles, waist and/or lower back, causing those parts to feel sore. This may also occur if one commences chi-gung practice without first stretching the muscles and tendons and loosening the joints with a series of preparatory warm-up exercises to limber and balance the body.

Headache and Eyeache

Aching sensations in the head and eyes are usually a result of incorrect breathing techniques during practice. If the mind is not kept focused on the breathing during practice, there is a tendency to retain the breath too long upon completion of inhalation. Since inhalation draws energy up the spinal channels into the head, retaining the breath for too long causes energy and blood to accumulate in the head, creating stagnation and pressure there that can cause painful throbbing, particularly in the eyes. Another possible cause of discomfort in the head and eyes is muscular tension in the neck and shoulders, which blocks free flow of energy and blood to the head. A third source of this reaction is failure to conclude a practice session with a series of cool-down exercises to collect and store energy in the lower abdomen. When this happens, excess energy is left lingering in the head, which can cause a painful throbbing sensation.

In still sitting practice, the eyes may ache when the practitioner tries to focus his or her eyes on the tip of the nose as a means of internalizing attention. When practising chi-gung, whether moving or still, the eyes should always be kept unfocused and completely relaxed. Trying to keep them focused on a specific point throughout a practice session causes tension in the muscles of the eyeballs, resulting in a throbbing eyeache. This can be relieved by rubbing the palms together till warm, then placing them over closed eyes and holding them there for a minute or two.

Headache and eyeache are therefore not signs of progress, but rather indicators of incorrect technique. When breathing is smooth, eyes are kept unfocused, and tension in the neck and shoulders is released, these sensations usually subside immediately.

Insomnia

Many practitioners experience a period of insomnia when they first take up chi-gung practice. This is quite normal and nothing to worry about. Chi-gung stimulates secretions of hormones and neurotransmitters, enhances circulation of blood and energy throughout the system, particularly the brain, and activates large areas of the brain that were formerly dormant. The overall result of these effects is to elevate vitality, awaken latent cerebral powers, and readjust the body's sleep rhythms. After the body and brain grow accustomed to the heightened state of vitality and the enhanced secretions of hormones and neurotransmitters, the system will settle into new sleep patterns that require less time asleep but provide deeper rest. Meanwhile, you can help yourself fall asleep at night during the initial period of insomnia by focusing attention on the exhalation stage of breathing when you go to bed at night. As you exhale, visualize each part of your body becoming more and more relaxed, starting from the feet and moving gradually up the legs and torso, down the arms to the hands, and up the neck to the head.

Sexual Excitation

Increased sexual excitation is a positive sign of progress in chi-gung, indicating that deep abdominal breathing is being correctly practised. When one breathes deeply into the abdomen, it stimulates secretion of hormones in the glands of the sacrum, particularly the testicles and ovaries, and this in turn increases sexual drive and sensitivity to sexual stimulation. Kidney-energy, which governs sexual drive, is also elevated by deep diaphragmic breathing due to the stimulating massage effect of the diaphragm descending against the adrenal cortex on top of the kidneys.

While this may be taken as a sign of progress, men must be especially careful not to misuse this enhanced sexual energy for hedonistic purposes. Sexual fluids are the basic fuel of internal alchemy, and if the extra supplies of sexual essence generated by chi-gung are wasted on ordinary sexual indulgence, rather than being transformed into energy and raised to the head to nurture spirit, the resulting loss of vitality is even greater than that experienced when not practising chi-gung, because greater amounts of fluid will be expelled from the body with each ejaculation. Therefore, it's advisable to practise Taoist sexual yoga with a partner or sexual self-massage without a partner to regulate and recirculate your sexual energy, as a supplemental regime to support and enhance your chi-gung practice.

Burps, Coughs and Gas

Chi-gung effectively drives toxic elements and stagnant energy from the internal organs, and sometimes these are expelled as burps, coughs and intestinal gas (flatulence). This is a normal sign of detoxification, and a positive indication that chi-gung is being correctly practised.

People with chronic stomach or liver problems, for example, may experience frequent bouts of burping during practice. If the lungs are congested, coughing may occur to loosen and eliminate phlegm. If the bowels are full of gas due to incomplete digestion or the presence of parasites, chi-gung will cause this gas to be passed out through the anus. These reactions should not be suppressed, for they indicate that a cleansing process is occurring. When the internal organs are rebalanced and their functions restored to normal, these reactions will naturally subside and cease.

If your system is highly toxic when you first take up chi-gung, particularly due to excessive consumption of alcohol and drugs, in addition to burping, coughing and passing gas, you might also experience a runny nose, watery eyes and frequent yawning. These too are normal signs of detoxification, and they will gradually subside as your system sloughs off the accumulated toxins. You can accelerate this process by increasing the time spent in practice until your body is thoroughly cleansed, then cut back a bit.

Dizziness

Dizziness can occur as the result of several factors. If there are imbalances in brain chemistry when chi-gung is started, or if large portions of the brain have been chronically deprived of sufficient oxygen for a long time, the restoration of adequate secretions of essential neurotransmitters and the enhanced oxygenation of brain tissues can result in sensations of dizziness. These usually subside after a few months, when the brain grows accustomed to functioning at a higher level of essence and energy.

Dizziness may also result from the elimination of accumulated toxins from the brain and neck. Toxins, particularly heavy metals, tend to accumulate around nerve tissues, which are most densely concentrated in the head and neck. As these toxic particles are loosened and eliminated, they can cause temporary sensations of dizziness as they circulate through the brain.

Dizziness can also be caused by retaining the breath for too long, or breathing too hard.

Itching

Itching sensations during chi-gung are quite normal during the early stages of practice. As energy circulates through the skin to strengthen the protective shield of Guardian Energy around the body, it sometimes feels like tiny insects are crawling around just below the surface of the skin. This can also happen when practising Energy Gate Breathing (see page 226). As energy is drawn into the body through various energy gates, an itching sensation may occur there, particularly on top of the head; this is a positive sign of progress.

Itching may also be caused by detoxification, as the body drives toxins out through the pores of the skin. When the toxins have been eliminated, this sort of itching will naturally disappear.

Heaviness and Lightness

Sensations of heaviness and lightness are normal reactions to increased assimilation of energy from nature and the cosmos. Strong infusions of terrestial energy from the earth tend to cause feelings of heaviness, while enhanced inflow of celestial energy from the sky can cause feelings of lightness, as though the body were about to lift off the ground and float away. This is simply the way the nerves respond to increased levels of energy from Heaven and Earth as they circulate through the human system. The heaviness will subside after a period of time, as the body grows accustomed to the extra inflow of terrestial energy. Sensations of lightness, however, may continue to occur indefinitely, particularly in still sitting practice, which tends to elevate energy upward in the human system and sometimes even projects the energy of spiritual awareness out through the gates on the crown or forehead. This is a positive indication of progress, but when it happens, you should apply intent to draw your awareness back into your body before terminating a meditation session.

Laughing, Weeping and Shouting

Sudden outbursts of laughter or weeping or spontaneous bouts of shouting during chi-gung practice are perfectly normal reactions, indicating that deep-seated imbalances within the vital organs and their associated energies are being successfully rebalanced. However, many people become so alarmed by this phenomenon that they abruptly terminate their practice. Far from being a cause for alarm, these are positive signs of progress, indicating that health is being restored at the deepest levels.

Recall that each of the emotions is associated with a particular organ, such as anger with the liver, fear with the kidneys, joy with the heart, and so forth. Speech is one of the most powerful manifestations of energy in the human system. Therefore, if there is a lot of anger bottled up in the liver, chi-gung will bring it up and purge it from the system, thereby restoring proper balance to the liver. Shouting is one of the most effective ways to vent such pent-up anger and disperse it into the atmosphere. Similarly, grief may be expelled from the lungs by sudden outbursts of weeping, and laughter may be used to rebalance the joyful energy of the heart. The resulting emotional equilibrium is one of chi-gung's most beneficial effects on health.

These reactions are also ways of eliminating other forms of stagnant energy from the system. You may suddenly feel a strong surge of energy running up the spine and erupting as an outburst of uncontrolled laughter. Or you may feel compelled to burst out in song. Don't be alarmed by any of these reactions, for they are very effective ways whereby the energy system rebalances itself spontaneously.

Spontaneous Movement

This is another normal chi-gung reaction that sometimes alarms newcomers to the field. When body, breath and mind enter a deep state of calm during practice, sudden movements of the head, limbs, torso or whole body may occur spontaneously without any volition by the practitioner. This indicates that deep-seated imbalances within the energy system are being corrected, and that stagnant energy is being driven out of the system through various channels and gates. If there are obstructions in any of the meridians, spontaneous movements in the parts of the body where the obstructions are seated may suddenly erupt as energy pushes through and opens circulation there. A dancer, for example, may experience spontaneous uncontrolled movements in the legs, as the energy in those channels is rebalanced. A person with back problems may start shaking and shimmying the entire spine, as though dancing the 'Twist' to a tune that only he or she can hear. This indicates that long-blocked spinal channels are reopening and that spinal energy circulation is being restored and rebalanced. Such spontaneous movements, which are always a sign of progress, should neither be encouraged nor discouraged. Simply let them occur naturally, take their course and pass of their own accord. If they become especially intense, you may get down on the floor and roll around to facilitate the process of rebalancing.

Supernatural Powers

The manifestation of supernatural powers indicates progress in the highest levels of practice. As internal alchemy progresses and primordial spirit is progressively awakened, a variety of spiritual powers may be spontaneously activated. While this is a very good sign, it also calls for great self-discipline and spiritual virtue, lest one become distracted by them or, worse yet, try to put them to use for personal fame and fortune. According to all the world's great mystical traditions, the manifestation of esoteric spiritual powers is a clear sign that the practitioner is approaching the highest state of awareness. These powers are a blessing from the universe, but they also represent a real test of the practitioner's sincerity and spiritual integrity, for there is always the temptation to utilize such powers for profit. When that happens, the entire basis upon which the powers were gained is eroded, and they are soon lost, leaving the practitioner with nothing but regret.

Supernatural powers may manifest as luminous visions of deities, energies or cosmic phenomena that appear in the 'mind's eye', sounds or voices heard in the 'mind's ear', and spontaneous insights into the past, present or future. Visions of deities may indicate the attainment of the power to commune with higher spiritual entities in other dimensions of the universe. Voices may be the sound of deities or other spirits trying to communicate with the awakened practitioner, or incoming thought-waves from other people's minds, indicating the awakening of telepathic powers.

Intuitive visions of particular events unfolding in the future reflect the achievement of clairvoyance. All such signs must be handled with the greatest respect and vigilance. It also takes time to learn how to interpret such visions, voices and insights, and how to properly utilize them. One should never discuss them with anyone else other than a highly qualified spiritual master, nor should one focus too much attention or attach too much value to them. Whenever they occur during practice, take mental note of them, and perhaps record them in a private journal, but never engage in practice exclusively for the purpose of cultivating these phenomena. Ultimately, they are side-effects of practice, signposts along the way to the final goal. So if you shift the focus of your practice to the signs, you will certainly lose track of the path and lose sight of the goal.

As for utilizing such esoteric spiritual powers for practical purposes, one must be extremely careful to do so only when absolutely necessary to help others in distress, and only when conventional methods have failed. Most important, one should never take personal credit or demand rewards for such revelations and insights, but rather credit them to the universe from which they came and offer them as gifts to those who need them. And whenever they occur, one should make a gesture of acknowledgement and appreciation to the universe, such as a slight bow of the head, a whispered prayer of thanks, or reciting an appropriate sacred syllable (mantra). Such gestures reinforce the growing bond between one's individual spirit and the primordial spirit of the universe and help keep the personal ego from trying to claim credit for or profit from these powers.

Deviations and Corrections

Headache

The sort of headache discussed on page 267 is a sign of incorrect techniques in the beginning stages of chi-gung practice and usually stops occurring when the basic precepts of practice are more carefully observed. However, if headaches continue to occur even after one has been practising regularly for several months, and if they persist even after a practice session is over, this indicates that a deviation in energy may have occurred and should be corrected.

Headaches of this sort are most often caused by excess energy and blood getting trapped in the head. If breathing is property performed and posture is correct, then the cause is most likely to be found in the mind. Some practitioners are so eager to gain quick results from their practice that they tend to force their minds to concentrate exclusively and excessively on looking for results, rather than simply concentrating in a more relaxed manner on the basic points of practice. When this happens, too much energy is drawn into the head and held there by the state of mental concentration. This in turns draws excess blood to the brain – 'blood follows where energy leads' – causing pressure that can easily give rise to headaches.

If insufficient attention to breath also occurs as a result of such over-concentration on results, one tends to retain the breath too long, which deprives the brain of sufficient oxygen and allows carbon dioxide levels to rise, and this may contribute to headaches. Such impatience can also cause one to neglect the final cool-down stage of practice, which again compounds the problem by leaving all the excess blood and energy that has accumulated in the brain lingering there throughout the day and night. Finally, any sort of impatience during practice tends to cause muscular tension in the neck, which blocks the outflow of blood and energy from the head, thereby prolonging such headaches.

• **Corrections.** Whenever this sort of headache occurs, you should immediately stop practising and take measures to draw the excess blood and energy out of the head. First of all, roll the shoulders and stretch the neck to release tension there. Regulate your breathing in such a way that the compression stage is eliminated (i.e. do not pause to compress after inhalation) and focus attention entirely on long, slow exhalations through pursed lips, as though blowing out candles on a birthday cake. This sort of breathing prompts energy to descend down the front of the body into the lower abdomen, and if the neck is completely relaxed, the outflow of energy from the head will not be impeded.

Another measure you can take is to massage the temples with the knuckles or fingertips, and apply acupressure to the Wind Pond points, located at the base of the skull-bone, where the neck enters the head (see the section on acupressure in Chapter 6, page 155). You may also rub the palms together till warm, then place one palm on the crown of the head and rub gently in a circular motion, while placing the other palm on the navel and rubbing that spot in a circular motion as well. As you do this, visualize energy pouring down the front of the body like a waterfall, draining the head and filling the lower elixir field.

Finally, devote some extra time to the cool-down stage after your main practice to draw excess energy down into the lower abdomen for storage. Continue practising these measures until you stop getting headaches.

Pressure in the Upper Elixir Field

When excess energy accumulates in the upper elixir field in the head, particularly after prolonged periods of Microcosmic Orbit meditation in the sitting posture it can cause a dull throbbing sensation between the eyes. This means that instead of flowing smoothly *through* that point, energy is collecting *in* it, resulting in a build-up of stagnant energy there. This is a deviation of energy that, unless corrected, can eventually cause chronic headaches, eyeaches and blurry vision.

• **Corrections.** Whenever such throbbing pressure is felt between the eyes, take a break from your practice to release the energy there. Rub palms together till warm, then use the tips of the index and middle fingers to slowly rub the area between the eyes in a circular motion. After six or seven circular rubs, draw the energy out to the sides of the head by pressing the fingertips firmly against the ridgeline just above the eyebrows and moving them sideways towards the temples. When they reach the temples, continue pressing evenly and moving the fingertips downward past the ears, along the jawline to the chin, then flick the fingertips out and away from the chin to expel the excess energy into the atmosphere. Another way to do this is to use the fingertips to draw the stagnant energy down between the eyes, along both sides of the nose, down around the corners of the mouth, and flick them downward from the chin to expel the energy from the head.

Pressure in the Middle Elixir Field

Uncomfortable sensations of pressure in the solar plexus usually indicate stagnant energy accumulated there or over-exertion of the diaphragm, or both. If this deviation is not corrected, it can lead to painful inflammation of the diaphragm and a bloating sensation in the solar plexus due to stagnation of energy in this major energy centre. It can be caused by trying to force the diaphragm to breathe more deeply than its flexibility naturally allows, particularly when practising reverse abdominal breathing, by practising when there is tension in the chest and ribs, and/or by practising in a state of emotional turmoil, which tends to trap energy in the solar plexus.

• **Corrections**. First of all, pay careful attention to your breathing and make sure that you are not using too much force to move the diaphragm. It usually takes three to six months of regular practice before the diaphragm becomes sufficiently flexible to breathe deeply without exerting excess force on it. If you find yourself forcing the breath during your practice, ease up a bit and let the diaphragm expand only as far as its natural flexibility allows. The diaphragm's natural flex will increase gradually, and your breath will grow proportionately deeper by itself, without forcing it.

A more immediate corrective measure is to rub the palms together till warm, then place one palm directly over the solar plexus and the other palm over the first palm, and rub in circles with a firm and even pressure. After six to eight circular rubs, draw the palms apart in opposite directions, rubbing them along the lower ribs and out to the sides of the ribcage, then down the sides to the hips. When palms reach the hips, flick them out to the sides to expel the stagnant energy into the atmosphere.

Pressure in the Lower Elixir Field

Throbbing pressure and uncontrollable trembling in the region of the navel indicates that energy has become stuck in the abdominal wall and grown stagnant there. For purposes of collection and storage, energy should enter deep into the lower elixir field behind and below the navel, in which case it does not cause pressure or become stagnant, since it circulates freely from there through the eight major channels of the Macrocosmic Orbit. Throbbing pressure in the abdominal wall, however, occurs when too much energy has been drawn into the abdominal muscles during deep-breathing practice. This is usually the result of tensing the abdominal wall too much in an attempt to deepen the breath. While the abdominal wall must certainly move in order to breathe with the diaphragm, the expansion and contraction should occur with a minimum of muscular exertion. Excess exertion draws excess blood and energy into those tissues, and the resulting muscular tension traps them there, causing pressure, tremors and stagnation. If this is not corrected, it can give rise to indigestion, gas and discomfort in the stomach and lower intestinal tract.

• **Corrections.** Check your breathing to make sure that you are not over-exerting your abdominal muscles, and adjust your technique accordingly. For more immediate relief, rub the palms together till warm, place one palm over the navel and the other palm over the first, and rub in circles. After six to eight rubs, draw the palms apart without taking them from the surface of the body and rub downward towards the crotch, past the sexual organs and down along the inside of the thighs to the knees. When palms reach the knees, flick them out to the sides and away from the legs to disperse the stagnant energy into the atmosphere.

Pressure and/or Pain in the Lower Back

Pressure and pain in the lower back is usually due to incorrect posture, especially in still sitting practice. If the spine is not kept straight and the back is allowed to slump during chi-gung, energy becomes blocked and stagnates there, causing sensations of pressure and pain. The resulting diminishment in blood circulation reduces delivery of oxygen and permits accumulation of carbon dioxide, lactic acid and other metabolic wastes in the muscles supporting the spine, causing tension and sometimes cramps. This in turn further blocks energy flow and increases pressure and pain, and if the deviation continues uncorrected, it can also begin to interfere with nerve transmissions through the spinal cord.

• **Corrections**. If you notice throbbing pressure and pain in the lower spine during practice, first pause to correct it and restore free flow of blood and energy, then adjust your posture to prevent a recurrence. Rub palms together till warm, place them over the kidneys, and rub downward to the buttocks repeatedly. You may also help restore circulation by using the backs of the hands to vigorously tap both sides of the lower spine from the kidneys down to the coccyx. Another corrective measure is to practise the spinal stretch introduced as a warm-up exercise for still meditation in Chapter 10 (see page 246). If you're using the cross-legged posture for sitting practice and still feel pressure in the lower back even after adjusting your posture, try placing a thicker cushion, or adding a folded towel to the cushion you're using under the buttocks to further elevate the pelvis and reduce the burden on the lower spine.

Nocturnal Emissions

This deviation usually occurs only in males and indicates that excessive amounts of sexual secretions are accumulating in the sacrum, without being transformed into energy and raised up to the head to combine with celestial energy and nurture spirit. Deep abdominal breathing stimulates the sexual glands in the sacrum to increase production of hormones and semen, but if this enhanced sexual essence is not converted into energy and circulated through the rest of the system, it creates pressure for release below, and sometimes this release occurs involuntarily during sleep as nocturnal emission, or so-called 'wet dreams'.

In TCM as well as chi-gung, this way of losing semen is regarded as particularly harmful to men, because the ejaculations are completely uncontrolled. In addition to draining away all the extra supplies of precious semen produced as a result of chi-gung, it causes a total depletion of sexual energy. If such emissions occur once or twice a week, or more, and no corrective measures are taken, this deviation can result in a severe depletion of vitality, immune deficiency and lowered resistance, critical loss of cerebrospinal fluids (from which the body borrows to produce more semen), and impairment of mental clarity, memory and other cerebral functions.

• **Corrections.** If this deviation begins to manifest, men should correct it immediately with the following measures. Practise the anal lock frequently throughout the day and night to build up strength in the tissues of the urogenital canal so that semen does not flow out so readily. This also helps draws sexual energy from the sacrum up through the coccyx into the Governing Channel and upward to the head to nurture spirit, thereby reducing sexual pressure below. At night before going to sleep, practise the yoga posture known as the 'Candle' (shoulder stand with the palms placed firmly against the kidneys to form a foundation of support and the legs raised straight up above the head. This helps drain excess sexual fluids and energy out of the sacrum and reduces the pressure to ejaculate during sleep. Probably the best measure of all is to practise Dual Cultivation sexual yoga with a cooperative partner, engaging in prolonged sexual intercourse while deliberately holding back ejaculation. This practice greatly strengthens the contractive power of the urogenital canal and instils an instinctive response to contract the canal and withhold emission of semen whenever the urge to ejaculate arises, even in the throes of the wildest wet dream.

Energy Overflow

Building up your energy supply faster than your ability to circulate it smoothly through the channels can cause the deviation of energy overflow. This usually happens when beginning practitioners become over-eager for results and focus too much attention on drawing more external energy into the system than they can transform internally, with too little attention paid to the basic points of posture and breath and insufficient skill in circulating energy through the channels. This tendency to grab for more power than one's system is prepared to handle causes excess energy to accumulate in various parts of the body, and if it is not corrected, it can cause serious damage to the organs, overheat the blood, produce nervous tension and give rise to other problems.

• **Corrections.** If energy accumulates too quickly inside and starts causing pressure, excess body heat and tension, you should slow down or stop your practice for a while. Spend more time doing still sitting meditation and less time on moving exercises. Review the basic precepts of practice and focus more attention on body and breath. When working directly with energy, focus exclusively on circulating energy through the channels, not on drawing more energy into the system through the gates.

Mischannelled Energy

When energy has grown strong due to prolonged periods of

regular practice, but the mind remains distracted, agitated and out of tune with body and breath, energy may deviate and enter into the wrong channel, throwing the whole energy system off balance and causing congestion, excess heat, over-stimulation, energy conflict or other problems in the specific organs and tissues related to that channel. One of the first signs of mischannelled energy is unaccountable pain and pressure in particular parts of the body, especially in the solar plexus or abdomen, a twisting, screw-like sensation of pain that radiates outward and cannot be attributed to sore muscles, incorrect posture or poor circulation. If not corrected, this can cause impairment of vital functions, illness and intense discomfort.

• **Corrections.** If you feel that energy has been mischannelled, stop practice immediately, recline on your back in the 'Corpse' posture (see page 167), and make a conscious, patient effort to totally relax your whole body, as well as your mind. When the entire body becomes deeply relaxed and the mind grows calm, all the energy channels will open, allowing energy that has entered the wrong path to be re-routed in the right direction. This happens naturally, without any effort, but only when body and mind are totally relaxed and breath is well regulated. Refrain from further chi-gung practice for as long as you still feel pain or pressure in that area, but continue taking measures to relax the whole body until all deviant energy has been recirculated through normal channels and symptoms of discomfort disappear. When you commence regular practice again, go back to the basics for a while, working to balance body, breath and mind before focusing attention directly on energy again.

Fainting

This is a rare deviation in chi-gung, and the main danger involved here is failing on to a hard surface and hurting your head or bruising your bones when doing standing practice. Fainting can be caused by breathing too fast and too forcefully, retaining the breath too long during the compression stage, standing up too suddenly after a long session of sitting practice, or raising up the head too fast from a bowed-down position during moving exercises. All of these factors can result in abrupt shifts in blood circulation and oxygen levels in the brain, causing extreme dizziness and temporary loss of consciousness. If this deviation is not corrected and continues to occur frequently, it can cause serious imbalances in cerebral function and raise the risk of injury due to an uncontrolled fall.

• **Corrections.** The first corrective measure to prevent fainting is to ease up on the compression stage of breathing. Continue to practise deep diaphragmatic breathing, but don't use as much force to drive or hold the breath, and breathe slowly and gently enough so that you cannot hear the sound of your own breath.

Also be sure to apply the neck lock after inhalation to prevent too much blood from rushing up the carotid arteries into the brain. After a sitting session, stretch your arms and neck, rub or tap your head, and take a few long deep breaths to stimulate and rebalance blood circulation before slowly standing up. When practising moving exercises that call for the head to be lowered to waist level or below on exhalation, be sure to raise the head up again very slowly on inhalation and refrain from compressing the breath after such manoeuvres, to avoid excessively sudden shifts in the balance of blood and other fluids in the brain.

Signs, sensations and deviations can all be very useful in chi-gung as indicators of how energy is moving and developing within the system and how one's practice is progressing, and as guidelines for making positive adjustments in technique to prevent negative effects from faulty practice. Familiarity with these various sensations and side-effects also prevents unnecessary alarm and confusion when they arise and enables each practitioner to fine-tune his or her personal practice in accordance with the unique way each individual's system responds to energy work. Like road signs along the motorway, signs and sensations help keep your practice on track, signal you when it's time for a pit-stop, and prevent your energy work from drifting off course.

CHAPTER 12

Chi-Gung and the Tao of Cultivating Life: A Systematic Path to Health, Longevity and Spiritual Power

Chi-gung evolved as an integral part of a comprehensive system of healthcare and life extension known as *yang-sheng dao*, the 'Tao of Cultivating Life'. Based on traditional Taoist principles of balance and harmony, natural law and universal energy, the Tao of Cultivating Life is a synergistic system of self-cultivation that weaves every aspect of daily life into the fabric of chi-gung practice. Practising chi-gung without adopting the rest of the *yang-sheng* system greatly diminishes its overall health benefits and increases the possibility of energy deviations. For example, if you don't reform your diet to reduce consumption of acid-forming foods, your eating habits will conflict directly with your chi-gung practice, negating the alkalizing benefits of deep breathing. If you don't cultivate the universal virtues of wisdom and compassion along with the universal power of energy, your ego and emotions are more likely to bend your newfound power for deviant purposes. Therefore, if you decide to practise chi-gung to protect your health and prolong your life, you are advised to adopt the complete *yang-sheng* system as a whole way of life. This will make your body, energy and mind work together as a team to achieve your goals and keep them all firmly on the path of Tao, maximizing the benefits of practice and minimizing the defects and deviations caused by counterproductive habits of body and mind.

There are two sides to the coin of cultivating life with chi-gung. On one side, you learn to bring your chi-gung practice into every aspect of your daily life. On the other side, you learn to adjust every aspect of your daily life to supplement and support your chi-gung practice. Let's take a look at what this means.

Applying Chi-Gung to Daily Life

One of the most effective ways of promoting health and longevity through chi-gung is to apply the precepts of practice, and the principles of Tao in general, to the ordinary activities of daily life. By learning to regulate body, breath and mind in preparation for every activity in life the same way that you regulate them for a session of chi-gung, you expand your practice to encompass every aspect of life and you extend it to cover the whole day. In fact, one of the main purposes of chi-gung is to learn how to slow down, deepen, balance, harmonize and control every activity in daily life, based on how you work with body, breath and mind in practice sessions, and to apply the techniques of conserving and cultivating energy to ordinary affairs, not just to formal practice. As the Zen master Haikuin declared, 'Meditation in activity is infinitely superior to meditation in stillness.' By this he meant that meditators should carry their practice from the meditation cushion to the kitchen, bedroom, garden, workplace and everywhere else, twenty-four hours a day, and should conduct themselves at all times and places with the same spirit they cultivate while meditating in stillness.

A basic example of how to carry your practice into daily life is breathing. It's very important to breathe consciously and correctly at all times, not just while practising chi-gung. This alone will do more to protect your health and prolong your life than all the medicines in the world combined. Breathing correctly at work greatly enhances productivity and creativity, prevents fatigue, renders one virtually invulnerable to stress and emotional turmoil, and helps keep the mind focused on the task at hand. Correct breathing in the bedroom is the basis of Taoist sexual yoga, enabling males to control ejaculation and females to circulate orgasmic energy. Breathing properly while working in the garden, reading a book, standing in a queue at the bank, driving a car and so forth, transforms every activity into a sort of chi-gung session, and each and every breath taken in this manner contributes another measure of balanced energy to the long-term goals of health and longevity.

The 'Three S's' of movement in chi-gung practice – soft, slow and smooth – may be applied to all movements in daily life. Learn to move slowly and deliberately, to tread softly, to coordinate activities smoothly, and everything in life becomes a 'moving meditation'. These days people seem to feel that if they hurry and rush through the day, they will be able to accomplish more and 'save time', but that's a fallacy. The faster you move and the more you hurry, the more swiftly time seems to pass, the more mistakes you make along the way, and the less you actually accomplish. Rushing through life makes life pass more quickly, effectively shortening it. Time is, after all, relative, as Einstein proved to the satisfaction of modern science. The relative point of reference is the mind: the faster the mind moves, the faster time flies. On a more physiological, less philosophical level, moving slowly, softly and smoothly at all times keeps the autonomous nervous system in the restorative, life-prolonging parasympathetic mode of operation, even while working, especially if deep abdominal breathing is practised at all times. Here again we see how we can transform every activity into a form of practice and bring the healing, life-preserving benefits of practice into our daily activities. It's simply a matter of technique.

Balance and harmony, which are the primary precepts of practice, should also serve as general guidelines for all aspects of daily life. Practising moderation in all things, avoiding extremes, cultivating equilibrium, and cleaving to the 'Golden Mean' have always been central principles in the Tao of Cultivating Life, and today they are more important than ever. The roots of human life lie in nature and the cosmos, not in industry and technology, and chi-gung shows us how to nurture these roots and harmonize our lives with the natural rhythms and laws of the universe. Through chi-gung practice, we begin to realize the impact which external forces and power fields can have on our internal energies, not just during practice but at all times. This in turn might inspire us to clean up our energy environments by minimizing our exposure to harmful electromagnetic fields, such as those generated by television, electric hair dryers, and other household appliances, to adapt our diets to seasonal shifts in ambient energy rather than to the latest food fads and to take other practical measures to balance our internal energy and harmonize our systems with external fields.

Perhaps the most fundamental lesson of all which chi-gung practice holds for daily life is to focus more attention on internal energy as the primary factor in life and pay less attention to external appearances. When meeting new people, when selecting a suitable location to work and live, when picking colours for clothing and decor, when settling disputes, when analysing a situation of any kind, we should train ourselves to look more closely at the underlying energy factors involved and not to be fooled by appearances or swayed by rationalizations. Once you've determined the basic equation of energy at work in a particular situation or decision, it's a relatively simple matter to apply the same basic principles which prevail in chi-gung to achieving balance in all of the energy equations of life. Energy manifests in manifold ways – colour, smell, sound, food, sex, emotion – but its fundamental nature is universal, and therefore it always responds to the same universal laws of nature. Chi-gung familiarizes us with the basic nature of energy and teaches us the universal laws which govern it. By applying that nature and those laws to all aspects and activities in daily life, we save a lot of time and energy, and time and energy are, after all is said and done, life's most precious commodities.

Cultivating Life as the Ground for Chi-Gung

The *yang-sheng* system of cultivating life is an ancient Chinese approach to health and longevity based on the same basic principles that run through all of the traditional Taoist arts and sciences. From these philosophical roots grows a tree of health with branches in diet, herbs, exercise, sex, meditation and other disciplines, all of which work with the same basic energies of Heaven and Earth and conform to the same fundamental principles of balance and harmony.

Chi-gung itself works directly with energy, which makes it the central practice in the Tao of Cultivating Life. Other practices such as diet, supplements and sexual yoga focus on various other manifestations of energy in the body, while cultivating the right attitude, behaviour and spiritual virtues provides proper leadership for energy in the mind. The *yang-sheng* system weaves together many different threads of life to produce a tapestry of health and longevity whose patterns reflect the eternal rhythms and universal laws of nature and the cosmos. To paraphrase Lao Tze in the *Tao Teh Ching*, 'Heaven and Earth endure precisely because they function in accordance with the Tao.' By harmonizing your life with Heaven and Earth and living in accordance with the Tao, you too may endure. Let's look at some of the ways this can be done.

Food

Food is the primary postnatal source of the True Energy that fuels corporeal human life on earth, providing the raw material for the essence-to-energy conversion stage of internal alchemy.

Nutritional scientists are fond of reminding us that 'you are what you eat', while chi-gung masters teach us that 'you are energy'.

Therefore, whatever you eat should provide the sort of energy that creates a healthy body and sustains life.

In the Tao of Diet, bioenergy rather than biochemistry is the basic barometer of nutritional value in food. The principles of Yin and Yang and the Five Elemental Energies that govern energy in chi-gung and regulate the vital organs and their functions in traditional Chinese medicine apply equally to establishing harmonious energetics in food and cultivating a 'balanced diet'. Take, for example, enzymes. Enzymes are involved in each and every metabolic function and biological activity in the body. In order to produce enzymes, the body must invest not only valuable proteins, vitamins and minerals, but also the most precious 'nutrient' of all – energy. Therefore, the more enzymes we assimilate with our food, the less energy we must expend to produce them in our bodies, and the more energy we save for other purposes. Modern diets are notoriously deficient in enzymes, which are destroyed when food is over-heated, chemically treated and industrially refined. Moreover, enzymes are required in great quantities for digestion, and therefore nature, in its universal wisdom, endowed wholefoods with abundant supplies of precisely the sort of enzymes each type of food requires to digest properly after it enters the digestive tract. But when we consume junk food, convenience food and other kinds of enzyme-dead food, not only do we fail to assimilate sufficient amounts of this essential nutrient to sustain health, we further tax our systems and drain our energy by forcing our bodies to produce large quantities of digestive enzymes just to process the nutritionally empty things we eat.

This sort of 'negative nutrition' depletes the body's reserves of nutritional essence and robs it of energy. Rather than providing the body with the basic building blocks of life and furnishing the energy system with the essential ingredients required to generate energy, modern diets strain the internal organs and drain our reservoirs of energy, impairing rather than protecting health.

As in chi-gung, the Great Principle of Yin and Yang is the main gauge of energy balance in food. All foods may be divided into Yin or Yang categories, depending on the sort of energies they release in the system when digested. Yang foods tend to warm and stimulate the internal organs, while Yin foods have a cooling, calming effect. This principle may be used to select foods in such a way that they help to achieve optimum energy balance in the human system. For example, for a person with slow metabolism and Yin constitution a balanced diet would include more warming, stimulating Yang foods and fewer Yin items, whereas a person with too much hot Yang energy would balance his or her diet by favouring cooling Yin foods and cutting down on warming Yang items. In Western nutrition, a 'balanced diet' is regarded as being the same for everyone, based on the biochemical composition of the food itself, while in traditional Chinese medicine diets are balanced according to the constitutional energy traits of each individual. This aspect of Yin and Yang balance in food may also be used to rebalance the diet throughout the year according to seasonal changes. In winter, when the body requires extra heat, more Yang foods are added to the diet, and in summer, external heat is counterbalanced by consuming more cooling Yin products.

The traditional Chinese approach to food energetics, which suggests dietary guidelines that produce effects on human energy which are synergistic with chi-gung practice, differ significantly from the Western approach. Take, for example, raw vegetable salads, which Western nutritionists extol as an excellent choice for everyone every day in every season and which many Western women eat to the exclusion of all other food in order to control their weight. According to Yin/Yang energetics, raw vegetable salads are extremely Yin, which means that they generate very cold, Yin energy within the human system. Excessively cold Yin foods are contraindicated for most women in Chinese medicine, and for almost everyone during cold winter weather. If you're practising chi-gung and you do not observe Yin/Yang energy balance in your diet, you may end up creating deviations in your energy system which conflict directly with your practice and negate some of its benefits.

Another important aspect of Yin/Yang balance in food is alkaline and acid, or pH balance. People today consume far too much acid-forming (Yang) foods, resulting in chronic acidosis of the blood and intercellular fluids, and this is one of the primary contributing factors to many common degenerative conditions, such as arthritis, osteoporosis, high blood pressure, immune deficiency, cancer and many others. The major culinary culprit in this dietary folly is refined sugar, one of the most acidifying items in the world, and as discussed on page 197 the worst offender of all is sweet carbonated soft drinks. One 12-ounce (360ml) glass of the world's most popular cola contains about 9 teaspoons of refined sugar, and it's so acidifying to the human bloodstream that it would require thirty-two glasses of alkaline water to neutralize it. Obviously, no one chugs down thirty-two glasses of alkaline water every time they guzzle a can of cola. On the other hand, if the body did not take immediate measures to rebalance the pH of the blood after ingesting such an acid bomb, death would occur in less than a minute. So what the body does is leach calcium from the bones and teeth and draw it into the bloodstream to counteract the acidity caused by the sugar and carbonation from the cola. That's because calcium is the most effective nutrient alkalizer. But it also means that people who consume a lot of sugar, especially in the form of carbonated soft drinks, as well as other acid-forming foods such as meat and dairy products, are constantly draining calcium from their teeth and bones. That's why so many people in America lose their teeth and suffer from osteoporosis by the time they reach middle age.

Consequently, calcium has become one of the most essential nutrients that require supplemental sources in modern diets. Not only is calcium the most important building block in bones and teeth and the body's most effective alkalizing agent to counteract acidosis, it is also an absolutely essential element for nerve transmission and hormone secretion and therefore plays a vital role in the PNI healing response that is triggered by chi-gung. Without sufficient calcium in the diet, many of chi-gung's immunity-enhancing benefits are compromised. Besides consuming foods rich in calcium and avoiding foods that drain calcium due to their acidifying properties, it's also a good idea to take calcium supplements and drink water rich in ionized calcium. Remember, however, that the body cannot assimilate calcium without sufficient supplies of vitamin D, which the body produces in response to exposure of the skin to sunlight.

pH balance in the blood and other bodily fluids is closely connected with energy balance and energy circulation, which is why it is so important to regulate pH balance through diet. Proper pH is maintained mainly by alkaline minerals, particularly calcium, and diet is the body's sole source of these minerals. These minerals also serve as electrolytes to store and transmit energy in the body's various vital fluids. Energy does not flow freely through an acid medium, and therefore acidosis of the blood and other fluids counteracts the benefits of chi-gung practice. Chi-gung practitioners should pay close attention to the pH aspect of Yin/Yang balance in their diets, favouring foods that produce an alkalizing effect and avoiding excess consumption of acid-forming foods. The chart overleaf, which lists a variety of acid and alkaline foods in order of strength, may be used as a general guideline for selecting a pH-balanced diet:

Acid-Forming Foods	*Alkaline-Forming Foods*
sugar	ginger
rice	spinach
egg yolk	mushrooms
oats	cabbage
tuna	potatoes
chicken	radish
pork	squash
beef	bamboo shoots
cheese	turnips
barley	egg white
shrimp	pears, grapes
bread	watermelon
butter	tofu (bean curd)

The Five Elemental Energies also manifest their activity in foods, in the form of the Five Flavours, each of which has a 'natural affinity' for a particular organ-energy system in the body. Sour Wood foods may thus be consumed to tonify the liver and gall bladder, sweet Earth foods for the spleen and stomach, salty Water products for the kidneys and bladder and so forth. When using chi-gung to heal or boost a particular organ or vital function, this aspect of food energetics may be applied to supplement the therapeutic benefits of the chi-gung.

There are many ways that the precepts of chi-gung practice may be applied to cultivate dietary habits which produce nutritional energy effects that are synergistic with the benefits of chi-gung. A simple example is the principle of slowness, which governs both breathing and bodily movements in chi-gung. Applied to eating, this implies eating slowly, which means chewing food very well before swallowing it. This measure alone greatly improves digestion and assimilation, for it allows food to be pre-digested by salivary enzymes in the mouth. This saves a lot of enzyme power and other forms of digestive energy in the stomach and increases the amount of nutrients released for assimilation. The bottom line here is that you obtain more nutritional essence and energy per unit of food consumed, while also conserving a lot of vital enzyme essence and energy, when you eat as slowly and chew your food as deliberately at the table as you breathe and move your body in chi-gung practice.

The other way of regulating the diet and balancing the entire digestive system in Taoist tradition is to abstain entirely from all food from time to time. This regimen, known as *bi-gu* ('abstention from grains'), has already been discussed earlier. Periodic fasting is one of the best ways on earth to cleanse the digestive tract, purify and balance the blood, and detoxify the entire body. When practised in conjunction with chi-gung, it greatly enhances the efficiency of the internal alchemy of digestion and metabolism, training the system to extract more energy from the body's available reserves of essence. And just as food may be used to cure specific ailments, so abstention from food may be used to cure the whole body by triggering a full-scale internal house-cleaning operation that sweeps out all toxic residues and rejuvenates the entire system.

Readers who wish to reform their diets according to traditional Taoist nutritional principles and thereby bring their eating habits into harmony with their chi-gung practice may refer to the chapters on diet and nutrition in the author's previous works, *The Tao of Health, Sex, and Longevity* and *Guarding the Three Treasures*, in which the Tao of Diet is discussed in full detail.

Water

In terms of energy conductivity, water and ionized minerals are the two most important nutritional elements in the human system and together they constitute what are known as electrolytes, mineral-rich fluids that conduct and store energy in the tissues. Furthermore, water is the richest source of ionized minerals for the human body, but only if the water is pure, alkaline and free of chemical additives. One reason that Hindu yogis and Taoist hermits preferred to live and practise in high mountains is because mountain spring water is loaded with calcium and other essential alkaline minerals in ionized form, and also rich in oxygen. Drinking such water enhances internal energy to such a degree that the need for solid food is significantly decreased. It also provides a strong foundation for higher spiritual work by increasing the body's capacity to store, transform and circulate energy.

Oxygen is another important element in water. Oxygen helps maintain proper pH balance by promoting alkalinity and also assists the body in detoxifying the cells and tissues. Furthermore, with the available oxygen in the atmosphere reduced by half over the past two hundred years, water has become more important than ever as a supplementary source of oxygen. The best way to obtain oxygen from water is to infuse the water with ozone gas, then drink it. Ozonated water may also be used for bathing, for enemas and colonic irrigations, and for vaginal douches, all of which methods facilitate assimilation of abundant supplies of oxygen from ozonated water.

Unfortunately, public drinking water today has become a source of toxic chemicals rather than essential minerals and oxygen. Chlorine and fluoride, which are often added to public water supplies throughout the world, are both certified poisons. In addition, public water supplies are laced with lead, cadmium, aluminium and other toxic metals. 'You are what you drink' even more so than what you eat, because more than 80 per cent of the body's composition is water. Purity and proper pH balance in water is therefore even more essential to health and longevity than in food, and chi-gung practitioners would be wise to ensure that the water they drink works in conjunction rather than conflicts with their other health practices. The best way to prepare and balance drinking water so that it supports internal alchemy, stores and transmits energy, and promotes health is to first run it through a water ionizer to ionize the minerals, filter out toxins, remove acids, and alkalize the water (this produces what's known as 'microwater'), then suffuse it with ozone. Devices for both of these purposes are now commercially available and may be ordered from the supplier listed in the Appendix (see page 312).

Supplements

The judicious use of herbal and nutritional supplements can be very helpful as a form of synergistic support for chi-gung. In China, chi-gung and medicinal herbs have been used in close conjunction for thousands of years, both in the prevention and cure of disease as well as for martial arts and spiritual training. Chinese medicine categorizes and prescribes herbs according to their effects on the human energy system, and after more than 5000 years of clinical experience, the specific effects of the more than 2000 herbs in the Chinese pharmacopoeia have all been recorded in great detail. This information can be of great practical benefit in fine-tuning your energy system as your chi-gung practice progresses. Detailed information on the nature and use of more than one hundred individual herbs and three dozen compound formulas may be found in the author's previous work *A Handbook of Chinese Healing Herbs*.

Supplementary herbal formulas fall into three major categories. The category most highly favoured by chi-gung practitioners, and by the Chinese in general, are tonic herbs and formulas, known in Chinese as 'Superior Medicine' (*shang yao*). Tonics are meant to be taken only when you're in good health, and their purpose is to further elevate your health by boosting immunity, enhancing vitality and strengthening vital functions, including sexual potency and mental faculties. Due to their stimulating effects on hormone production, tonics are increasingly favoured for their age-retarding benefits as one grows older. They may be taken as pills, powders, teas, liquids, extracts or cooked into food.

The second category is constitutional formulas. These formulas are specifically combined to produce effects that compensate for constitutional imbalances in an individual's energy system. If a person has an innately weak digestive system, for example, he or she would take a herbal formula that enhances digestive functions. People with constitutional deficiencies may use specially blended herbal formulas to balance their systems, then gradually reduce and eliminate the herbs as chi-gung practice begins to correct the condition. Using herbs to boost the effects of chi-gung saves some time in such cases.

The third category is curative formulas, which are only used when symptoms of disease have already appeared. Curative herbs may be used to relieve symptoms as well as cure root causes of disease, and the formulas are adjusted every week or two as the cure progresses. When the system has regained balance and the disease is cured, herbal treatment stops, after which an appropriate tonic or constitutional formula may be taken to prevent a similar imbalance from occurring again.

The other type of supplement is nutritional, including vitamins, minerals, enzymes and food concentrates. Abundant information on this topic is available elsewhere and need not be repeated here, except to stress the particular importance of sufficient mineral supplementation in chi-gung practice. Due to their crucial role in the synthesis of electrolytes and enzymes, minerals are vital elements in all essence-to-energy transformations in the human body and are also involved in the storage and circulation of energy. It should also be noted that minerals are much more difficult to assimilate than other nutritional supplements, and therefore should be taken in several forms, to ensure sufficient supplies. All multi-vitamin formulas contain a spectrum of minerals, and these may be further supplemented by using alkaline water (preferably prepared by ionization), fresh raw vegetable juices and whole sea salt. And be especially careful to take enough calcium.

Sexual Yoga

'All the best medicines and good food in the world cannot help one achieve longevity unless one knows and practises the Tao of Yin and Yang.' So wrote the great Taoist alchemist Ko Hung seventeen centuries ago. Sexual yoga has played a central role in the Tao of Cultivating Life ever since the dawn of Chinese civilization 5000 years ago, when the Yellow Emperor is said to have attained immortality by using the method of 'contact without leakage' in his sexual relations with a harem of 1200 women. In *Secrets of the Jade Bedroom*, Peng Tze, the 'Chinese Methusela' who is reported to have lived to the age of 800, explains that for men semen is the fundamental fountain of life and must be carefully conserved in sexual intercourse:

> In sexual intercourse, semen must be regarded as a most precious substance. By saving it, a man protects his very life. Whenever he does ejaculate, the loss of semen must then be compensated by absorbing the woman's essence.

Sexual secretions constitute the body's most potent form of vital essence for internal alchemy, and sexual energy is the most powerful kind of energy for cultivating spiritual vitality. For men, the importance of conserving semen by carefully regulating frequency of ejaculation cannot be overstated, especially after the age of forty, for nothing erodes male vitality more quickly than reckless sexual activity. As the Plain Girl, the Yellow Emperor's chief advisor on sexual matters, explains to him, 'If a man can learn to control and regulate his ejaculations during sex, he may derive great benefits from this practice. The retention of semen is highly beneficial to man's health.'

While women do not need to worry about losing sexual essence during sex and may therefore enjoy as many orgasms as they wish, sexual yoga also serves the female very well by teaching her how to transform sexual energy and raise it up to the head to nurture spirit, and how to circulate it through the whole system to elevate vitality and enhance immunity. In Taoist sexual yoga, man and woman are equal, and the sexual act becomes a living metaphor for the internal alchemy activated by chi-gung. As the Plain Girl explains:

> When men and women indulge freely in sex, exchanging their bodily fluids and breathing each other's breath, it is like Fire and Water meeting in such perfect proportions that neither one defeats the other. Man and woman should ebb and flow in intercourse like the waves and currents of the sea, first one way, then another, but always in harmony with the Great Tide (female orgasm).

Many of the techniques used to regulate breath and energy in chi-gung practice may also be used by men to control ejaculation and by women to transform and circulate sexual energy during sexual intercourse. The anal lock, for example, is the primary preventive against premature ejaculation for men and the main technique for raising orgasmic energy from sacrum to cerebrum for women.

Learning How to 'Lock the Gate'

The rhythmic contraction and relaxation of the anal sphincter can be practised any time, anywhere, in any position. Be sure to contract both the external and internal sphincters and to hold the contraction for several seconds before relaxing it.

When utilizing the anal lock for ejaculation control, you should apply it strongly as your lungs fill up, hold it tightly while you briefly retain the breath, but *do not* release it during exhalation, as you would in ordinary breathing exercises. Hold it locked tightly through two or three complete breathing cycles, or for as long as necessary to regain composure and control. Only then should you release it, slowly and gently. Remember that this exercise also benefits women by toning up the entire urogenital diaphragm and drawing sexual energy upward.

The muscles that control the anal sphincters may be further contracted to exert control over the prostate, the ureter and the entire penile shaft. When properly applied, you can feel this extended contraction lift the entire pelvic floor upwards as it closes off the urogenital canal.

This enhanced anal, prostate and penile lock, combined with breath retention, is the key that 'locks the gate', a key that every man may forge for himself by daily practice of a single, simple exercise that is as easy to remember and perform as going to the toilet. Here's how it's done: while urinating, a few seconds before the flow of urine stops, sharply lock the anus and contract the penile shaft to 'squeeze off' the ureter and halt the flow, as if you were 'holding it' while looking for a toilet. After a second or two, relax the contraction, let the flow of urine resume, then immediately 'squeeze it off' again. Each squeeze will cause a strong spurt of residual urine as the ureter is contracted. Repeat this three to five times, or until no more urine spurts out when you squeeze, then hold the last contraction for 5 to 10 seconds while you tuck yourself back in and zip up. You can further enhance the effects of this exercise by standing up on your toes while doing it.

If a man performs this exercise habitually every time he urinates, he will automatically be practising the correct method of 'locking the gate' during intercourse – several times a day, every day.

The Orgasmic Upward Draw for Women

Men must learn ejaculation control in order to prevent depletion of essence and energy during sexual intercourse. While women need not worry about essence and energy loss through ejaculation, they do experience significant loss of vital energy as a result of menstruation and the gradual slackening of vaginal muscles. To reduce such losses, women may practise the 'Orgasmic Upward Draw'.

The key muscle in this exercise is the pubococcygeal muscle, also called the 'Love Muscle', which controls the labia, vagina and other parts of the female sexual organ. Before even attempting the Orgasmic Upward Draw, women should spend a few months tightening and toning the Love Muscle by practising deep contractions of the anus and perineum and extending the contraction all the way through the vagina. This exercise alone will eventually reduce menstrual bleeding, prevent loss of *chi* through the vagina, stimulate secretions in the sacral glands, and help open the lower channels of the Microcosmic Orbit.

The Orgasmic Upward Draw is the technique by which women may direct the energy of orgasm inward and upward through the spinal energy channels, so that the sexual energy spreads to all parts of the body and into all the vital organs via the meridian network. Not only does this conserve energy and tonify the organs, it results in a total body orgasm that only women are capable of experiencing.

To cultivate the Orgasmic Upward Draw, first practise alone and unaroused, as follows. Sit on the edge of a stool or chair and perform a few minutes of Bellows breathing (see page 171). Then inhale slowly and deeply, retain the breath and lock up the entire body by clenching feet and fists, contracting anus, perineum and vagina, and applying neck and abdominal locks as well. Press tongue to palate, tilt sacrum forward to straighten sway in lower spine, and roll eyes up towards top of head. Then slowly exhale through the nostrils as you gently release all locks and relax all muscles and visualize energy moving up the spine. After practising this exercise for a few weeks, try it in a state of self-arousal, applying the locks and retention when you are about 95 per cent towards the brink of orgasm.

When you start feeling heat gathering in the vagina and perineum and energy tingling up your spine during this exercise, then you are ready to practise it during sexual intercourse with a partner. During actual intercourse, the most important thing is to start applying the Orgasmic Upward Draw *before* actual orgasmic contractions of the vagina commence, but *after* the energy of orgasm has already been aroused inside. Just prior to orgasm, lock the gates, tighten the muscles, inhale deeply and retain the breath. Then tuck the pelvis forward to straighten the spine and perform six to nine deep contractions of the pubococcygeal muscle. When properly performed after long practice, this will cause orgasmic contractions to reverse the flow of sexual energy during orgasm, sending it coursing up the spinal channels instead of out through the vagina, and filling the entire body with the ecstatic sensation of orgasm.

Despite its novelty in the light of conventional sexuality, ejaculation control is really as natural as breathing and flexing muscles. What is most difficult for most conventional men to master is the mentality of ejaculation control. As semen gathers and the exquisite sensations associated with a mounting ejaculation flood the body, men tend to lose their mental resolve and abandon their physical discipline. A nagging little voice bleats inside their heads, tempting them with rhetorical arguments, 'Go ahead! Why not? To hell with Tao! Life is short!' Men who heed this devilish voice too often will indeed discover that 'life is short'.

Beginners often complain that retaining semen during intercourse is 'impossible', or that it leaves them with that full feeling in the scrotum known as 'lover's balls', or that their partners don't 'cooperate' enough. When first attempting semen retention, post-coital pressure in the testicles is perfectly natural and no cause for alarm. It is caused by a very fundamental change in physical habit and a complete reorganization of the ejaculatory apparatus. It is no different than the bloated or jittery feelings you get in your stomach whenever you make a major, permanent change in dietary habits. After the body grows accustomed to the mechanics and biochemistry of the new routine, all uncomfortable side-effects disappear entirely. In the meantime, you can relieve that 'full feeling' with a few minutes of post-coital deep breathing and by gently massaging the region between anus and scrotum.

In order to help smooth the way for beginners on the path to ejaculation control, the author offers the following five fundamental guidelines:

1. First and foremost, enlist your wife or lover as a partner. A man cannot master ejaculation control with strangers. He needs a woman who is fully familiar with him and with the principles and practices involved. An understanding and patient partner serves a novice male as the Plain Girl served the Yellow Emperor, guaranteeing complete cooperation and a carefree relationship. Once a man has mastered the methods, he may apply them with any partner.
2. Start out by practising ejaculation control during the daytime and promising yourself the treat of an ejaculation later on that day or night. This makes it a lot easier to ignore the advice of that bleating voice as ejaculation approaches, for you may look forward to an emission during a second round later.
3. Once you have learned to suppress ejaculation during daytime intercourse, try skipping the bribe of a later ejaculation, and start experimenting objectively with your physiological and psychological responses to intercourse without ejaculation. Take note of your physical vitality and mental alertness after sex without emission, take pride in your new-found self-control, and take pleasure in your partner's ever-growing satisfaction with your sexual skills.
4. When you have finally mastered both the methods and the mentality of ejaculation control, make it a permanent habit by adopting it as a form of birth control.
5. Follow your own instincts and personal experience in determining your own ideal ejaculation frequency. Every five or six years, decrease the frequency of emission according to the same factors, without decreasing your frequency of intercourse. This will automatically adjust your sexual habits to suit the requirements of advancing age and guarantees sufficient stores of essence and energy to replenish the depletions associated with ageing.

With diligent practice, some men can even learn to approach the very brink of ejaculation and enjoy all the exquisite sensations associated with it, without spilling a drop of semen. These sensations are similar to the series of 'mini-orgasms' women sometimes experience en route to the 'big bang' at the end.

Deep diaphragmic breathing with a prolonged retention during the compression stage is another way of controlling semen emission and circulating energy in Taoist sexual yoga. Conversely, the extra supplies of sexual essence and energy accumulated by practising Taoist sexual yoga provide potent fuel for internal alchemy in chi-gung, enhancing immunity, strength and spiritual vitality.

Another reason that serious practitioners of chi-gung should regulate their sexual activities according to the Tao of Yin and Yang is because when sexual energy gets involved with human emotions, as it normally does in life, it can turn a person's life topsy-turvy and cause all sorts of unnecessary complications in human relationships. Taoist sexual yoga bypasses the human emotions by drawing raw sexual energy up from the sacrum, refining it in the channels and energy centres along the spine, and raising it directly into the brain to nurture spirit. Not only does this prevent the animal instinct of sex from controlling human behaviour by inflaming the ego and agitating the emotions, it also puts sexual energy directly under the command of spirit, where it may be expressed with wisdom and compassion rather than lust.

Last but not least, sexual yoga produces sexual harmony and happiness between man and woman in marriage, and this in turn provides the sort of emotional stability required for swift progress in chi-gung. Like Fire, male sexual energy naturally tends to flare up quickly, burn intensely, then fizzle out, while female energy, like Water, usually takes a long time to warm up, but once it's hot, it stays hot for a long time. The Tao of Yin and Yang teaches men how to control their Fire so that it burns more slowly and lasts a lot longer, thereby enabling it to bring female Water to a full boil and keep it hot for as long as a woman needs to feel completely satisfied. The ever practical Tao thus provides a way for loving couples to utilize sexual energy for health, longevity and spiritual development, while also maximizing the mutual pleasure derived from the sexual act.

The Power of Emptiness

The term 'emptiness' crops up time and again in Eastern mystical teachings, for emptiness is the essential nature of all existence and the primordial ground from which all manifest form arises and ultimately returns. It is also the basic nature of energy and spirit, the immaterial forces that mould the manifest universe. In the modern world of commerce and compulsive consumerism, all empty space and time are obsessively filled with construction, decoration, billboards, sensory distractions and entertainment, and consequently the practical value and expressive power of emptiness have been largely forgotten. Yet in terms of functional utility, nothing is more practical and potent than emptiness, as Lao Tze so clearly illustrates in the *Tao Teh Ching:*

> We put thirty spokes together and call it a wheel;
> But it is on the space where there is nothing that the usefulness of the wheel depends.
> We turn clay to make a vessel;
> But it is on the space where there is nothing that the usefulness of the vessel depends.
> We pierce doors and windows to make a house;
> But it is on the spaces where there is nothing that the usefulness of the house depends.
> Therefore, just as we take advantage of what is, so we should recognize the usefulness of what is not.

Thus an ancient Taoist adage advises, 'Those who strive for longevity should maintain the "Four Empties".' The Four Empties are useful guidelines in the Tao of Cultivating Life, providing daily reminders of the utility of emptiness in all aspects of life:

- **Empty Mind.** What one does not think about is far more useful than the speculative chatter with which one usually fills the mind. Wisdom never arises from idle fantasy and discursive thought, but rather from direct intuitive perception of truth, which can only occur when the mind is still and empty of thought. The reason meditation is so important in Eastern mystical traditions is that meditation is the most effective way to experience the primordial purity and power of emptiness, even if for only a few moments, and because emptiness is the original ground of enlightened awareness. However, in order to be of practical utility in daily life, this emptiness of mind must be carried into ordinary activity as well; otherwise it remains a mere mental exercise.
- **Empty Stomach.** This is a reminder that gluttony paves a quick path to the grave and impedes progress on the path of self-cultivation. The human tendency to over-eat has been further aggravated today by supermarkets, fast food, convenience food shops, home delivery and mass advertising campaigns. Nothing on earth pollutes the body more swiftly than to overstuff the stomach with a haphazard combination of denatured foods that can only be partially digested and whose putrefied by-products linger and stagnate in the digestive tract for weeks, months and years, polluting the blood by osmosis and producing a chronic state of acidosis and toxaemia. On the other hand, leaving the stomach completely empty, as in the period is abstinence from food (*bi-gu*) practised by chi-gung adepts, is by far the best way to detoxify the system, purify the blood and alkalize the tissues and bodily fluids. Eat only when you feel hungry, but do not eat only to fill an empty

stomach. From the viewpoint of chi-gung practice, an empty stomach is far more useful for energy work than a full one.

• **Empty Kitchen.** A good way to maintain an empty stomach is to keep an empty kitchen. Storing large quantities of food in the kitchen not only promotes over-eating, it also allows food to get stale and grow mould. The less food you keep in the kitchen, the more careful you tend to be about eating, and the more often you must go out to purchase fresh food. Today, with deep freezers and microwave ovens, some people don't go shopping more than once a month, subsisting entirely on pre-cooked, industrially processed frozen foods heated up by microwaves. Anyone who wishes to fully benefit from regular practice of chi-gung would be well advised to consume only fresh foods in moderate quantities and to banish all pre-cooked and artificially processed foods from the kitchen. If you are simply too lazy to properly prepare fresh food at home, then go out and eat in restaurants that serve wholesome health food. Cost need not be a consideration here, because if you follow the 'empty stomach' guideline and cut down the quantity while elevating the quality of the food you consume, then you need not spend much money dining out.

• **Empty Room.** Walk into any disco on any night in any city in the world and you will experience the utter antithesis of 'empty room'. Ear-piercing music reverberates in the smoky, air-conditioned air, while flashing lights, lasers and strobes bombard the eyes and flood the brain with a constant barrage of sensory distraction that precludes even a moment of emptiness from arising in the mind. The same chaotic cacophony and visual clutter prevail in department stores, shopping malls, offices and private homes. As discussed earlier, the internal microcosm of the human system reflects the prevailing energy conditions of the external macrocosm, and whatever external energies we expose our systems to imprint their patterns on our internal energies. Thus the more clutter and chaos we perceive in our immediate environment, the more chaotic and cluttered become our minds and energies. There's not much you can do to simplify and harmonize the prevailing energies in public spaces, but you can certainly control your own private living space. Zen gardens and room decor in Japan are designed to still and empty the mind by imparting their simplicity and natural harmonics to the human energy system, thereby sweeping away the artifice and complexity of human thought and allowing emptiness to arise naturally in the mind. Though spartan in appearance, an empty room is pregnant with potential insight and energy; when the human mind perceives such a room and tunes itself into the prevailing emptiness, all sorts of energy and awareness will spontaneously begin to stir, suffusing the mind with the sort of primordial power and awareness that can only arise from emptiness.

Chi-gung and other Taoist health regimes are founded on the potential power and awareness that arise from emptiness. Moreover, the principle of emptiness manifests itself in many other subtle ways in the Tao of Cultivating Life, such as in the superiority of restraint over aggression, silence over noise, not-doing over doing, stillness over speed, abstinence over indulgence, and so forth. It is the human attachment to material form that creates so much greed and illusion in life, and drives people to value material gain over spiritual virtue, only to realize at the moment of death that 'you can't take it with you'. Awareness, however, is an eternal asset that follows you from life to life, so whatever spiritual insights you acquire in life become permanent dividends of everlasting value. To gain such valuable insight, one must cultivate an implicit understanding and appreciation of the power of emptiness. Cultivating the Four Empties in daily life teaches us to recognize the value and practical utility of emptiness and familiarizes us with the terrain of spiritual immortality.

Cultivating the Right Mind for Practice

'Right Mind' is one of the basic precepts of the 'Noble Eight-Fold Path' taught by the Buddha as a way to end suffering and achieve spiritual liberation. Without the right attitude and a wholesome outlook on life, no practice in the world can bring you peace of mind, physical health, happiness and longevity. There is a very strong tendency today to believe that everything can be accomplished entirely through science and technology, modern medicine and diet, physical exercise and various other external methods, without the slightest consideration for the most important factor of all – consciousness.

One of the main purposes of chi-gung is to cultivate 'right energy' as a functional basis for 'right mind'. When our energy systems are deficient and imbalanced, clogged with stagnant energies, obstructed with toxins and tensions, and out of tune with the forces of nature and the cosmos, not only does this cause physical disease and degeneration, it also gives rise to mental distress and emotional imbalance. When your energy is pure, strong and well balanced, so are your body and mind. On the other hand, since 'spirit commands energy', it's equally important to cultivate spiritual virtue as a basis for energy work. A mean spirit always generates mean energy, and an angry mind causes the energy cultivated by chi-gung to deviate into anger. While chi-gung can certainly help balance and harmonize the mind by nurturing spirit with the pure primordial energy generated by internal alchemy, there is a limit to how far energy can influence spirit.

As we already know, spirit is the ultimate authority in the human system, and therefore it has the power to over-rule energy. Thus a conscious effort must be made by mind itself to cultivate spiritual virtue as a basis for practice. No matter how much energy is harvested from the universe and how well it is cultivated within the human system, if the human mind deviates from the path of wisdom and compassion paved by primordial spirit and defies the universal laws of nature and the cosmos, then energy will heed the same deviant call and manifest the same delinquent activity, for energy always follows the mind. Indeed, one reason that so many people today are so unhealthy, short-lived and spiritually stunted is that they subvert their own vital energy resources with perverse thoughts and deviant intentions.

We have already discussed the power of positive thinking as a basis for awakening the body's own natural healing responses. Positive thinking includes one's entire outlook on life and cultivates an optimistic point of view, precluding the cynical attitudes and dark pessimism which have become so fashionable these days. All too often people discount positive thinking as mere 'wishful thinking', because they're afraid to trust the power of spirit and unwilling to cultivate 'right mind' as a basis for life. There is, however, a tremendous reservoir of transformative power locked inside the mind, and the key to unleashing this power is a positive attitude towards life. What this basically means is that your energy is capable of accomplishing whatever you believe it can do, for 'spirit commands energy'. A positive attitude always propels energy in a positive direction, and 'right mind' naturally guides energy the 'right way'.

All true chi-gung masters make a strong point of teaching their students that their ordinary behaviour in daily life sets the tone for their entire practice, and that private practice and public life can never be separated. If you truly understand and accept the view that all phenomena in life reflect the interplay of universal energies and that all relationships are governed by the interaction between the personal energy fields of the individuals involved, then you must realize the truth of the statement that 'no man is an island'. In terms of energy, there are no concrete boundaries between objects or between people, because all energy fields radiate outward infinitely, and therefore they ultimately intersect with everything else in the universe.

Thus, if half the people on the planet are suffering and unhappy, that negative energy is bound to affect the rest of the people on the planet, whether they are aware of it or not. Unhappy minds project unhappy energies, and unhealthy bodies generate unhealthy energy fields, and those energies and fields broadcast a miasma of misery out in all directions, producing a planetary pall that ultimately affects everyone else in the world. Building high walls and installing steel gates around your home may keep out burglars and protect your material possessions from theft, but they won't keep out the negative energy of other people's misery nor protect you from its negative influence.

According to this view, greedy, selfish behaviour towards others is always counterproductive because it causes others to project negative energy that bounces back and harms the perpetrators of greed. Similarly, whenever we help others and make others happy, we thereby also help ourselves and make ourselves happy, because the happiness we bring others with our helpful behaviour is projected straight back to us from their minds.

Even if we cannot bring ourselves to be overtly helpful to others, at the very least we should refrain from being harmful and thereby avoid invoking the negative impact of others' enmity. If we go one step further and actually go out of our ways to help others, we then earn their everlasting gratitude. Gratitude and enmity are very different qualities in terms of the type of energy they generate and project on to others. If you earn the enmity of enough people, there is no question that the cumulative effects of the negative energy they project to you will have a strongly negative impact on your life, just as the energy of gratitude can be of tremendous benefit. This point goes beyond moral considerations: it's a basic fact of life, a universal principle of energy, and therefore an important point of practice.

It is due to the primacy of energy in life that human relationships provide such fertile ground for training in energy work. This is especially true of personal family relationships, in which emotions come into play. As everyone knows, the Chinese put great stock in family relationships, viewing the family as a microcosm of society, the state, and the entire cosmos. The energy dynamics between parents and children and among siblings is a training ground for how personal energy is expressed in the world at large. Relationships between teacher and student, master and disciple, were also regarded as sacred, because the teacher or master taught younger people how to harness their instinctive animal energies to serve the higher purposes of Heaven, Earth and Humanity. All such relationships in life may contribute valuable lessons in chi-gung practice, and all the precepts of balance and harmony which govern chi-gung may be applied with equally beneficial results to human relationships.

Perhaps the most important element of all in cultivating the right mind for life on the path of spiritual practice and energy work is love. Love, in the altruistic sense of selfless unconditional compassion for others, seems to have gone completely out of style in the modern world, and few people today attribute the rapid decline in human health throughout the world to the absence of love. It is not an accident that all of the world's great religious and mystical traditions consistently stress the over-riding importance of love. The great martial artist Chang San-feng, who is credited with developing Tai Chi Chuan six hundred years ago, summed up his entire approach to life by saying, 'Therefore, to those who want to know the way to deal with the world, I suggest, Love People.'

This is not a goody-two-shoes, pie-in-the-sky moral injunction to be a nice guy or girl, but rather a very basic lesson in energy work and spiritual power. The universe from which we harness power when we practise chi-gung is a living organism with spirit, and that spirit is guided by wisdom and compassion. All of our energy comes from the universe and ultimately returns to it. In order to fuel our lives, we borrow as much energy from the universe as we need, or as much as our practice permits, but in order for it to work positively for us, universal energy must be utilized in accordance with the other two universal virtues with which it is inseparably linked at its primordial source – wisdom and compassion. In this pragmatic age of science and technology, people are prone to overlook the power of love, but it doesn't take much vision to see very clearly that science and technology, which can be said to represent energy unbridled by love, have certainly brought neither health nor happiness to the world. If love were taken seriously as a guideline for utilizing energy, then atomic energy would never have been allowed to be used to produce weapons of mass destruction. This may seem obvious, and perhaps naïve, but the fact remains that love is the best safeguard against the deviant use of energy, and spiritual self-cultivation is the best way to understand how wisdom, love and energy are inseparable triunal virtues that must always be cultivated together.

To cultivate love, you must practise it daily, just as you do to cultivate energy and wisdom. Here are a few ways to cultivate love as 'the way to deal with the world'.

- Try to hug someone at least half a dozen times per day. Make it a real bear hug, and do it the same way you practise chi-gung – with body relaxed, breath deep and slow, mind still and empty. If you really relax into a hug and pay attention to how you feel, you'll be amazed at how much positive energy it generates – and how much negative energy it releases from the system.
- Learn to say, 'I love you'. It's amazing how difficult these words are for most people to say today. When you say 'I love you' to someone and mean it, you beam healing energy to them and enhance their health and happiness. That seems simple enough in principle, but in practice many people have trouble doing it. Furthermore, if you can say it with an open heart, you'll notice that it feels very good and stirs a lot of power between you and the recipient, and that somehow it feels right.
- Laugh a lot. Laughter is a very positive expression of energy, and it's closely related to love. Laughter comes from the heart, so when you laugh, you open your heart and balance your heart energy. Laughter does not always have to be prompted by humour; simple happiness suffices to stimulate a good belly laugh. For releasing physical as well as mental and emotional tension, nothing compares to the power of laughter, and in this sense, it is a very effective form of chi-gung.
- Avoid anger like the plague. Anger completely wilts the most carefully cultivated garden of love. Anger generates highly volatile, very destructive energy, and the person who suffers most from anger is the one who expresses it, not the one at whom it is directed. Therefore, getting angry only hurts yourself, not others, although temper tantrums can certainly be annoying to others. In terms of chi-gung, a brief burst of anger totally negates the cumulative benefits of many weeks of practice, so here again, as with love, it is the individual who expresses that energy who is most deeply affected by it.
- Practice the 'Golden Rule': do not do unto others what you would not have them do unto you. Simple as this seems, people consistently do things that are harmful to others, as long as they believe that they can 'get away with it'. But you never get away with anything when it comes to generating energy. If you do something deliberately, knowing that the result of your action will harm someone else, that sets in motion a chain reaction of energy dynamics which ultimately backfires on you. This is the basis of karma in Oriental thought. By refraining from harming others, you

also refrain from causing harm to yourself.

• Always give before you receive, and you will never want for anything. Giving is an expression of love. If there's something you really want in life, the quickest way to get it is to give others what they want, and this in turn will establish a flow of positive energy back to you. Whenever you express your personal energy with love, such as in giving, you receive energy from others in the same spirit. Like everything else related to love, this may strike the modern man and woman in the age of science and technology as facile, but in actual practice it works. Try it – you'll love it!

Chi-gung is without doubt one of the swiftest paths to health and longevity in the world, but in order for it to work for you, you must practise it within the total context from which it arose. That means cultivating wisdom and compassion together with energy, and utilizing energy with wisdom and compassion. Most important of all is to take full personal responsibility for protecting your own health, and for curing your own disease when preventive measures fail, and take responsibility for your own behaviour and its consequences in your life. Chi-gung teaches us how to take our lives into our own hands by showing us how to manage our personal energy and cultivate a direct personal relationship with the universe. Like all relationships from which we learn something and obtain beneficial results, respect is an essential factor in the relationship between a human being and the spirit of the universe. The spirit of the universe creates life by organizing the power of energy with wisdom and love. Those who call upon that power must do so with due respect for the wisdom and love that command it, for in the grand order of the universe wisdom, love and power are inseparably linked. Thus it behoves those who practise chi-gung to cultivate wisdom and love along with energy, so that the power they cull from the universe is not co-opted for deviant purposes by the ignorance, greed and aggression of the human mind. The Tao of Cultivating Life provides the most suitable context for chi-gung practice precisely because it regulates every aspect of human life with the same basic principles of wisdom and love that govern power at the highest levels of the universe, drawing every facet of daily life into one's practice and leaving no loopholes for self-deception and deviation.

Afterword

In the preface to *Guarding the Three Treasures*, the author states, 'What counts in medicine is its utility in practice, not its theoretical agreement with culturally conditioned concepts'. This is particularly true of chi-gung. The basic Chinese medical premise that energy imbalance is the primary cause of all disease, mental as well as physical, and that energy work is therefore the most effective way to cure as well as prevent disease, does not agree in any way with the chemical/mechanical paradigm of human health and healing to which modern Western medicine still subscribes. Nevertheless, the very fact that chi-gung has worked so well for so long for so many people to prevent and cure disease, retard ageing and prolong life, balance the emotions and 'please the spirit', is reason enough to start practising chi-gung today, while ongoing studies to further prove its efficacy in terms of modern Western science continue. Moreover, people who practise chi-gung as a way to cultivate health and nurture life soon discover for themselves, without requiring any further proof, that chi-gung builds the firmest foundation for health and longevity, while also paving an effective path for spiritual development. In chi-gung, the proof is in the practice.

Chi-gung develops conscious awareness of the underlying, overriding connection between body and mind, and cultivates volitional command over that energy as a pivotal bridge linking the mental faculties of spirit with the physical functions of body. Concurrently, chi-gung fosters acute awareness of the constant interaction between the internal world of blood and breath, bone and flesh, thought and feeling, within the human system, and the external world of land and sea, sky and earth, planets and stars that surround it. Here too *chi* serves as a functional intermediary between the two, linking the energies of the human microcosm with the forces of the universal macrocosm. Chi-gung thus provides a practical way for each and every individual to establish a direct personal relationship with the universe and tap into its infinite reservoirs of primordial power, while also cultivating the wisdom and compassion that spring from the same source. To those who've never felt the uplifting effects of chi-gung on body, energy and mind, all this may sound too good to be true, but those who practise chi-gung daily know from experience that a well-balanced body, dynamic energy system and harmonious spirit attract all good things in life, just as surely as a flame attracts a moth.

Chi-gung teaches the practitioner two practical lessons of manifold utility in life. First, it demonstrates how the mind can control the body by invoking its primordially ordained command over energy in the 'Triplex Union' of essence, energy and spirit, and conversely, how the body can nurture the mind by means of the internal alchemy of the Three Treasures, whereby essence is transformed to produce energy and energy is refined to nurture spirit. Second, chi-gung teaches us that the internal world of the human system and the external world of nature and the cosmos reflect and mutually influence one another, and that whatever happens in the macrocosm always has direct repercussions in the microcosm. This knowledge enables us to cultivate a healthy, harmonious homeostasis between our internal energies and the external forces that shape them, and to use our minds creatively to harness the power of the universe for the benefit of ourselves and others.

A long time ago in Tibet, the Fifth Dalai Lama, who understood and utilized the alchemical equation between sexuality and spirituality, remarked, 'If people practised spiritual work with as much energy and enthusiasm as they devote to sexual pursuits, everyone would become a fully enlightened Buddha in this very lifetime!' To paraphrase him, if people today spent as much time and effort working with and saving energy as they do playing with and wasting it, everyone would enjoy good health and longevity in this very lifetime.

Energy is life's most precious commodity, and chi-gung shows us how to manage our personal energy portfolios so that they pay maximum benefits in health and longevity, while also yielding spiritual dividends and providing us with an inexhaustible well of power that, as Lao Tze assures us in the *Tao Teh Ching*, 'Draw on it as you will, it never runs dry.'

Appendix

Useful Addresses

The addresses listed here may be helpful in locating qualified chi-gung teachers, courses and workshops, as well as books, videos and other materials about chi-gung and related topics. This list is only a small sample of what's available now in the field of chi-gung and is provided as a means for interested readers to establish their own networks of contacts with teachers, associations, practitioners and suppliers of products related to chi-gung.

Chi-Gung Associations

USA and Canada:

The Qiqong Institute and the East West Academy of Healing Arts
450 Sutter Street, Suite 2104, San Francisco, CA 94108
Tel: (415) 788-2227 Fax: (415) 788-2242
(Private courses in chi-gung; chi-gung therapy; private health consultations; chi-gung networking and references; materials)

Dr Wong Chung-siu
940 Washington Street, San Francisco, CA 94108
Tel: (415) 788-1008
(Representative of Guo Lin Research Society for chi-gung cancer therapy; personal health consultations and treatments)

The International Chi-Kung Directory
PO Box 19708, Boulder, CO 80301
Tel: (303) 422-3131 Fax: (303) 442-3141
(provides references to chi-gung teachers and associations throughout North America)

Chi Kung Association of America
571 Selby Avenue, St Paul, MN 55102
Tel: (888) 218-7788 / (612) 291-7772 Fax: (612) 291-7779

Yang's Martial Arts Association (YMAA)
38 Hyde Park Avenue, Jamaica Plains, MA 02130-4132
Tel: (617) 524-9235 Fax: (617) 524-4184 / (800) 669-8892
(courses in martial arts, chi-gung, chi-gung massage; personal counselling in chi-gung; instructional books and videos)

Sun Do ('Way of the Immortals') Centre
Master Hyunmoon Kim, 45 South Main Street, Suite 90, West Hartford, CT 06107
Tel: (860) 523-5260

Qigong Human Life Research Foundation
PO Box 5327, Cleveland, OH 44101
Tel: (216) 475-4712
(courses in chi-gung; newsletter; references)

Chinese National Chi Kung Institute
2068 Sunnyside Drive, Brentwood, TN 37027
Tel: (615) 370-8992 Fax: (615) 371-8990
(chi-gung courses; instructional videos and correspondence courses; mail orders)

Qigong Academy
8103 Marlborough Avenue, Cleveland, OH 44129
Tel: (216) 842-9628
(private courses in chi-gung)

The Chi-Kung School
PO Box 19708, Boulder, CO 80301
Tel: (303) 442-3131 Fax: (303) 442-2141
(private courses in chi-gung; personal health counselling)

China Healthways Institute
117 Avenida Granada, San Clemente, CA 92672
Tel: (714) 361-3976 Fax: (714) 498-0947 / (800) 743 5608
(information, references and courses in chi-gung; distributors of the 'Qigong Machine' produced in China)

East West Academy of Healing Arts
PO Box 18097, 2225 West 41st Avenue, Vancouver, BC V6M 4L3
Tel: (604) 224-1824 / 527-5477
(chi-gung courses and workshops; private consultations)

Shou-yu Liang Wushu Institute
7951 No. 4 Road, Richmond, BC
Tel: (604) 228-3604 / 273-9648
(courses in chi-gung and martial arts)

Yan Xin Qi Gong Culture Center
198 Allendale Road, Suite 402, King of Prussia, PA 19406
Tel: (601) 265-3370
e-mail: alp@ op.net;www.qigong.net

Australia:

Qigong Association of Australia
458 White Horse Road, Surrey Hills, Victoria 3127
Tel: 61 03 9836-6961 Fax: 61 03 9830-5608
(courses, workshops, references)

Tai Chi and Qiqong Institute
GPOF Box 66, Adelaide 5001, SA
Tel: 61 85 9281-8555 Fax: 61 85 9282240
(courses and information on Tai Chi Chuan and chi-gung)

Great Britain:

The Qigong Institute
18 Swan Street, Manchester M4 5JN, Lancs.
Tel: (44) 0161 832-8204
(courses and workshops in chi-gung; personal consultations)

British Acupuncture Council
206-208 Latimer Road, London W10 6RE
Tel: (44) 0181 964-0222
(contact for schools and colleges of Chinese medicine,
and details of practitioners)

Council for Complementary and Alternative Medicine
38 Mount Pleasant, London WC1X 0AP

Register of Chinese Herbal Medicine
21 Warbreck Road, London W12 8NS
(contact for details of qualified herbal practitioners)

Register of Chinese Massage Therapy
PO Box 8739, London N28

Chi-Gung practitioners:

Linda Chase Broda
The Village Hall, 168 Palatine Road, Manchester M20 2GH
Tel: (44) 0161 445-1568 Fax: (44) 0161 445-9568

Zhi-Zing and Zhen-Di Wan
Chinese Heritage, 15 Dawson Place, London W2 4TH
Tel: (44) 0171 229-7187

Lin Jun Wen
3 New College Parade, Finchley Road, London NW3 5EP
Tel: (44) 0171 722-9808 Fax: (44) 0171 722-7341

Feng Shui Network
PO Box 2133, London WlA 1RL
Tel: (44) 0171 935-8935 Fax: (44) 0171 935-9295

British Council for Martial Arts
Senior Coach
28 Linden Farm Drive, Countesthorpe, Leicester LE8 5SX
Tel/Fax: (44) 0116 277-4260

The Zero Balancing Association UK
36 Richmond Road, Cambridge CB4 3PU
Tel/Fax: (44) 01223 315-480

China:

The World Academic Society of Medical Qigong
He Ping Jie Bei Kou
Bei San Huan Lu 29, Beijing 100013
Tel: 86 10 422-5566, ext: 2347 Fax: 86 10 421-1591
(information on medical chi-gung and references to teachers and chi-gung healers)

The International Qigong Science Association
Somatic Science Research Center, Dept of Electrical Engineering,
Xan Jiao Tong University, Xian, Shaanxi Province 710049
(research papers; scientific data; references to teachers and healers)

China Wushu Association
3 An-Din Road, Chao-Yang District, Beijing 100101
Tel: 86 10 491-2150
(courses in martial arts and chi-gung; references; information)

Taiwan:

Lo Te-hsiu
136 Lung Men Street, Sanchung District, Taipei, Taiwan
Tel: 8862 975-8768 Fax: 8862 873-6222
(private courses in chi-gung; workshops; personal consultations)

Sung Yang Taoist Meditation Center (Master Han Yu-mo)
33-8, Ta-Lin Village, Ping Ling District, Taipei, Taiwan
Tel: 8862 665-6995 Fax: 8862 665-6996
(courses and printed materials on Taoist meditation)

Planetary Energy Gemstones

Astral Gemstone Talismans
Richard S. Brown, Planetary Gemologist & Designer
Langsuan Balcony, 3rd Floor
99/22 Soi 7, Langsuan Road, Bangkok 10330, Thailand
Tel: 66 2 252-1230 / 251-0577 Fax: 66 2 252-1231 / 241-2535
e-mail: agt-gems@comnet4.ksc.net.th/http://www.agt-gems.com/
(astral gemstone talismans custom designed to balance cosmic energies according to personal requirements)

Electromagnetic Energy Devices, Negative Ion and Ozone Generators and Related Products

Tools for Exploration
47 Paul Drive, San Rafael, CA 94903, USA
Tel: (415) 499-9050 Fax: (415) 499-9047 / (888) 748-6657
(high-tech electromagnetic devices for enhancing and balancing human energies; negative ion and ozone generators; water ionizers, ozonators, and purifiers; full-spectrum solar lighting, etc.)

Index

Alphabetical order is word-by-word, and hyphens are treated as spaces. **Bold** type indicates main references. *Italics* indicate illustrations. Short entries are given under both Chinese and English forms; longer entries are referred from Chinese to English.